AS-Level Chemistry

The Revision Guide

Editors:
Sharon Keeley, Simon Little

Contributors:
Martin Chester, Vikki Cunningham, Ian H. Davis, John Duffy, Max Fishel, Emma Grimwood, Richard Harwood, Philippa Hulme, Munir Kawar, Lucy Muncaster, Glenn Rogers, Emma Singleton, Derek Swain, Sharon Watson

Proofreaders:
Jeremy Cooper, Maureen Darling-Reid, John Moseley.

Published by Coordination Group Publications Ltd.

This book is suitable for:

Edexcel, Edexcel Nuffield, AQA, OCR and OCR Salters.

There are notes at the tops of double pages to tell you if there's a bit you can ignore for your syllabus.

ISBN: 1 84146 976 9
Groovy website: www.cgpbooks.co.uk
Jolly bits of clipart from CorelDRAW
Printed by Elanders Hindson, Newcastle upon Tyne.

Contents

The Atom

This stuff about atoms and elements should be ingrained on your brain from GCSE. You do need to know it perfectly though if you are to negotiate your way through the field of man-eating tigers which is AS Chemistry.

Atoms are made up of Protons, Neutrons and Electrons

Atoms are the stuff **all** elements and compounds are made of.
They're made up of 3 types of particle — **protons**, **neutrons** and **electrons**.

Electrons

1) Electrons have **-1** charge.
2) They whizz around the nucleus in **orbitals**. The orbitals take up most of the **volume** of the atom.

Nucleus

1) Most of the **mass** of the atom is concentrated in the nucleus.
2) The **diameter** of the nucleus is rather titchy compared to the whole atom.
3) The nucleus is where you find the **protons** and **neutrons**.

The mass and charge of these subatomic particles is **really small** so **relative mass** and **relative charge** are used instead.

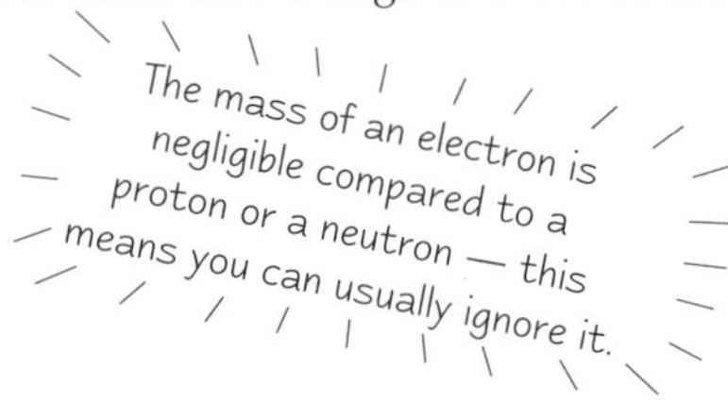
The mass of an electron is negligible compared to a proton or a neutron — this means you can usually ignore it.

Subatomic particle	Relative mass	Relative charge
Proton	1	+1
Neutron	1	0
Electron, e^-	$\frac{1}{1836}$	–1

Nuclear Symbols Show Numbers of Subatomic Particles

You can figure out the **number** of protons, neutrons and electrons from the **nuclear symbol**.

$$^{A}_{Z}X$$

Mass number
This tells you the **total** number of **protons** and **neutrons** in the nucleus.

Element symbol

Atomic (proton) number

1) This is the number of **protons** in the nucleus — it identifies the element.
2) **All** atoms of the same element have the **same** number of protons.

Sometimes the atomic number is left out of the nuclear symbol, e.g. ^{7}Li. You don't really need it because the element symbol tells us its value.

1) For **neutral** atoms with no overall charge, the number of electrons is **the same as** the number of protons.
2) The number of neutrons is just **mass number minus atomic number**, i.e. 'top minus bottom' in the nuclear symbol.

Nuclear symbol	Atomic number, Z	Mass number, A	Protons	Electrons	Neutrons
$^{7}_{3}Li$	3	7	3	3	7 – 3 = **4**
$^{80}_{35}Br$	35	80	35	35	80 – 35 = **45**
$^{24}_{12}Mg$	12	24	12	12	24 – 12 = **12**

Ions have Different Numbers of Protons and Electrons

Negative ions have **more electrons** than protons...

E.g.

Br^-

The – charge means that there's 1 more electron than there are protons.
Br has 35 protons (see table above), so Br^- must have 36 electrons.
The overall charge = + 35 – 36 = –1.

...and **positive** ions have **less electrons** than protons. It kind of makes sense if you think about it.

E.g.

Mg^{2+}

The 2+ charge means that there's 2 less electrons than there are protons.
Mg has 12 protons (see table above), so Mg^{2+} must have 10 electrons.
The overall charge = +12 – 10 = +2.

The Atom

Isotopes are *Atoms of the* **Same Element** *with Different Numbers of* **Neutrons**

Make sure you **learn** this definition and totally **understand** what it means —

Isotopes of an element are atoms with the same number of protons but different numbers of neutrons.

Chlorine-35 and chlorine-37 are examples of isotopes.

35 – 17 = 18 neutrons ← **Different** mass numbers mean different numbers of neutrons. → **37 – 17 = 20 neutrons**

$^{35}_{17}Cl$

The **atomic numbers** are the same. **Both** isotopes have 17 protons and 17 electrons.

$^{37}_{17}Cl$

1) It's the **number** and **arrangement** of electrons that decides the **chemical properties** of an element. Isotopes have the **same configuration of electrons**, so they've got **virtually identical** chemical properties.
2) Isotopes of an element do have slightly different **physical properties** though, such as different densities, rates of diffusion, etc. This is because **physical properties** tend to depend more on the **mass** of the atom.

Here's another example — naturally occurring **magnesium** consists of 3 main isotopes.

^{24}Mg (79%)	^{25}Mg (10%)	^{26}Mg (11%)
12 protons	12 protons	12 protons
12 neutrons	**13** neutrons	**14** neutrons
12 electrons	12 electrons	12 electrons

The periodic table gives the atomic number for each element. The other number isn't the mass number, it's the relative atomic mass (see page 10). They're a bit different, but for all but the most accurate work, you can assume they're equal.

Practice Questions

Q1 Draw a diagram showing the structure of the atom, labelling each part.

Q2 Define the term isotope and give an example.

Q3 Draw a table showing the relative charge and relative mass of subatomic particles.

Q4 Using an example, explain the terms atomic number and mass number.

Q5 Where is the mass concentrated in an atom and what makes up most of the volume of an atom?

Exam Questions

Q1 Hydrogen, deuterium and tritium are all isotopes of each other.
- a) Identify 1 similarity and 1 difference between these isotopes. [2 marks]
- b) Deuterium can be written ^{2}H. Determine the number of protons, neutrons and electrons in neutral deuterium. [3 marks]
- c) Write a nuclear symbol for tritium, given that it has 2 neutrons. [1 mark]

Q2 This question relates to the atoms or ions A to D: A. $^{32}S^{2-}$, B. ^{40}Ar, C. ^{30}S, D. ^{42}Ca.
- a) Identify the similarity for each of the following pairs, justifying your answer in each case.
  - (i) A and B. [2 marks]
  - (ii) A and C. [2 marks]
  - (iii) B and D. [2 marks]
- b) Which of the 2 atoms or ions are isotopes of each other? Explain your reasoning. [2 marks]

Got it learned yet? — isotope so...

This is a nice straightforward page just to ease you in to things. Remember that positive ions have fewer electrons than protons and negative ions have more electrons than protons. Get this straight in your mind otherwise you'll end up in a right mess. There's nowt too hard about isotopes neither. They're just the same element with different numbers of neutrons.

Electronic Structure

Those little electrons prancing about like mini bunnies decide what'll react with what — it's what chemistry's all about.

Electron Shells are Made up of *Sub-Shells* and *Orbitals*

1) Electrons move around the nucleus in **shells** (sometimes called **energy levels**). These shells are all given numbers known as **principal quantum numbers**.
2) Shells **further** from the nucleus have a greater energy level than shells closer to the nucleus.
3) The shells contain different types of **sub-shells**. These sub-shells have different numbers of **orbitals** which can each hold up to **2 electrons**.

This table shows the number of electrons that fit in each type of sub-shell.

Sub-shell	Number of orbitals	Maximum electrons
s	1	1 × 2 = 2
p	3	3 × 2 = 6
d	5	5 × 2 = 10
f	7	7 × 2 = 14

And this one shows the sub-shells and electrons in the first four energy levels.

Shell	Sub-shell	Total number or electrons	
1st	1*s*	2	= 2
2nd	2*s* 2*p*	2 + (3 × 2)	= 8
3rd	3*s* 3*p* 3*d*	2 + (3 × 2) + (5 × 2)	= 18
4th	4*s* 4*p* 4*d* 4*f*	1 + (3 × 2) + (5 × 2) + (7 × 2)	= 32

Orbitals Have *Characteristic Shapes*

There's a few things you need to know about orbitals...like what they are —

1) An orbital is the **bit of space** which an electron moves in. Orbitals within the same sub-shell have the **same energy**.
2) The electrons in the orbitals have to spin in **opposite** directions — this is called **spin-pairing**.
3) s orbitals are **spherical** — p orbitals have **dumbbell shapes**. There's 3 p orbitals at right angles to one another.

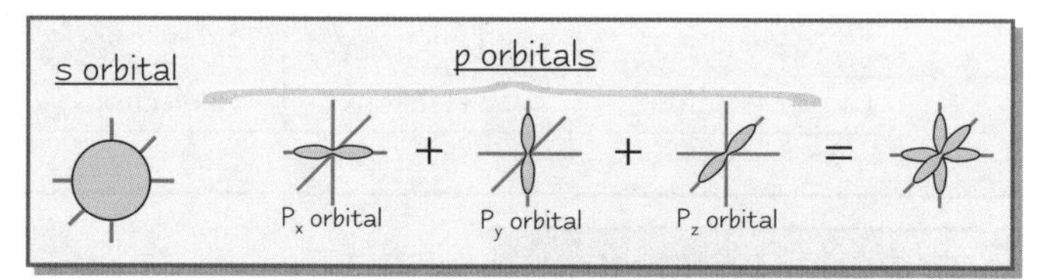

Work Out *Electron Configurations* by Filling the *Lowest* Energy Levels First

You can figure out most electronic configurations pretty easily, so long as you know a few simple rules —

1) Electrons fill up the **lowest** energy sub-shells first.

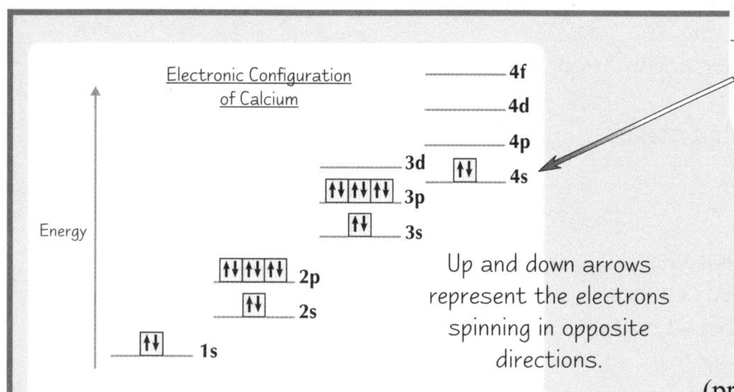

There's always got to be an exception to mess things up. The 4*s* sub-shell has a lower energy level than the 3*d* sub-shell, even though its principal quantum number is bigger. This means the 4*s* sub-shell fills up first.

Sub-shell notation is another way of showing electronic configuration. The electronic configuration of **calcium** is:

$$1s^2\ 2s^2\ 2p^6\ 3s^2\ 3p^6\ 4s^2$$

Energy level / shell (principal quantum number) — Sub-shell — Number of electrons

2) Electrons fill orbitals **singly** before they start sharing.

	1s	2s	2p
Nitrogen	↑↓	↑↓	↑ | ↑ | ↑
Oxygen	↑↓	↑↓	↑↓ | ↑ | ↑

See the next page for more on the s and p block.

3) For the configuration of **ions** from the **s** and **p** blocks of the periodic table, just **remove or add** the electrons to or from the highest energy occupied sub-shell. E.g. $Mg^{2+} = 1s^2\ 2s^2\ 2p^6$, $Cl^- = 1s^2\ 2s^2\ 2p^6\ 3s^2\ 3p^6$

Watch out — **inert gas symbols**, like that of Argon (Ar), are sometimes used in configurations. For example, calcium ($1s^2\ 2s^2\ 2p^6\ 3s^2\ 3p^6\ 4s^2$) can be written as $[Ar]4s^2$, where $[Ar] = 1s^2\ 2s^2\ 2p^6\ 3s^2\ 3p^6$.

Electronic Structure

Transition Metals *Behave Unusually*

1) **Chromium** (Cr) and **copper** (Cu) are badly behaved. They donate one of their **4s** electrons to the **3*d* sub-shell.** It's because they're happier with a **more stable** full or half-full d sub-shell.
   Cr atom (24 e^-): $1s^2\ 2s^2\ 2p^6\ 3s^2\ 3p^6\ 3d^5\ 4s^1$ Cu atom (29 e^-): $1s^2\ 2s^2\ 2p^6\ 3s^2\ 3p^6\ 3d^{10}\ 4s^1$
2) And here's another weird thing about transition metals — when they become **ions**, they lose their **4s** electrons **before** their 3d electrons, even though 3d is at a higher energy level.
   Fe atom (26 e^-): $1s^2\ 2s^2\ 2p^6\ 3s^2\ 3p^6\ 3d^6\ 4s^2 \rightarrow Fe^{3+}$ ion (23 e^-): $1s^2\ 2s^2\ 2p^6\ 3s^2\ 3p^6\ 3d^5$

Electronic Structure Decides the **Chemical Properties** *of an Element*

The number of **outer shell electrons** decides the chemical properties of an element.

Sub-shells and the periodic table
1s 2s 3s 4s 5s 6s 7s 3d 4d 5d 2p 3p 4p 5p 6p 1s

1) The **s block** elements (Groups I and II) have 1 or 2 outer shell electrons. These are easily **lost** to form positive ions with an **inert gas configuration**. E.g. Na — $1s^2\ 2s^2\ 2p^6\ 3s^1 \rightarrow Na^+$ — $1s^2\ 2s^2\ 2p^6$ (the electronic configuration of neon).
2) The elements in Groups V, VI and VII (in the p block) can **gain** 1, 2 or 3 electrons to form negative ions with an **inert gas configuration**. E.g. O — $1s^2\ 2s^2\ 2p^4 \rightarrow O^{2-}$ — $1s^2\ 2s^2\ 2p^6$. Groups IV to VII can also **share** electrons when they form covalent bonds.
3) Group 0 (the inert gases) have **completely filled** s and p sub-shells and don't need to bother gaining, losing or sharing electrons — their full sub-shells make them **inert**.
4) The **d block elements** (transition metals) tend to **lose** s and d electrons to form positive ions.

Practice Questions

Q1 Write down the sub-shells in order of increasing energy up to 4*f*.

Q2 How many electrons would full s, p and d sub-shells contain?

Q3 Draw diagrams to show the shapes of an s and a p orbital.

Q4 What does the term 'spin-pairing' mean?

Exam Questions

Q1 Potassium can react with oxygen to form potassium oxide, K_2O.

a) Using sub-shell notation, give the electron configuration of the K atom and K^+ ion. [2 marks]

b) Using arrow-in-box notation, give the electron configuration of the oxygen atom. [2 marks]

c) Explain why it is mainly the outer shell electrons, not those in the inner shells, which determine the chemistry of potassium and oxygen. [2 marks]

Q2 This questions concerns electron configurations in atoms and ions.

a) What is the electron configuration of manganese, Mn? [1 mark]

b) Identify the element with the 4th shell configuration of $4s^2 4p^2$. [1 mark]

c) Suggest the identity of an atom, a positive ion and a negative ion with the configuration $1s^2\ 2s^2\ 2p^6\ 3s^2\ 3p^6$. [3 marks]

d) Using arrow-in-box notation, give the electron configuration of the Al^{3+} ion. [2 marks]

She shells sub-sells on the shesore...

The way electrons fill up the orbitals is kind of like how strangers fill up seats on a bus. Everyone tends to sit in their own seat till they're forced to share. Except for the huge, scary, smelly man who comes and sits next to you. Make sure you learn the order the sub-shells are filled up, so you can write electron configurations for any atom or ion they throw at you.

Ionisation Energies

This page gets a trifle brain-boggling, so I hope you've got a few aspirin handy...

Ionisation is the Removal of One or More Electrons

When electrons are removed from an atom or molecule, it's been **ionised**.
The energy you need to remove the first electron is called the **first ionisation energy**:

> The **first ionisation energy** is the energy needed to remove 1 electron from **each atom** in **1 mole** of **gaseous** atoms to form 1 mole of gaseous 1+ ions.

You can write **equations** for this process. Here's the equation for the **first ionisation of oxygen** —

$$O_{(g)} \rightarrow O^{+}_{(g)} + e^{-} \qquad \text{1st ionisation energy} = +1314 \text{ kJ mol}^{-1}$$

Here's a few rather important points about ionisation energies:

1) You **must** use the gas state symbol, **(g)**, because ionisation energies are measured for gaseous atoms.
2) Always refer to **1 mole** of atoms as stated in the definition, rather than to a single atom.
3) The **lower** the ionisation energy, the **easier** it is to form an ion.

There's **3 main things** that affect the size of ionisation energies:

1) **Atomic radius** — the further the outer shell electrons are from the positive nucleus, the less they'll be attracted towards the nucleus. So, the ionisation energy will be **lower**.
2) **Nuclear charge** — the **more protons** there are in the nucleus, the more it'll attract the outer electrons — it'll be harder to remove the electrons, so the ionisation energy will be **higher**.
3) **Electron shielding** — the inner electron shells **shield** the outer shell electrons from the attractive force of the nucleus. Because more inner shells mean more shielding, the ionisation energy will be **lower**.

Successive Ionisation Energies Involve Removing Additional Electrons

Skip this bit if you're doing AQA.

1) You can remove **all** the electrons from an atom leaving only the nucleus. Each time you remove an electron, there's a **successive ionisation energy**.
2) The definition for the **second ionisation energy** is —

> The **second ionisation energy** is the energy required to remove 1 electron from **each ion** in **1 mole** of **gaseous** 1+ ions to form 1 mole of gaseous 2+ ions.

And here's the equation for the **second ionisation of oxygen** —

$$O^{+}_{(g)} \rightarrow O^{2+}_{(g)} + e^{-} \qquad \text{2nd ionisation energy} = +3388 \text{ kJ mol}^{-1}$$

3) A **graph** of successive ionisation energies (like the one for sodium below) shows the **shell structure** of atoms.

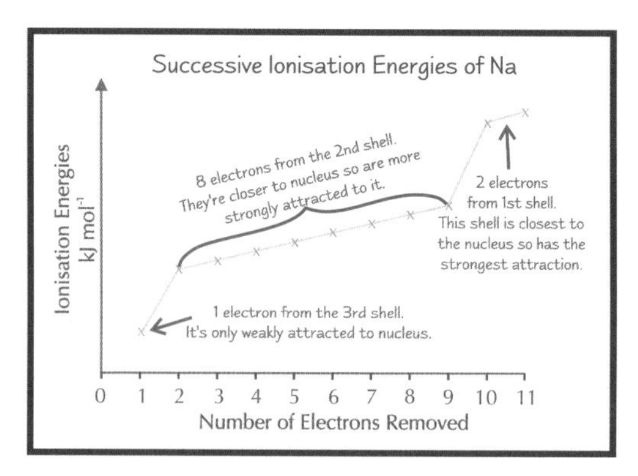

1) **Within each shell**, successive ionisation energies **increase**. This is because electrons are being removed from an **increasingly positive ion**, so the attraction between the nucleus and the remaining electrons increases. Also, there's **less repulsion** amongst the remaining electrons.
2) The **big jumps** in ionisation energy happen when a new shell is broken into — an electron is being removed from a shell **closer** to the nucleus.

Ionisation Energies

The First Ionisation Energies of **Group II Decrease** Down the Group

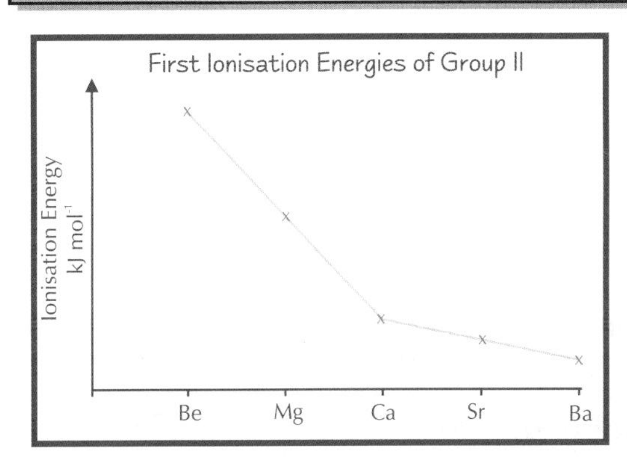

The first ionisation energy **decreases** down Group II because there's **less attraction** between the nucleus and outer electrons. This shows that the electrons are arranged in **energy levels** (and it's not all lies):

1) As you go down the group, the outer electrons are in shells **further** from the nucleus, so they're attracted to the nucleus **less**.
2) The amount of shielding **increases** because there's more filled inner shells. This means **less nuclear attraction** for the outer shell electrons.
3) Although the number of **protons** increases down the group, this **doesn't** lead to an increase in ionisation energy because it's a less important factor than either shielding or the distance of the outer electrons from the nucleus.

A First Ionisation Energy Plot for **Period 3** Shows **Shell** and **Sub-shell Structure**

There's a **general increase** in first ionisation energy **across a period** because of the **increasing attraction** between the outer shell electrons and the nucleus. Across the period:

1) **Nuclear charge** increases since the number of protons increases.
2) **Shielding** stays **about the same** since each additional electron is added to the same shell.

Ionisation energies show sub-shell structure:

1) For Na and Mg, the **3s** sub-shell is filling.
2) The three **3p** orbitals are further out, so the outer electrons are **easier** to remove.
3) With **two** electrons in the same orbital there's **extra repulsion** between them, so they're easier to remove.

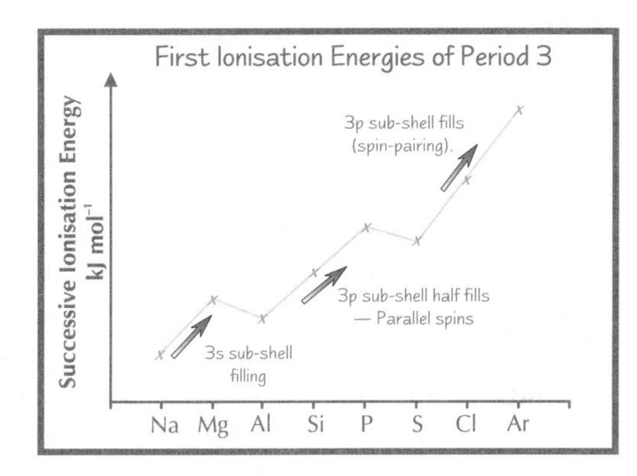

Practice Questions

Q1 Define first ionisation energy and give an equation as an example.

Q2 Describe the 3 main factors that affect ionisation energies.

Q3 Explain why ionisation energies decrease down Group II.

Q4 How do first ionisation energy plots give you information about atomic sub-shell structure?

Exam Question

Q1 The graph shows how first ionisation energy varies across Period 2.

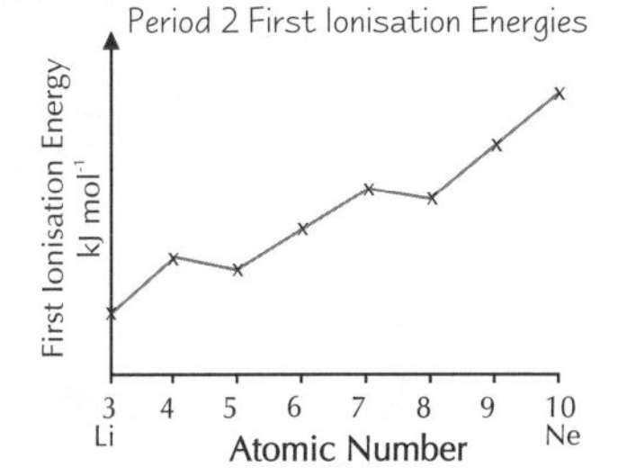

a) Explain why there is a general increase in ionisation energy across the period. [2 marks]

b) Explain how the graph provides evidence for the electronic structure of these elements. [3 marks]

Shirt crumpled — ionise it...

When you're talking about ionisation energies in exams, always use the 3 main factors — shielding, nuclear charge and atomic radius. It's really important that you know what's going on in the graphs and why they look like dogs' hind legs. Recite the definition of the first and second ionisation energies to yourself until the men in white coats get to you. Then stop.

Nuclear Fusion, Atomic Spectra & Radiation

These two pages are just for people doing OCR Salters, so the rest of you can put your feet up and have a cup of tea.

Nuclear Fusion — Forming Elements in Stars

1) **Nuclear fusion** is when two nuclei combine to make one larger nucleus — it happens naturally in **stars**.
2) Our Sun's core contains **hydrogen nuclei** which combine to make **helium nuclei**, releasing **huge** amounts of **energy**.

$$^{2}_{1}H + ^{2}_{1}H \rightarrow ^{3}_{2}He + ^{1}_{0}n$$

3) When the hydrogen in a star's core runs out, the **temperature** of the core starts to rise. In a big enough star it'll get **hot** enough to fuse **heavier elements**, starting with helium.

Atomic Spectra — Exciting Electrons with Electromagnetic Radiation

OK...here's a bit of brain-frying stuff coming at you —

1) Atoms in their **ground state** have all their electrons in their **lowest** possible orbitals. Each energy level is given a **quantum number**. The quantum number, n, for 1s electrons is 1.
2) If the electrons take in **energy** from their surroundings they can move to **higher energy levels**, further from the nucleus. At higher energy levels, electrons are said to be **excited**. (More excited than you are right now, I'll bet.)
3) The energy levels all have **certain fixed values** — they're **discrete**. Electrons can jump from one energy level to another by **absorbing** or **releasing** a fixed amount of energy.
4) Energy is related to **wavelength**. When **electromagnetic radiation** is passed through a gaseous element, the electrons only absorb **certain wavelengths,** corresponding to **differences between the energy levels**. That means the radiation passing through has certain wavelengths missing. A spectrum of this radiation is called an **atomic absorption spectrum**. The missing wavelengths show up as **dark bands**.

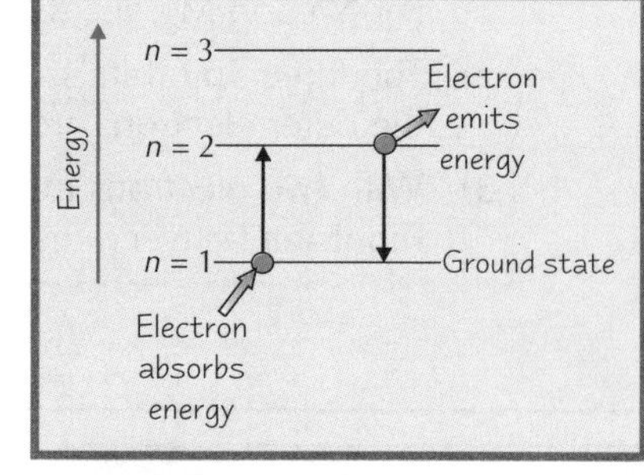

5) When electrons **drop** to lower energy levels, they **give out** certain amounts of energy. This produces lines in the spectrum too — but this time it's called an **emission spectrum**. The wavelengths in an emission spectrum are the **same** as those missing in the corresponding absorption spectrum.
6) Each element has a **different** electron arrangement, so the wavelengths of radiation absorbed and emitted are different. This means the **spectrum** for each element will be unique too.

The Atomic Emission Spectrum of Hydrogen is made up of Sets of Lines

1) Spectra often seem to make as much sense as bar codes. But the emission spectrum of **hydrogen** is fairly simple because hydrogen only has **one** electron that can move.
2) The atomic emission spectrum of hydrogen shows **sets of lines** — you need to know about three of them, the **Lyman series**, the **Balmer series** and the **Paschen series**.

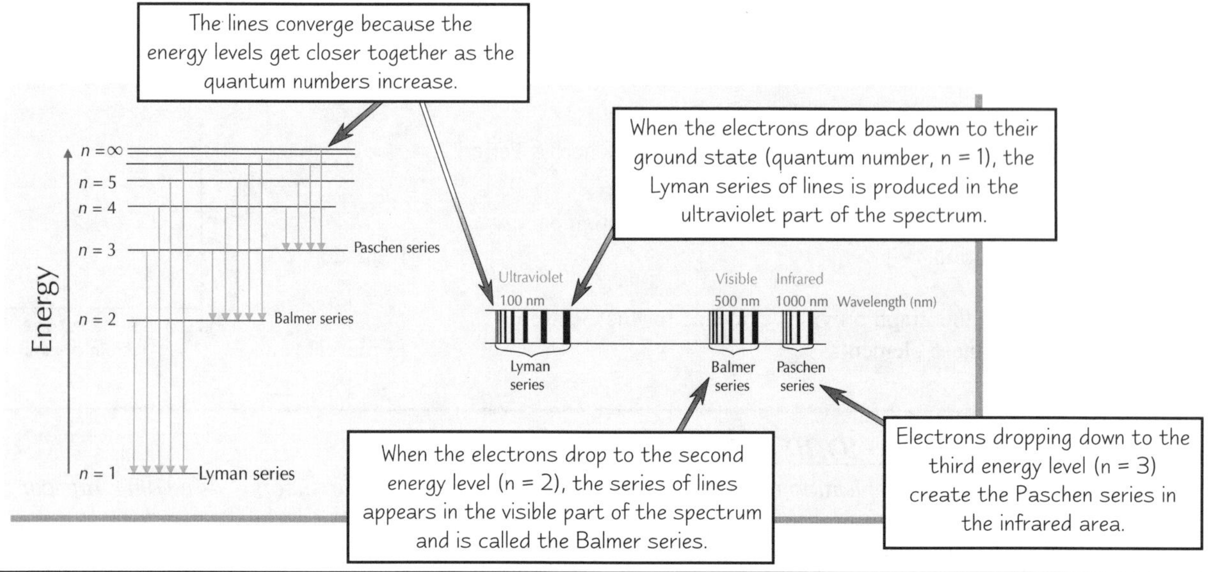

Nuclear Fusion, Atomic Spectra & Radiation

Nuclear radiation — Alpha, Beta and Gamma

Radioactive decay happens **spontaneously** to unstable nuclei. '**Spontaneously**' means you don't have to boil them or tickle them or anything — they just decay when they feel like it.
Alpha, **beta** or **gamma** radiation can be emitted. Learn the properties of these types of radiation.

	Alpha (α) Particles	Beta (β) Particles	Gamma (γ) Rays
What they are	Helium nuclei ^4_2He	Fast-moving electrons $^0_{-1}e$	Very short wave electromagnetic waves
Penetrating power	Stopped by paper	Stopped by thin aluminium sheets	Stopped by very thick lead
Ionising ability	Strong	Moderate	Weak
Deflection in electric field	Slight	large	Not deflected

Nuclear Equations — Balance the Mass and Atomic Numbers

To find out what type of **radiation** or **element** is produced, balance the **top** and **bottom** numbers in the equation.

Example 1: What type of radiation is being lost?

$^{14}_{6}C \rightarrow ^{14}_{7}N + ^{\square}_{\square}\square$ ← 14 – 14 = 0, 6 – 7 = – 1 → so radiation must be $^{0}_{-1}e$

Example 2: Which element is produced?

$^{208}_{81}Tl \rightarrow ^{\square}_{\square}\square + ^{0}_{-1}e$ 208 – 0 = 208, 81 – (–1) = 82 ← Atomic Number = Pb → $^{208}_{82}Pb$

Radioactive Tracers are used in Medicine and Industry

1) In medicine, isotopes can be **injected** into the bloodstream or **swallowed** and their movement around the body monitored using an **external detector**. **Gamma or beta** (never alpha) isotopes are used so that the radiation passes out of the body. They also have a **short half-life** so the radioactivity quickly disappears.
2) Radioactive isotopes are also used to find **leaks in pipes** — this is really useful for underground pipes as it means you don't have to dig up half the road.

One radioactive tracer too many.

Practice Questions

Q1 What is an excited electron?

Q2 Describe what the atomic emission spectrum of hydrogen shows.

Q3 Construct a table of the properties of alpha, beta and gamma radiation.

Q4 Describe how radioactive tracers are used in medicine.

Exam Questions

Q1 A radioactive isotope of the element polonium underwent two stages of radioactive decay. Complete the nuclear equations to identify the type of radiation produced in the first stage of decay and the final element produced.

$^{216}_{84}Po \rightarrow ^{212}_{82}Pb + ^{\square}_{\square}\square$ $\quad ^{212}_{82}Pb \rightarrow ^{\square}_{\square}\square + ^{0}_{-1}e$ [2 marks]

Q2 a) Label the diagram to show how a helium electron can be excited.

b) Show how the electron can then emit its extra energy in two stages. [2 marks]

Q3 Explain why isotopes which produce gamma radiation are used in medicine and not those that produce alpha particles. [2 marks]

Radioactive tracers are like Ready Brek — you'll have a warm glow all day...

This page is a mish-mash of a few different things. Atomic spectra are pretty hard to get your head round — so go over them again and again until it's crystal clear. As for the stuff on radiation — make sure you have the properties of alpha, beta and gamma radiation nailed down firmly in your memory. It'll be fun...I promise...and I also promise you'll win the lottery.

Relative Mass

Relative mass...What? Eh?...Read on...

Relative Masses are Masses of Atoms Compared to Carbon-12

The actual mass of an atom is **very, very tiny**. Don't worry about exactly how tiny for now, but it's far **too small** to weigh. So, the mass of one atom is compared to the mass of a different atom. This is its **relative mass**.
There's 4 definitions here for you to learn.

The **relative atomic mass**, A_r, is the **average mass** of an atom of an element on a scale where an atom of **carbon-12** is 12.

Relative isotopic mass is the mass of an atom of an **isotope** of an element on a scale where an atom of **carbon-12** is 12.

Relative atomic mass is an average, so it's not usually a whole number. Relative isotopic mass is always a whole number (at AS level anyway). E.g. a natural sample of chlorine contains a mixture of ^{35}Cl (75%) and ^{37}Cl (25%), so the relative isotopic masses are 35 and 37. But its relative atomic mass is 35.5.

The **relative molecular mass** (or **relative formula mass**), M_r, is the mass of a **molecule** or **formula unit** on a scale where an atom of **carbon-12** is 12.

To find the relative molecular mass, just add up the relative atomic mass values of all the atoms in the molecule, e.g. $M_r(C_2H_6O) = (12 \times 2) + (1 \times 6) + 16 = 46$.

Relative formula mass is used for compounds that are ionic (or giant covalent, such as SiO_2). To find the relative formula mass, just add up the relative atomic masses (A_r) of all the ions in the formula unit. (A_r of ion = A_r of atom. The electrons make no difference to the mass.) E.g. $M_r(CaF_2) = 40 + (2 \times 19) = 78$.

Relative Masses can be Measured Using a Mass Spectrometer

You can use a **mass spectrometer** to find out loads of stuff. It can tell you the **relative atomic mass**, **relative molecular mass**, **relative isotopic abundance**, **molecular structure** and your **horoscope** for the next fortnight.

There are **5** things that happen when a sample is squirted into a mass spectrometer.

1. **Vaporisation** — the sample is turned into **gas** (**vaporised**) using an electrical heater.
2. **Ionisation** — the gas particles are bombarded with **high-energy electrons** to ionise them. Electrons are knocked off the particles leaving **positive ions**.
3. **Acceleration** — the positive ions are accelerated by an **electric field**.
4. **Deflection** — The positive ions' paths are altered with a **magnetic field**. **Lighter ions** have less momentum and are deflected **more** than heavier ions. For a given magnetic field, **only** ions with a particular **mass/charge ratio** make it to the detector.
5. **Detection** — the magnetic field strength is **slowly increased**. This **changes** the mass/charge ratio of ions that can reach the detector. A **mass spectrum** is produced.

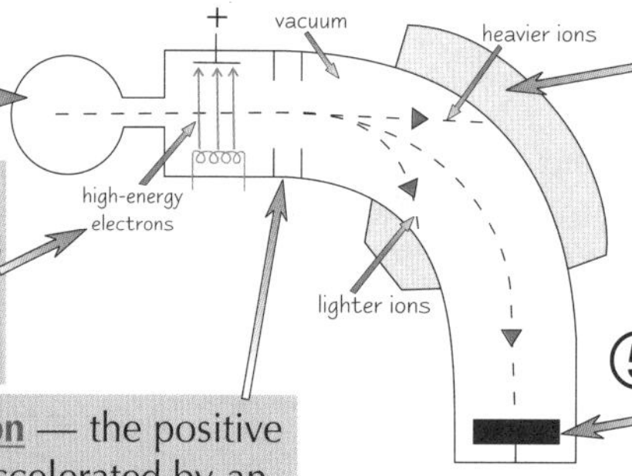

A Mass Spectrum

The **y-axis** gives the **abundance of ions**, often as a percentage. For an element, the **height** of each peak gives the **relative isotopic abundance**, e.g. 75.5% are the ^{35}Cl isotope.

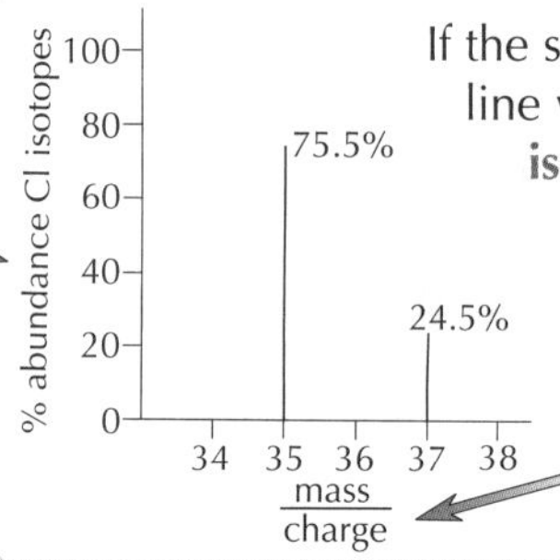

If the sample is an **element**, each line will represent a **different isotope** of the element.

The **x-axis** units are given as a '**mass/charge**' ratio. Since the charge on ions is mostly **+1**, you can often assume the x-axis is simply the **relative mass**.

Relative Mass

A_r and Relative Isotopic Abundance can be Worked Out from a Mass Spectrum

You need to know how to calculate the **relative atomic mass** (A_r) of an element from the **mass spectrum**.

Here's how to calculate A_r for magnesium, using the mass spectrum below —

Step 1: For each peak, read the **% relative isotopic abundance** from the y-axis and the **relative isotopic mass** from the x-axis. **Multiply** them together to get the total mass for each isotope. 79 × 24 = 1896; 10 × 25 = 250; 11 × 26 = 286

Step 2: **Add** up these totals. 1896 + 250 + 286 = 2432

Step 3: **Divide by 100** (since percentages were used). $A_r(\text{Mg}) = \frac{2432}{100} = 24.32 \approx \mathbf{24.3}$

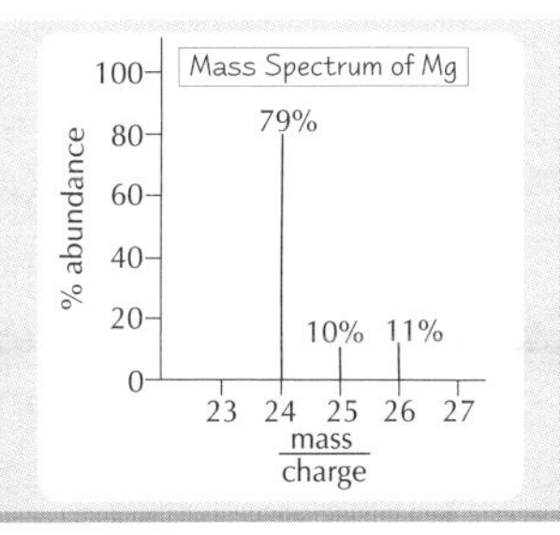

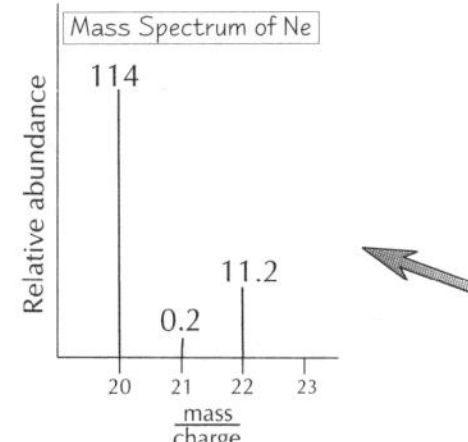

If the relative abundance is **not** given as a percentage, the total abundance may not add up to 100. In this case, don't panic. Just do steps 1 and 2 as above, but then divide by the **total relative abundance** instead of 100 — like this:

$$A_r(\text{Ne}) = \frac{(114 \times 20) + (0.2 \times 21) + (11.2 \times 22)}{114 + 0.2 + 11.2} \approx 20.18$$

Mass spectroscopy is a good way to identify elements and molecules (it's kind of like a fingerprint). For instance, a small mass spectrometer was used in the 1999 Mars probe to find out what the Mars atmosphere is made of.

Mass Spectroscopy can be used to Find Out M_r

You can also get a mass spectrum for a **molecular sample**, such as ethanol (CH_3CH_2OH).

1) A **molecular ion**, $M^+_{(g)}$, is formed when the bombarding electrons remove 1 electron from the molecule. This gives the peak in the spectrum with the **highest mass** (furthest to the right, ignoring isotopes). The mass of M^+ gives $\mathbf{M_r}$ for the molecule, e.g. $CH_3CH_2OH^+$ has M_r 46.
2) But it's not that simple — bombarding with electrons makes some molecules break up into fragments. These all show up on the mass spectrum, making a **fragmentation pattern**. For ethanol, the fragments you get include: CH_3^+ (M_r = 15), $CH_3CH_2^+$ (M_r = 29) and CH_2OH^+ (M_r = 31). Fragmentation patterns are actually pretty cool because you can use them to identify **molecules** and even their **structure**.

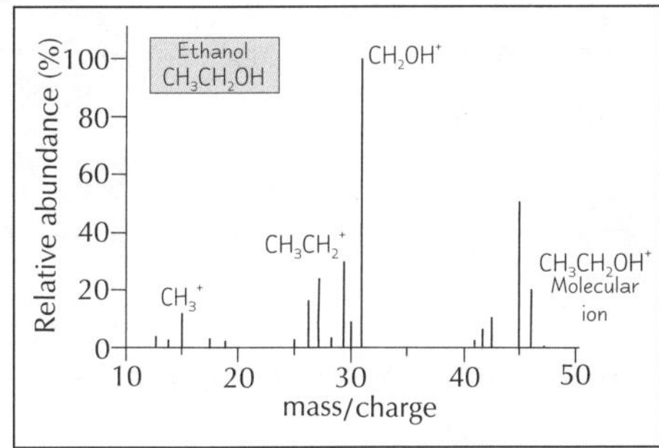

Practice Questions

Q1 Explain what relative atomic mass (A_r) and relative isotopic mass mean.

Q2 Explain the difference between relative molecular mass and relative formula mass.

Q3 A sample of argon is injected into a mass spectrometer. Outline the main things that happen.

Exam Questions

Q1 Copper, Cu, exists in two main isotopic forms, ^{63}Cu and ^{65}Cu.

a) Calculate the relative atomic mass of Cu using the information from the mass spectrum. [2 marks]

b) Explain why the relative atomic mass of copper is not a whole number. [2 marks]

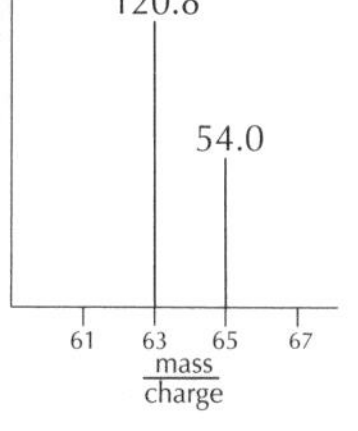

Q2 The percentage make-up of naturally occurring potassium is 93.11 % ^{39}K, 0.12 % ^{40}K and 6.77 % ^{41}K.

a) What method is used to determine the mass and abundance of each isotope? [1 mark]

b) Use the information to determine the relative atomic mass of potassium. [2 marks]

You can't pick your relatives, you just have to learn them...

Working out M_r is dead easy — and using a calculator makes it even easier. It'll really help if you know the mass numbers for the first 20 elements or so, or you'll spend half your time looking back at the periodic table. I hope you've done the Practice Questions, cos they pretty much cover the rest of the stuff, and if you can get them right, you've nailed it.

The Mole

It'd be handy to be able to count out atoms — but they're way too tiny. You can't even see them, never mind get hold of them with tweezers. But not to worry — using the idea of relative mass, you can figure out how many atoms you've got.

A **Mole** is Just a (Very Large) **Number of Particles**

1) Amount of substance is measured using a unit called the **mole** (**mol** for short) and given the symbol ***n***.
2) One mole is roughly **6×10^{23} particles** (**Avogadro's number, L**).
3) It **doesn't matter** what the particles are. They can be atoms, molecules, penguins — **anything**.
4) Here's a nice simple formula for finding the number of moles from the number of atoms or molecules:

$$\text{Number of moles} = \frac{\text{Number of particles you have}}{\text{Number of particles in a mole}}$$

Example:
I have 1.5×10^{24} carbon atoms.
How many moles of carbon is this?

$$\text{Number of moles} = \frac{1.5 \times 10^{24}}{6 \times 10^{23}} = \textbf{2.5 moles}$$

Molar Mass is the Mass of **One Mole**

Molar mass, **M**, is the mass of **one mole** of something.

But the main thing to remember is:

Molar mass is just the same as the relative molecule mass, M_r

That's why the mole is such a ridiculous number of particles (6×10^{23}) — it's the number of particles for which the weight is the same as the relative molecular mass.

The only difference is you stick a 'g' for grams on the end...

Example: Find the molar mass of $CaCO_3$.

Relative molecular mass, M_r, of $CaCO_3$ = 40 + 12 + (3 × 16) = 100
So the molar mass, M, is **100 g**. — i.e. 1 mole of $CaCO_3$ weighs 100 g.

Here's another formula. This one's really important — you need it **all the time**:

$$\text{Number of moles} = \frac{\text{mass of substance}}{\text{molar mass}}$$

Example: How many moles of aluminium oxide are present in 5.1 g of Al_2O_3?

Molar mass of Al_2O_3 = (2 × 27) + (3 × 16) = 102 g

Number of moles of Al_2O_3 = $\frac{5.1}{102}$ = **0.05 moles**

In a Solution the **Molarity** is the **Concentration** in **mol dm^{-3}**

1) The molarity (or **concentration**) of a solution is how many **moles** are dissolved per **1 dm³** of solvent. The units are **mol dm^{-3}** (or M).
2) Here's the formula to find the **number of moles**.

$$\text{Number of moles} = \frac{\text{Concentration} \times \text{Volume (in cm}^3\text{)}}{1000}$$

1 dm³ = 1000 cm³ = 1 litre

Example: What mass of sodium hydroxide needs to be dissolved in 50 cm³ to make a 2 M solution?

$$\text{Number of moles} = \frac{2 \times 50}{1000} = 0.1 \text{ moles of NaOH}$$

Molar mass, M, of NaOH = 23 + 16 + 1 = 40 g

Mass = number of moles × M = 0.1 × 40 = **4 g**

The Mole

All Gases Take Up the **Same Volume** under the Same Conditions

If temperature and pressure stay the same, **one mole** of **any** gas always has the **same volume**.
At **room temperature and pressure** (r.t.p.), this happens to be **24 dm^3**, (r.t.p is 298 K (25 °C) and 101.3 kPa).
Here's 2 formulas for working out the number of moles in a volume of gas. Don't forget — **ONLY** use them at r.t.p.

$$\text{Number of moles} = \frac{\text{Volume in } dm^3}{24} \quad \text{OR} \quad \text{Number of moles} = \frac{\text{Volume in } cm^3}{24\,000}$$

Example: How many moles are there in 6 dm^3 of oxygen gas at r.t.p.?

$$\text{Number of moles} = \frac{6}{24} = \mathbf{0.25 \text{ moles of oxygen molecules}}$$

Ideal Gas equation — pV = nRT

This bit's just for people doing AQA.
In the real world (and AQA exam questions), it's not always room temperature and pressure.
The **Ideal Gas Equation** lets you find the **number of moles** in a certain volume at **any temperature and pressure**.

pV = nRT

Where: p = pressure (Pa)
V = volume (m^3)
n = number of moles
R = 8.31 J $K^{-1}mol^{-1}$
T = temperature (K)

The gas constant — don't worry about what it means, just learn it.

1 cm^3 = 1 x 10^{-6} m^3
1 dm^3 = 1 x 10^{-3} m^3

K = °C + 273

Example:
At a temperature of 60 °C and a pressure of 250 kPa, a gas occupied a volume of 1100 cm^3 and had a mass of 1.6 g. Find its relative molecular mass.

$$n = \frac{pV}{RT} = \left(\frac{(250\times10^3)\times(1.1\times10^{-3})}{8.31\times333}\right) = 0.1 \text{ moles}$$

1100 cm^3 = 1.1 × 10^{-3} m^3

If 0.1 moles is 1.6 g, then 1 mole = $\frac{1.6}{0.1}$ = 16 g. So the relative molecular mass (M_r) is **16**.

Practice Questions

Q1 How many molecules are there in one mole of ethane molecules?

Q2 What volume does 1 mole of gas occupy at r.t.p.?

Q3 Which has the most particles, a solution of concentration 0.1 mol dm^{-3} or one that is 0.1 M?

Exam Questions

Q1 Calculate the mass of 0.36 moles of ethanoic acid, CH_3COOH. [2 marks]

Q2 What mass of H_2SO_4 is needed to produce 60 cm^3 of 0.25 M solution? [2 marks]

Q3 What volume will be occupied by 88 g of propane gas (C_3H_8) at r.t.p.? [2 marks]

Put your back teeth on the scale and find out your molar mass...

You need this stuff for loads of the calculation questions you might get, so make sure you know it inside out. Before you start plugging numbers into formulas, make sure they're in the right units. If they're not, you need to know how to convert them or you'll be tossing marks out the window. Learn all the definitions and formulas then have a bash at the questions.

Empirical and Molecular Formulas

Here's another page piled high with numbers — it's all just glorified maths really.

Empirical and Molecular Formulas are Ratios

You have to know what's what with empirical and molecular formulas, so here goes...

1) The **empirical formula** gives just the smallest whole number ratio of atoms in a compound.
2) The **molecular formula** gives the **actual** number of atoms in a molecule.
3) The molecular formula is made up of a whole **number** of empirical units.

Example: A molecule has an empirical formula of $C_4H_3O_2$, and a molecular mass of 166 g. Work out its molecular formula.

Compare the empirical and molecular mass.

First find the **empirical mass** — $(4 \times 12) + (3 \times 1) + (2 \times 16)$
$= 48 + 3 + 32 = 83$ g

Empirical mass is just like the relative formula mass... (if that helps at all...).

But the **molecular mass** is 166 g,

so there are $\frac{166}{83} = 2$ empirical units in the molecule.

The molecular formula must be the **empirical formula × 2**,
so the molecular formula = $C_8H_6O_4$. So there you go.

Empirical Formulas are Calculated from Experiments

You need to be able to work out empirical formulas from **experimental results** too.

Example: When a hydrocarbon is burnt in excess oxygen, 4.4 g of carbon dioxide and 1.8 g of water are made. What is the empirical formula of the hydrocarbon?

First work out how many moles of the products you have.

No. of moles of $CO_2 = \frac{\text{mass}}{M} = \frac{4.4}{12+(16\times2)} = \frac{4.4}{44} = 0.1$ moles

1 mole of CO_2 contains 1 mole of carbon atoms, so you must have started with **0.1 moles of carbon atoms.**

No. of moles of $H_2O = \frac{1.8}{(2\times1)+16} = \frac{1.8}{18} = 0.1$ moles

1 mole of H_2O contains 2 moles of hydrogen atoms (H), so you must have started with **0.2 moles of hydrogen atoms.**

Ratio C : H = 0.1 : 0.2 . Now you divide both numbers by the **smallest** — here it's 0.1.
So, the ratio C : H = 1 : 2. So the empirical formula must be CH_2.

This works because the only place the carbon in the carbon dioxide and the hydrogen in the water could have come from is the hydrocarbon.

As if that's not enough, you also need to know how to work out empirical formulas from the **percentages** of the different elements.

Example: A compound is found to have percentage composition 56.5% potassium, 8.7% carbon and 34.8% oxygen by mass. Calculate its empirical formula.

If you assume you've got 100 g of the compound, you can turn the % straight into mass, and then work out the number of moles as normal.

In **100 g** of compound there are:

Use $n = \frac{\text{mass}}{M}$

$\frac{56.5}{39} = 1.449$ moles of K $\frac{8.7}{12} = 0.725$ moles of C $\frac{34.8}{16} = 2.175$ moles of O

Divide each number of moles by the **smallest number** — in this case it's 0.725.

K: $\frac{1.449}{0.725} = 2.0$ C: $\frac{0.725}{0.725} = 1.0$ O: $\frac{2.175}{0.725} = 3.0$

The ratio of K : C : O = 2 : 1 : 3. So you know the empirical formula's got to be K_2CO_3.

Empirical and Molecular Formulas

Molecular Formulas are Calculated from Experimental Data Too

Once you know the empirical formula, you just need a bit more info and you can work out the **molecular formula** too.

Example:

When 4.6 g of an alcohol, with molar mass 46 g, is burnt in excess oxygen, it produces 8.8 g of carbon dioxide and 5.4 g of water.

Calculate the empirical formula for the alcohol and then its molecular formula.

Alcohols contain C, H and O.

The carbon in the CO_2 and the hydrogen in the H_2O must have come from the alcohol — work out the number of moles of each of these.

No. of moles of $CO_2 = \frac{\text{mass}}{\text{M}} = \frac{8.8}{44} = 0.2$ moles

1 mole of CO_2 contains 1 moles of C. So, 0.2 moles of CO_2 contains **0.2 moles of C**.

No. of moles $H_2O = \frac{\text{mass}}{\text{M}} = \frac{5.4}{18} = 0.3$ moles

1 mole of H_2O contains 2 moles of H. So, 0.3 moles of H_2O contain **0.6 moles of H**.

Mass of C = no. of moles × M = 0.2 × 12 = 2.4 g

Mass of H = no. of moles × M = 0.6 × 1 = 0.6 g

Mass of O = 4.6 – (2.4 + 0.6) = 1.6 g

Number of moles O = $\frac{\text{mass}}{\text{M}} = \frac{1.6}{16} = 0.1$ moles

Now work out the mass of carbon and hydrogen in the alcohol. The rest of the mass of the alcohol must be oxygen — so work out that too. Once you know the mass of O, you can work out how many moles there is of it.

Molar Ratio = C : H : O = 0.2 : 0.6 : 0.1 = 2 : 6 : 1

Empirical formula = C_2H_6O

Mass of empirical formula = (12 × 2) + (1 × 6) + 16 = 46 g

In this example, the mass of the empirical formula equals the molecular mass, so the empirical and molecular formulas are the same.

Molecular formula = C_2H_6O

When you know the number of moles of each element, you've got the molar ratio. Divide each number by the smallest.

Compare the empirical and molecular mass.

Practice Questions

Q1 Define empirical formula.

Q2 What is the difference between molecular formula and empirical formula?

Exam Questions

Q1 Hydrocarbon X has a molecular mass of 78 g. It is found to have 92.3% carbon and 7.7% hydrogen by mass. Calculate the empirical and molecular formulae of X. [3 marks]

Q2 When 1.2 g of magnesium ribbon is heated in air, it burns to form a white powder, which has a mass of 2 g. What is the empirical formula of the powder? [2 marks]

Q3 When 19.8 g of an organic acid, A, is burnt in excess oxygen, 33 g of carbon dioxide and 10.8 g of water are produced. Calculate the empirical formula for A and hence its molecular formula, if $M_r(A) = 132$. [4 marks]

Hint: organic acids contain C, H and O.

The Empirical Strikes Back...

With this stuff, it's not enough to learn a few facts parrot fashion, to regurgitate in the exam — you've gotta know how to use them. The only way to do this is to practise. Go through all the examples on these two pages again, this time working the answers out for yourself. Then test yourself on the Practice Exam Questions. It'll help you sleep at night — honest.

Equations and Calculations

Balancing equations'll cause you a few palpitations — as soon as you make one bit right, the rest goes pear-shaped.

*Balanced Equations have **Equal Numbers** of each Atom on **Both Sides***

1) Balanced equations have the **same number** of each atom on **both** sides. They're..well...you know...balanced.
2) You can only add more atoms by adding **whole compounds**. You do this by putting a number **in front** of a compound or changing the one that's already there. You **can't** mess with formulas — ever.

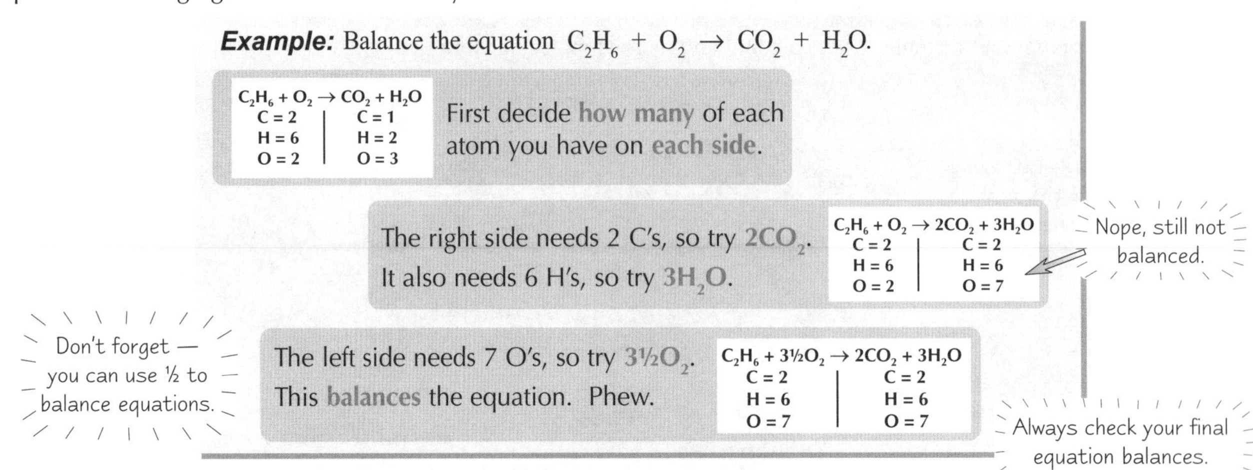

Example: Balance the equation $C_2H_6 + O_2 \rightarrow CO_2 + H_2O$.
$C_2H_6 + O_2 \rightarrow CO_2 + H_2O$
C = 2 | C = 1
H = 6 | H = 2
O = 2 | O = 3
First decide how many of each atom you have on each side.
The right side needs 2 C's, so try $2CO_2$. It also needs 6 H's, so try $3H_2O$.
$C_2H_6 + O_2 \rightarrow 2CO_2 + 3H_2O$
C = 2 | C = 2
H = 6 | H = 6
O = 2 | O = 7
Nope, still not balanced.
Don't forget — you can use ½ to balance equations.
The left side needs 7 O's, so try $3\frac{1}{2}O_2$. This balances the equation. Phew.
$C_2H_6 + 3\frac{1}{2}O_2 \rightarrow 2CO_2 + 3H_2O$
C = 2 | C = 2
H = 6 | H = 6
O = 7 | O = 7
Always check your final equation balances.

*In **Ionic Equations** the **Charges** must Balance too*

In ionic equations, only the **reacting particles** are included. You don't have to worry about the rest of the stuff.

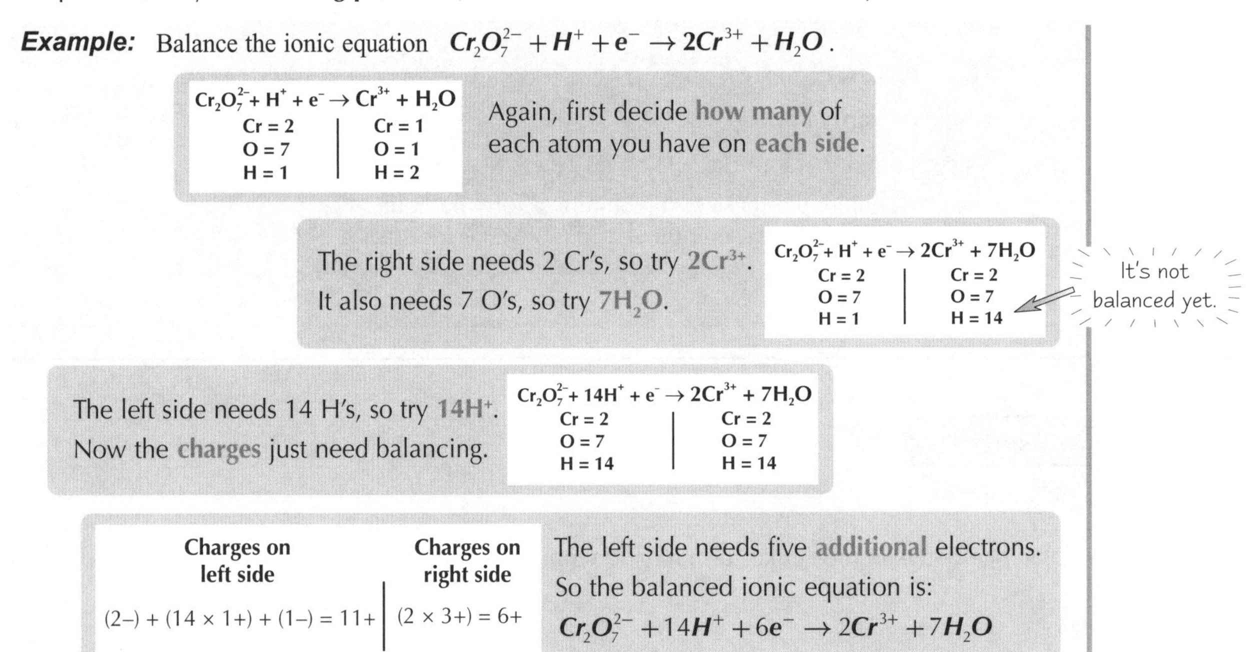

Example: Balance the ionic equation $Cr_2O_7^{2-} + H^+ + e^- \rightarrow 2Cr^{3+} + H_2O$.
$Cr_2O_7^{2-} + H^+ + e^- \rightarrow Cr^{3+} + H_2O$
Cr = 2 | Cr = 1
O = 7 | O = 1
H = 1 | H = 2
Again, first decide how many of each atom you have on each side.
The right side needs 2 Cr's, so try $2Cr^{3+}$. It also needs 7 O's, so try $7H_2O$.
$Cr_2O_7^{2-} + H^+ + e^- \rightarrow 2Cr^{3+} + 7H_2O$
Cr = 2 | Cr = 2
O = 7 | O = 7
H = 1 | H = 14
It's not balanced yet.
The left side needs 14 H's, so try $14H^+$. Now the charges just need balancing.
$Cr_2O_7^{2-} + 14H^+ + e^- \rightarrow 2Cr^{3+} + 7H_2O$
Cr = 2 | Cr = 2
O = 7 | O = 7
H = 14 | H = 14
Charges on left side
$(2-) + (14 \times 1+) + (1-) = 11+$
Charges on right side
$(2 \times 3+) = 6+$
The left side needs five additional electrons.
So the balanced ionic equation is:
$Cr_2O_7^{2-} + 14H^+ + 6e^- \rightarrow 2Cr^{3+} + 7H_2O$

Balanced Equations** can be used to Work out **Masses

Example: Calculate the mass of iron oxide produced if 28 g of iron is burnt in air.

$$2Fe + \tfrac{3}{2}O_2 \rightarrow Fe_2O_3$$

The molar mass, M, of Fe = 56 g, so the number of moles in 28 g of Fe = $\frac{\text{mass}}{M} = \frac{28}{56}$ = 0.5 moles

From the equation: 2 moles of Fe produces 1 mole of Fe_2O_3, so 0.5 moles of Fe produces 0.25 moles of Fe_2O_3.

M of Fe_2O_3 = (2 × 56) + (3 × 16) = 160 g

Mass of Fe_2O_3 = no. of moles × M = 0.25 × 160 = **40 g**. And that's your answer.

Once you know the number of moles and the molar mass (M) of Fe_2O_3, it's easy to work out the mass.

Equations and Calculations

That's not all... Balanced Equations can be used to Work out Gas Volumes

It's pretty handy to be able to work out **how much gas** a reaction will produce, so that you can use **large enough apparatus**. Or else there might be a rather large bang.

Example: How much gas is produced when 15 g of sodium is reacted with excess water at r.t.p.?

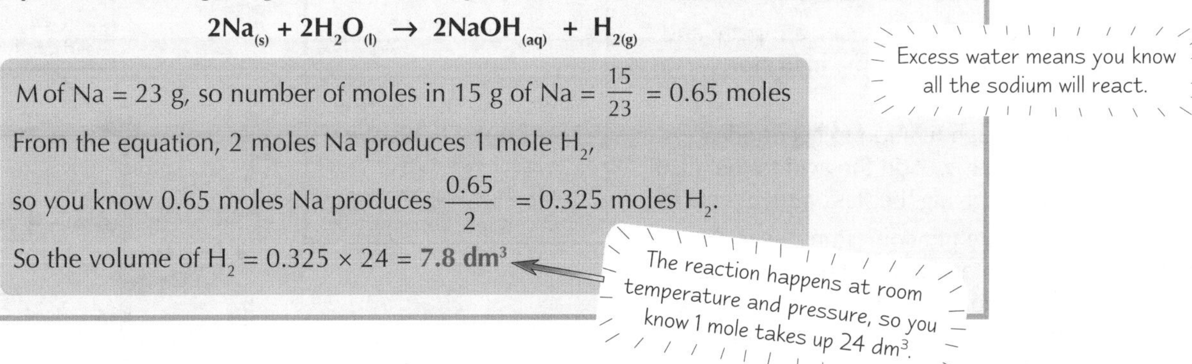

$$2Na_{(s)} + 2H_2O_{(l)} \rightarrow 2NaOH_{(aq)} + H_{2(g)}$$

M of Na = 23 g, so number of moles in 15 g of Na = $\frac{15}{23}$ = 0.65 moles

From the equation, 2 moles Na produces 1 mole H_2,

so you know 0.65 moles Na produces $\frac{0.65}{2}$ = 0.325 moles H_2.

So the volume of H_2 = 0.325 × 24 = **7.8 dm³**

Excess water means you know all the sodium will react.
The reaction happens at room temperature and pressure, so you know 1 mole takes up 24 dm³.

State Symbols Give a bit More Information about the Substances

State symbols are put after each compound in an equation. They tell you what **state of matter** things are in.

s = solid
l = liquid
g = gas
aq = aqueous (solution in water)

To show you what I mean, here's an example —

$$CaCO_{3(s)} + H_2SO_{4(aq)} \rightarrow CaSO_{4(aq)} + H_2O_{(l)} + CO_{2(g)}$$

solid, solution, solution, liquid, gas

Practice Questions

Q1 What is the state symbol for a solution of hydrochloric acid?

Q2 What is the difference between a full balanced equation and an ionic equation?

Exam Questions

Q1 Calculate the mass of ethene required to produce 258 g of chloroethane, C_2H_5Cl.

$C_2H_4 + HCl \rightarrow C_2H_5Cl$ [4 marks]

Q2 15g of calcium carbonate is heated strongly. $CaCO_{3(s)} \rightarrow CaO_{(s)} + CO_{2(g)}$

a) Calculate the mass of calcium oxide. [3 marks]

b) Calculate the volume of gas produced. [3 marks]

Q3 Balance this equation: $KI + Pb(NO_3)_2 \rightarrow PbI_2 + 2KNO_3$ [2 marks]

Don't get in a state about equations...

You're probably completely fed up of all these equations, calculations, moles and whatnot...well hang in there, there's just one more double page coming up. I've said it once, and I'll say it again — practise, practise, practise...it's the only road to salvation (by the way, where is salvation anyway?). Keep going...we're nearly there.

Titrations

*Titrations are used to find out the **concentration** of acid or alkali solutions. They're also handy when you're making salts of soluble bases.*

*Titrations need to be done **Accurately***

1) **Titrations** allow you to find out **exactly** how much acid is needed to **neutralise** a quantity of alkali.
2) You measure out some **alkali** using a pipette and put it in a flask, along with some **indicator**, e.g. **phenolphthalein**.
3) First of all, do a rough titration to get an idea where the **end point** is. Add the **acid** to the alkali using a **burette** — giving the flask a regular **swirl**.
4) Now do an **accurate** titration. Run the acid in to within 2 cm^3 of the end point, then add the acid **dropwise**. If you don't notice exactly when the solution changed colour you've **overshot** and your result won't be accurate.
5) **Record** the amount of acid used to **neutralise** the alkali. It's best to **repeat** this process a few times, making sure you get the same answer each time.

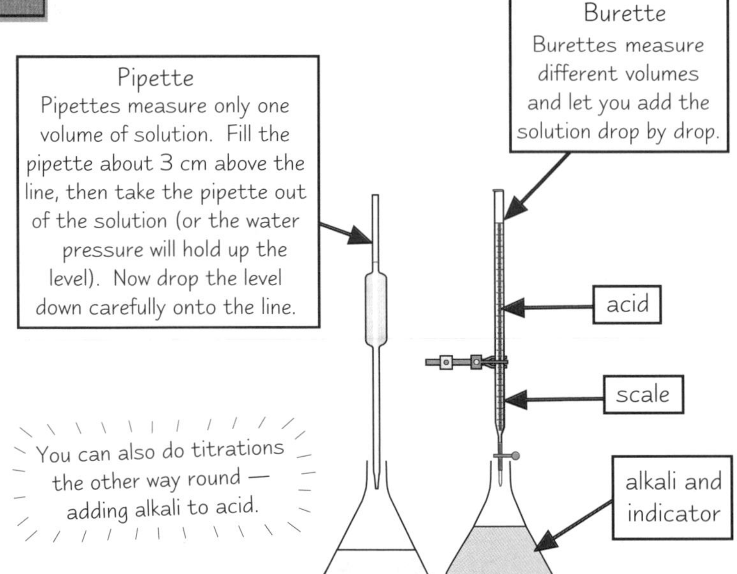

Pipette
Pipettes measure only one volume of solution. Fill the pipette about 3 cm above the line, then take the pipette out of the solution (or the water pressure will hold up the level). Now drop the level down carefully onto the line.
Burette
Burettes measure different volumes and let you add the solution drop by drop.
acid
scale
alkali and indicator
You can also do titrations the other way round — adding alkali to acid.

Indicators** Show you when the Reaction's **Just Finished

Indicators change **colour**, as if by magic. In titrations, indicators that change colour quickly over a **very small pH range** are used so you know **exactly** when the reaction has ended.

The main two indicators for **acid/alkali reactions** are —

methyl orange — turns **yellow** to **red** when adding acid to alkali.
phenolphthalein — turns **red** to **colourless** when adding acid to alkali.

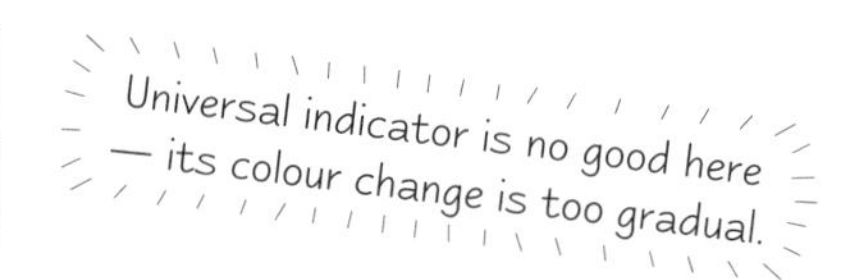

Universal indicator is no good here — its colour change is too gradual.

*You can Calculate **Molarities** from Titrations*

Now for the calculations...

Example: 25 cm^3 of 0.5 M HCl was used to neutralise 35 cm^3 of NaOH solution. Calculate the concentration of the sodium hydroxide solution.

First write a **balanced equation** and decide **what you know** and what you **need to know**:

$$\underset{\substack{25cm^3 \\ 0.5\,M}}{HCl} + \underset{\substack{35cm^3 \\ ?}}{NaOH} \rightarrow NaCl + H_2O$$

Now work out how many **moles of HCl** you have:

It's just the formula from page 12.

$$\text{Number of moles HCl} = \frac{\text{concentration} \times \text{volume (cm}^3)}{1000} = \frac{0.5 \times 25}{1000} = 0.0125 \text{ moles}$$

From the equation, you know 1 mole of HCl neutralises 1 mole of NaOH.
So 0.0125 moles of HCl must neutralise **0.0125** moles of NaOH.

Now it's a doddle to work out the **concentration of NaOH**.

$$\text{Concentration of NaOH}_{(aq)} = \frac{\text{moles of NaOH} \times 1000}{\text{volume (cm}^3)} = \frac{0.0125 \times 1000}{35} = \mathbf{0.36\ mol\ dm^{-3}}$$

Titrations

You use a **Pretty Similar Method** to Calculate **Volumes** for Reactions

This is usually used for **planning experiments**.

You need to use this formula again, but this time **rearrange** it to find the volume. →

$$\text{number of moles} = \frac{\text{concentration} \times \text{volume (cm}^3)}{1000}$$

Example: 20.4 cm^3 of a 0.5 M solution of sodium carbonate reacts with 1.5 M nitric acid. Calculate the volume of nitric acid required to neutralise the sodium carbonate.

Like before, first write a **balanced equation** for the reaction and decide **what you know** and what you **want to know**:

$Na_2CO_3 + 2HNO_3 \rightarrow 2NaNO_3 + H_2O + CO_2$

Na_2CO_3	$2HNO_3$
20.4 cm^3	**?**
0.5 M	**1.5 M**

Now work out how many **moles** of Na_2CO_3 you've got:

$$\text{No. of moles of } Na_2CO_3 = \frac{\text{concentration} \times \text{volume (cm}^3)}{1000} = \frac{0.5 \times 20.4}{1000} = 0.0102 \text{ moles}$$

1 mole of Na_2CO_3 neutralises 2 moles of HNO_3,
so 0.0102 moles of Na_2CO_3 neutralises **0.0204 moles of HNO_3**.

Now you know the number of moles of HNO_3 and the concentration, you can work out the **volume**:

$$\text{Volume of } HNO_3 = \frac{\text{number of moles} \times 1000}{\text{concentration}} = \frac{0.0204 \times 1000}{1.5} = \mathbf{13.6\ cm^3}$$

Practice Questions

Q1 Describe the procedure for doing a titration.

Q2 What colour change would you expect to see if you added hydrochloric acid to a conical flask containing sodium hydroxide and methyl orange?

Exam Questions

Q1 Calculate the concentration of a solution of ethanoic acid, CH_3COOH, if 25.4 cm^3 of it is neutralised by 14.6 cm^3 of 0.5 M sodium hydroxide solution. **$CH_3COOH + NaOH \rightarrow CH_3COONa + H_2O$** [3 marks]

Q2 You are supplied with a 0.75 g of calcium carbonate and a solution of 0.25 M sulphuric acid.
What volume of acid will be needed to neutralise the calcium carbonate?
$CaCO_3 + H_2SO_4 \rightarrow CaSO_4 + H_2O + CO_2$ [4 marks]

Burettes and pipettes — big glass things, just waiting to be dropped...

Titrations are annoyingly fiddly. But you do get to use big, impressive looking equipment and feel like you're doing something important. It's really tempting to rush it and let half the acid gush into the alkali first. But it's totally not worth it, cos you'll just have to do it again. Yep, this is definitely one of those slow-and-steady-wins-the-race situations.

Ionic Bonding

Every atom's aim in life is to have a full outer shell of electrons. Once they've managed this, that's it — they're happy.

Compounds are Atoms of Different Elements Bonded Together

1) When different elements join or bond together, you get a **compound**.
2) There's two main types of bonding in compounds — **ionic** and **covalent**. You need to make sure you've got them **both** totally sussed.

When the elements hydrogen (H_2) and oxygen (O_2) combine, the compound water (H_2O) is formed.

Ionic Bonding is when Ions are Stuck Together by Electrostatic Attraction

1) Ions are formed when electrons are **transferred** from one atom to another.
2) The simplest ions are single atoms which have either lost or gained 1, 2 or 3 electrons so that they've got a **full outer shell**.

Here's some examples of ions:

A sodium atom (Na) **loses** 1 electron to form a sodium ion (Na^+)	$Na \rightarrow Na^+ + e^-$
A magnesium atom (Mg) **loses** 2 electrons to form a magnesium ion (Mg^{2+})	$Mg \rightarrow Mg^{2+} + 2e^-$
A chlorine atom (Cl) **gains** 1 electron to form a chloride ion (Cl^-)	$Cl + e^- \rightarrow Cl^-$
An oxygen atom (O) **gains** 2 electrons to form an oxide ion (O^{2-})	$O + 2e^- \rightarrow O^{2-}$

3) **Electrostatic attraction** holds positive and negative ions together — it's **very** strong. When atoms are held together like this, it's called **ionic bonding**.

Sodium Chloride and Magnesium Oxide are Ionic Compounds

1) The formula of sodium chloride is **NaCl**. It just tells you that sodium chloride is made up of **Na^+ ions** and **Cl^- ions** (in a 1:1 ratio).
2) You can use '**dot and cross**' diagrams to show how ionic bonding works in sodium chloride —

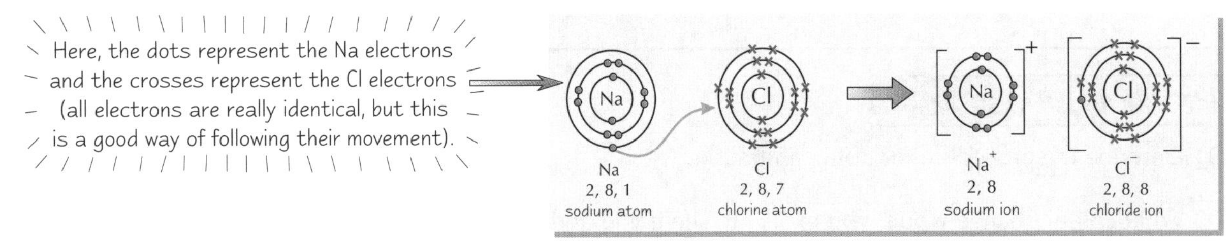

3) **Magnesium oxide**, MgO, is another good example:

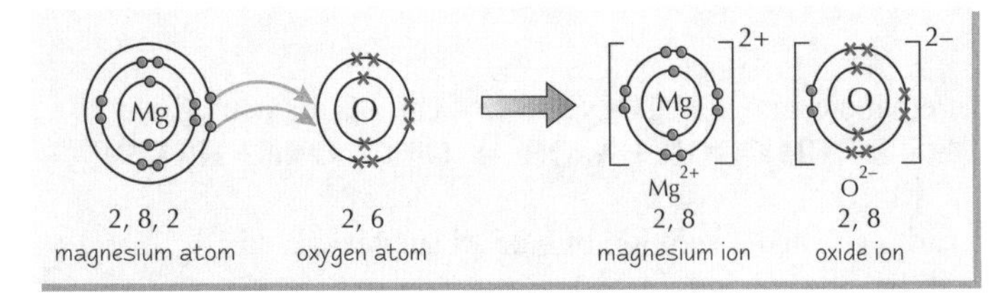

Some bonds will always be better than others..

The positive charges in the compound **balance** the negative charges exactly — so the total overall charge is **zero**. This is a dead handy way of checking the formula.

- In **NaCl**, the single + charge on the Na^+ ion balances the single – charge on the Cl^- ion.
- In magnesium chloride, **$MgCl_2$**, the 2+ charge on the Mg^{2+} ion balances the two individual – charges on the two Cl^- ions.

Ionic Bonding

Sodium Chloride has a **Giant Ionic Lattice** Structure

1) In **sodium chloride**, the Na^+ and the Cl^- ions are packed together in a regular structure called a **lattice**.
2) The structure's called '**giant**' because it's made up of the same basic unit repeated over and over again.
3) The sodium chloride lattice is **cube** shaped — different ionic compounds have different shaped structures, but they're all still giant lattices.
4) Sodium chloride's got very strong **ionic bonds**, so it takes loads of **energy** to break up the lattice. This gives it a high melting point (801°C).

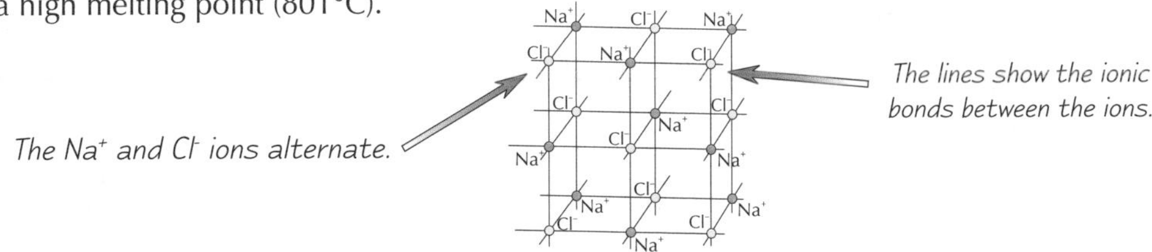

The Na^+ and Cl^- ions alternate.
The lines show the ionic bonds between the ions.

But it's not just melting points — the structure decides other **physical properties** too...

Ionic Structure Explains the **Behaviour** of Ionic Compounds

1) **Ionic compounds conduct electricity when they're molten or dissolved — but not when they're solid.** The ions in a liquid are free to move (and they carry a charge). In a solid they're fixed in position by the strong ionic bonds.
2) **Ionic compounds can be electrolysed (split up by electricity).** If a current is passed through a molten or dissolved ionic compound, the ions migrate (move) towards the electrode with the opposite charge to the ion — positive ions move to the negative electrode and vice versa.
3) **Ionic compounds are crystalline.** Crystalline just means that the atoms or ions are arranged regularly in structures with sharp edges.

Practice Questions

Q1 What's a compound?

Q2 Draw a 'dot and cross' diagram showing the bonding between magnesium and oxygen.

Q3 What type of force holds ionic substances together?

Q4 What happens when a current is passed through a dissolved ionic compound?

Exam Questions

Q1 a) Draw a labelled diagram to show the structure of sodium chloride. [3 marks]

b) What is the name of this type of structure? [1 mark]

c) Would you expect sodium chloride to have a high or a low melting point? Explain your answer. [4 marks]

Q2 a) Ions can be formed by electron transfer. Explain this and give an example for a positive and a negative ion. [3 marks]

b) Solid lead bromide does not conduct electricity, but molten lead bromide does. Explain this with reference to ionic bonding. [5 marks]

A black fly in your Chardonnay — isn't it ionic...

This stuff's easy marks in exams. Just make sure you can draw dot and cross diagrams showing the bonding in ionic compounds and you're sorted. Remember — atoms are lazy. It's easier to lose two electrons to get a full shell than it is to gain six, so that's what an atom's going to do. Practise drawing sodium chloride too, and don't stop till you're perfect.

Covalent Bonding

And now for covalent bonding — this is when atoms share electrons with one another so they've all got full outer shells.

Molecules are Groups of Atoms Bonded Together

Molecules are the **smallest parts** of compounds that can take part in chemical reactions.
They're formed when **2 or more** atoms bond together — it doesn't matter if the atoms are the **same** or **different**.
Chlorine gas (Cl_2), carbon monoxide (CO), water (H_2O) and ethanol (C_2H_5OH) are all molecules.

Molecules are held together by **covalent bonds**. In covalent bonding, two atoms **share** electrons, so they've **both** got full outer shells of electrons.

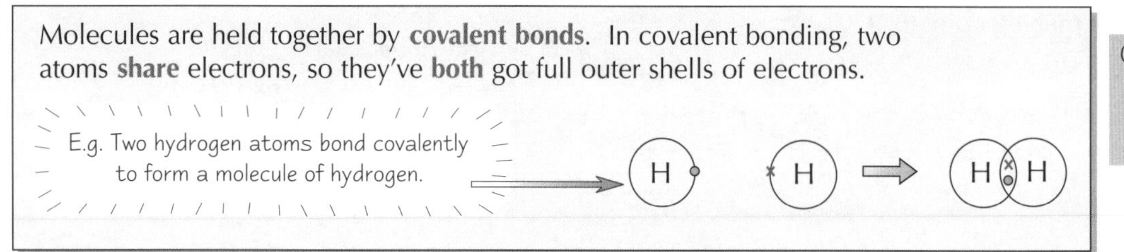

E.g. Two hydrogen atoms bond covalently to form a molecule of hydrogen.
H
H
H H

Covalent bonding happens between non-metals. Ionic bonding is between a metal and a non-metal.

Covalent Bonds can be Sigma (σ) Bonds...

1) The two hydrogen atoms above each have an electron in an **s orbital** (have a look back at page 4 if you've forgotten what an s orbital is). When the hydrogen atoms form an H_2 molecule, the two s orbitals overlap to make a **σ bond** (sigma bond):
2) The two s orbitals overlap in a straight line — this gives the **highest possible electron density** between the two nuclei. This is a **single** covalent bond and is shown as a single line between the atoms, like this: H — H

H H H_2

...or Pi (π) Bonds

1) A **π bond** is formed when two electrons in **p orbitals** overlap.
2) It's got **two parts** to it — one 'above' and one 'below' the molecular axis. This is because the π orbitals which overlap are **dumbbell shaped** (again, see page 4 if you're bewildered).
3) The π bond is **less tightly bound** to the two nuclei than the σ bond, so the **electron density** is lower. This means π bonds are **weaker** than σ bonds and molecules with π bonds are **more reactive**.

Atoms don't just form single bonds — **double** or even **triple covalent bonds** can form too. An example of a compound with a double bond is **ethene**, C_2H_4.

Its carbon-carbon **double** bond is drawn as C=C, but you're not really going to get little equals signs holding atoms together. The double bond is actually made up of a **σ bond** plus a **π bond**.

Ethene's π bond makes it lots **more reactive** than ethane, which has only got σ bonds.

σ bond
p orbitals
π bond

Ethene

You can also show ethene's bonding as a **dot and cross diagram**.

Covalent Bonding

Make sure you can Draw the Bonding in these Molecules

These diagrams don't show all the electrons in the molecules, just the ones in the **outer shells** —

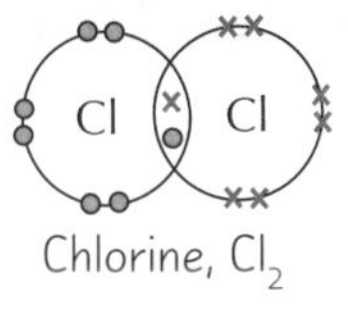

Chlorine, Cl_2

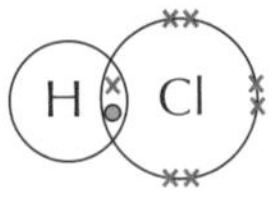

Hydrogen chloride, HCl

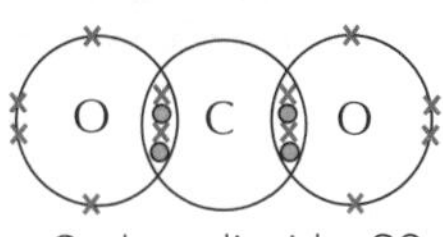

Carbon dioxide, CO_2

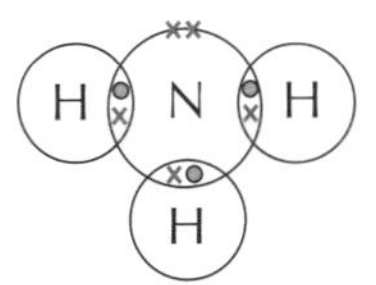

Ammonia, NH_3

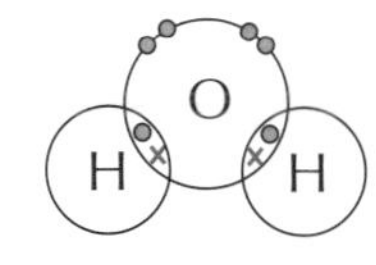

Water, H_2O

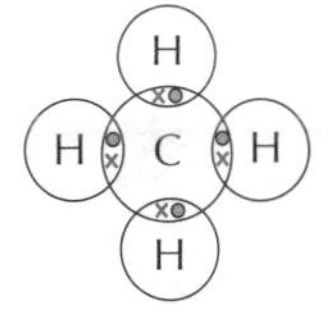

Methane, CH_4

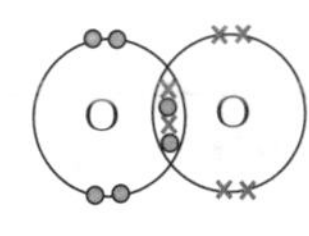

Oxygen, O_2

Dative Covalent Bonding is where Both Electrons come from One Atom

The **ammonium ion** (NH_4^+) is formed by dative (or coordinate) covalent bonding — it's an example the examiners love. It forms when the nitrogen atom in an ammonia molecule **donates a pair of electrons** to a proton (H^+) —

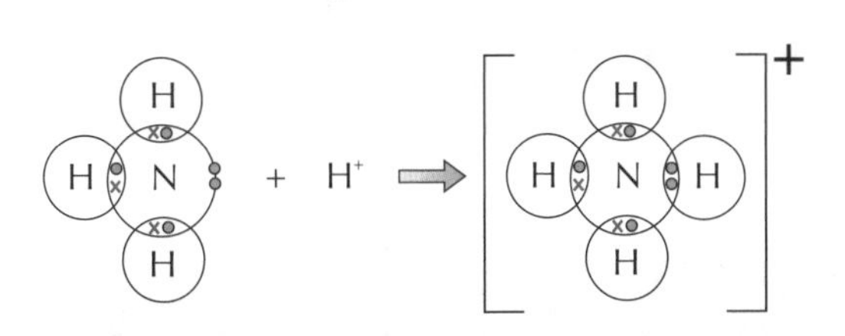

or

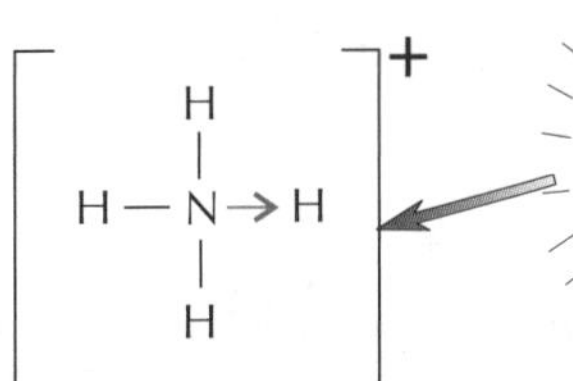

Dative covalent bonding is shown in diagrams by an arrow, pointing away from the 'donor' atom.

Hydrated metal ions use dative covalent bonding too.

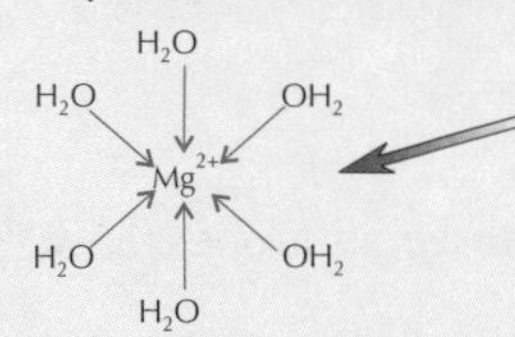

In complex ions like the (how's this for a good scrabble score) **hexaaquamagnesium ion**, $[Mg(H_2O)_6]^{2+}$, the oxygen atoms from six H_2O molecules each **donate** a pair of electrons to a Mg^{2+} ion, forming dative bonds with it. Molecules or ions that do this with metal ions like this are called **ligands**. (The overall charge of the hydrated ion is the same since the water molecules weren't charged to start with.)

Practice Questions

Q1 a) When two or more atoms combine, they form a ____________.

b) In covalent bonding, electrons are ________ between atoms.

Q2 Draw a dot and cross diagram to show the arrangement of the outer electrons only in a molecule of hydrogen chloride.

Exam Questions

Q1 Methane, CH_4, is an organic molecule.

a) What type of bonding would you expect it to have? [1 mark]

b) Draw a dot and cross diagram to show the full electronic arrangement in a molecule of methane. [2 marks]

Q2 a) In terms of covalent bonds, explain why ethene is more reactive than ethane. [4 marks]

b) i) What type of bonding is present in the hexaaquacopper(II) ion, $[Cu(H_2O)_6]^{2+}$? [1 mark]

ii) Explain how this type of bonding operates. [2 marks]

Steak and kidney — a great pie bond...

More pretty diagrams to learn here folks — practise till you get every single dot and cross in the right place. It's totally amazing to think of these titchy little atoms sorting themselves out so they've got full outer shells of electrons. Remember — covalent bonding happens between two non-metals, whereas ionic bonding happens between a metal and a non-metal.

Giant Molecular Structures & Metallic Bonding

Atoms can form giant structures as well as piddling little molecules — well...'giant' in molecular terms anyway. Compared to structures like the Eiffel Tower or even your granny's carriage clock, they're still unbelievably tiny.

Diamond, Graphite and Silicon(IV) Oxide have Giant Molecular Structures

1) **Giant molecular** structures have a huge network of **covalently** bonded atoms. (They're sometimes called **macromolecular structures** too.)
2) The reason **carbon** and silicon atoms can form this type of structure is that they can each form four strong, covalent bonds.

Diamond is the Hardest known Substance

Diamond is made up of **carbon atoms**. Each carbon atom is **covalently bonded** with σ bonds to **four** other carbon atoms. The atoms arrange themselves in a **tetrahedral** shape — this is a crystal lattice structure.

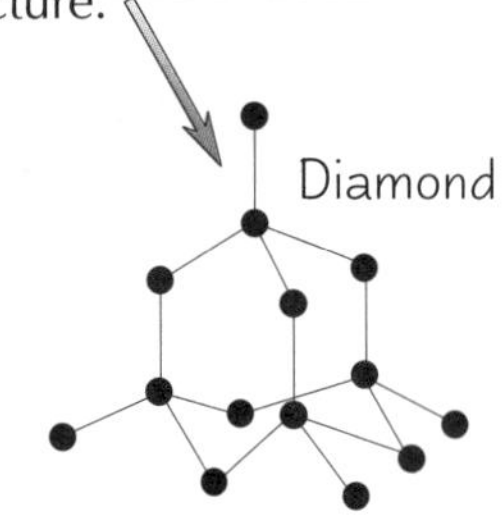

Because of its **strong covalent** bonds:
1) Diamond has a **very high melting point** — it actually sublimes at over 3800 K.
2) Diamond is extremely **hard** — it's used in diamond-tipped drills and saws.
3) **Vibrations** travel easily through the stiff lattice, so it's a **good thermal conductor**.
4) It **can't conduct** electricity — all the electrons are held in localised electron bonds.
5) It won't dissolve in **any** solvent.

You can 'cut' diamond to form gemstones. The regular structure makes it refract light a lot, which is why it sparkles.

'Sublimes' means it changes straight from a solid to a gas, skipping out the liquid stage.

Graphite is another Allotrope of Carbon

Allotropes are different forms of the **same element** in the **same state**. Carbon actually forms **three** allotropes, **graphite**, **diamond** and **fullerenes** — luckily, you only need to know about the first two.

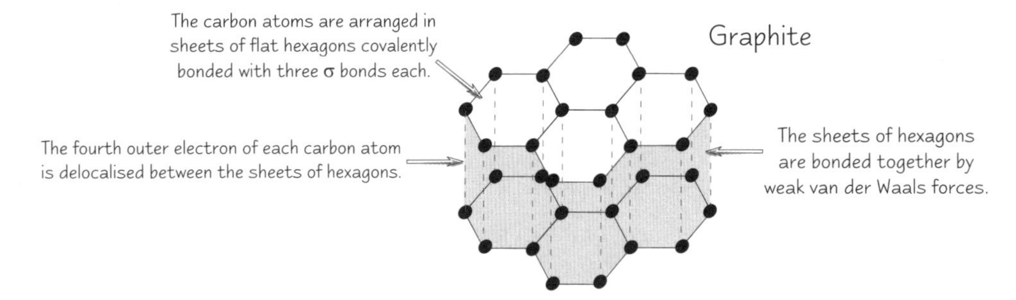

Graphite
The carbon atoms are arranged in sheets of flat hexagons covalently bonded with three σ bonds each.
The fourth outer electron of each carbon atom is delocalised between the sheets of hexagons.
The sheets of hexagons are bonded together by weak van der Waals forces.

Graphite's **structure** means it has some **different properties** from diamond.

1) The weak bonds **between** the layers in graphite are easily broken, so the sheets can slide over each other — graphite feels **slippery** and is used as a **dry lubricant** and in **pencils**.
2) The **'delocalised'** electrons in graphite aren't attached to any particular carbon and are **free to move** along the sheets, so an **electric current** can flow.

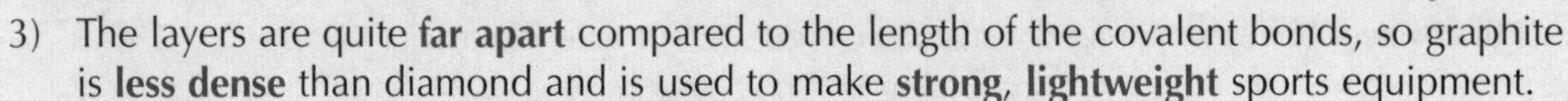

3) The layers are quite **far apart** compared to the length of the covalent bonds, so graphite is **less dense** than diamond and is used to make **strong, lightweight** sports equipment.
4) Because of the **strong covalent bonds** in the hexagon sheets, graphite also has a **very high melting point** (it sublimes at over 3900 K).
5) Like diamond, graphite is **insoluble** in any solvent. The covalent bonds in the sheets are **too difficult** to break.

Giant Molecular Structures & Metallic Bonding

Silicon(IV) Oxide has a Tetrahedral Arrangement

This bit's just for people doing OCR Salters.

1) **Silicon dioxide** or **silica** (SiO_2) is found as **quartz** or **sand** (sand's not pure, it's got lots of bits of other stuff in too).
2) Each silicon atom **covalently bonds** with **four oxygen atoms** in a **tetrahedral** arrangement to form a big **crystal lattice**.
3) Its structure **isn't** exactly the same as diamond's, because the oxygen atoms can only bond with **two silicon atoms**.

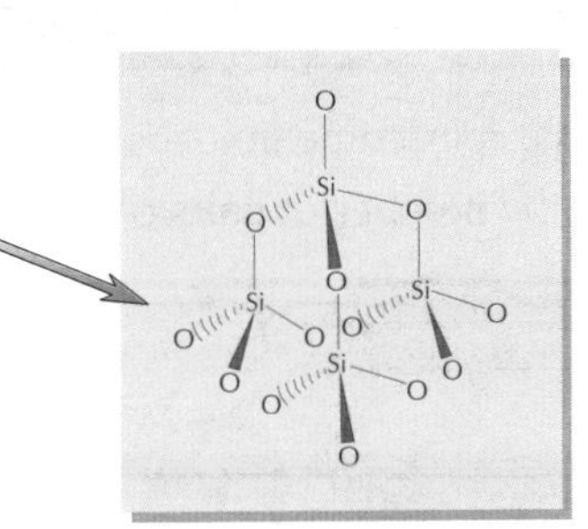

Metals have Giant Structures Too

Metal elements exist as **giant metallic lattice structures**.

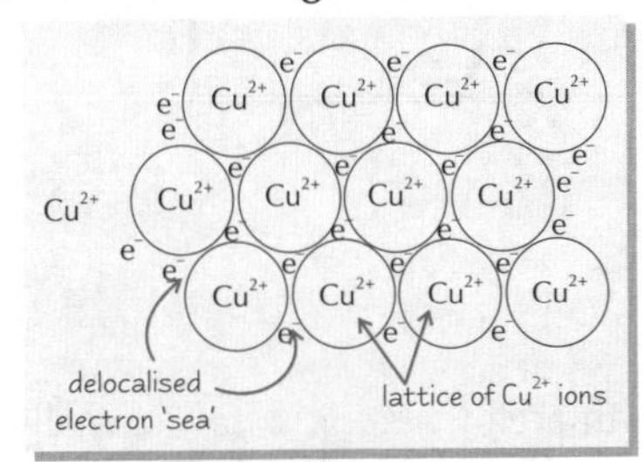

1) The outermost shell of electrons on a metal atom is **delocalised** and free to move. This leaves a **positive metal ion**, e.g. Na^+, Mg^{2+}, Al^{3+}.
2) The positive metal ions are **attracted** to the delocalised negative electrons. They form a lattice of closely packed positive ions in a **sea** of delocalised electrons — this is **metallic bonding**.

Metallic bonding explains why metals do what they do —

1) The **number of delocalised electrons per atom** affects the melting point. The **more** there are, the **stronger** the bonding will be and the **higher** the melting point. Mg^{2+} has **two** delocalised electrons per atom, so it's got a **higher melting point** than Na^+, which only has **one**. The **size** of the metal ion and the **lattice structure** also affect the melting point.
2) As there are **no bonds** holding specific ions together, the metal ions can "**creep**" when the structure is pulled, so metals are **malleable** (a posh word for bendable) and **ductile** (can be drawn into a wire).
3) The delocalised electrons can pass **kinetic energy** to each other, making metals **good thermal conductors**.
4) Metals are **good electrical conductors** because the **delocalised electrons** can carry a **current**.
5) Metals are **insoluble**, except in other **liquid metals**, because of the **strength** of the metallic bonds.

Practice Questions

Q1 How are the carbon sheets in graphite held together?

Q2 In silica, how many oxygen atoms are bonded to each silicon atom?

Q3 Why are metals malleable?

Exam Questions

Q1 Carbon can be found as the allotropes diamond and graphite.

a) What type of structure do diamond and graphite display? [1 mark]

b) Draw diagrams to illustrate the structures of diamond and graphite. [2 marks]

c) Compare and explain the electrical conductivities of diamond and graphite in terms of their structure and bonding. [4 marks]

Q2 Illustrate with a suitable labelled diagram the structure of copper and explain what is meant by metallic bonding. [4 marks]

Carbon is a girl's best friend...

Examiners love giving you questions on diamond and graphite. Close the book and do a quick sketch of each allotrope, together with a list of their properties — then look back at the page and see what you missed. It might be less fun than ironing your underwear, but it's much more useful and the only way to make sure you sparkle in the exam.

Shapes of Molecules

Chemistry would be heaps more simple if all molecules were flat. But they're not.

Molecular Shape depends on **Electron Pairs** on the **Central Atom**

Molecules and molecular ions come in loads of **different shapes**.

The shape depends on the **number of pairs** of electrons in the outer shell of the central atom.

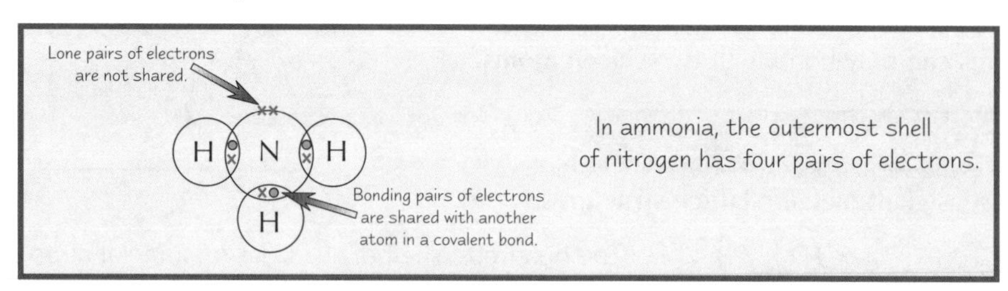
Lone pairs of electrons are not shared.
H
N
H
H
Bonding pairs of electrons are shared with another atom in a covalent bond.
In ammonia, the outermost shell of nitrogen has four pairs of electrons.

Electron Pairs exist as **Charge Clouds**

Bonding and lone pairs of electrons exist as **charge clouds**. A charge cloud is an area where you have a really **big chance** of finding an electron pair. The electrons don't stay still — they **whizz around** inside the charge cloud.

- The charge cloud for a **bonding-pair** is '**sausage**' shaped, because the electrons are attracted towards two different nuclei.
- The charge cloud for a **lone-pair** is more '**football**' shaped, because the electrons are pulled closer to the nucleus of the **central atom**.

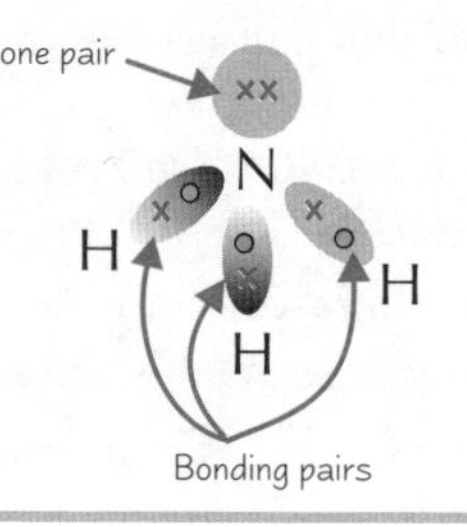
Lone pair
N
H
H
H
Bonding pairs

Here's ammonia again, but this time with charge clouds shown.

Electron Charge Clouds **Repel** Each Other

1) Electrons are all **negatively charged**, so it's pretty obvious that the charge clouds will **repel** each other as much as they can.
2) This sounds straightforward, but the **shape** of the charge cloud affects **how much** it repels other charge clouds. Lone-pair charge clouds repel **more** than bonding-pair charge clouds.
3) So, the **greatest** angles are between **lone-pairs** of electrons, and bond angles between bonding pairs are often **reduced** because they are pushed together by lone-pair repulsion.

Lone-pair/lone-pair bond angles are the biggest.	*Lone-pair/bonding-pair bond angles are the second biggest.*	*Bonding-pair/bonding-pair bond angles are the smallest.*

4) This is known by the long-winded name '**Valence-Shell Electron-Pair Repulsion Theory**'.

The central atoms in these molecules all have **four pairs** of electrons in their outer shells, but they're all **different shapes**.

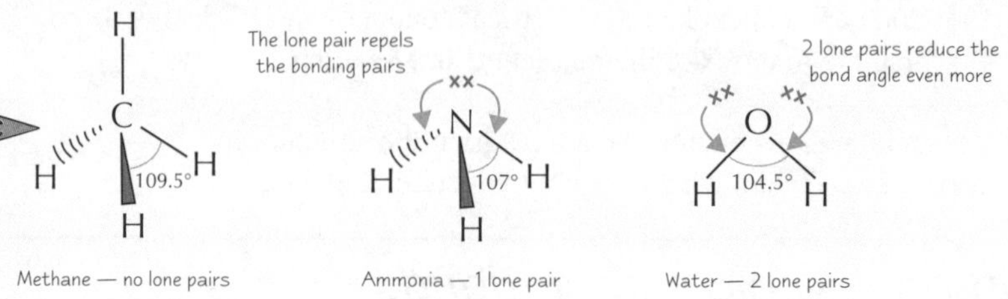

109.5°

Methane — no lone pairs

The lone pair repels the bonding pairs

107°

Ammonia — 1 lone pair

2 lone pairs reduce the bond angle even more

104.5°

Water — 2 lone pairs

Shapes of Molecules

Practise **Drawing** these Molecules

Just treat double bonds the same as single bonds (even though there might be slightly more repulsion from a double bond).

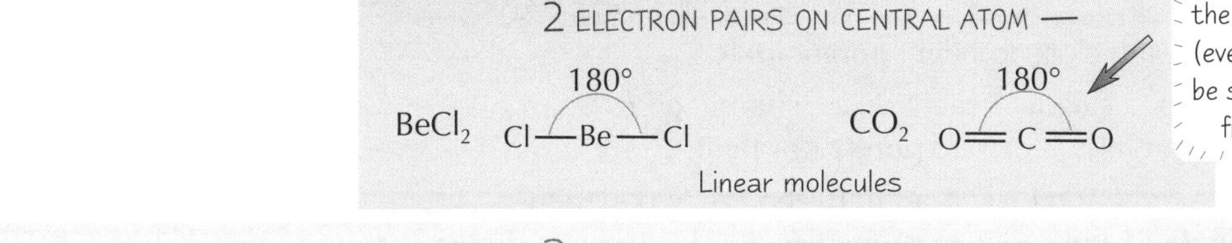

3 ELECTRON PAIRS ON CENTRAL ATOM —

BF_3 120° CO_3^{2-} 120° NO_3^- 120°

no lone pairs — trigonal planar

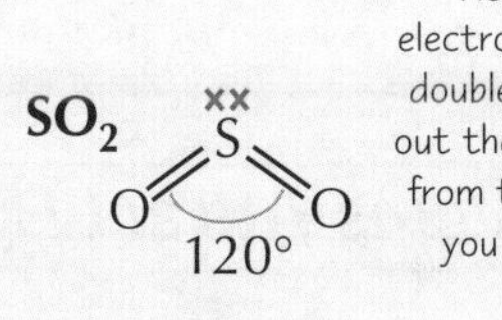

1 lone pair — non-linear or 'bent'

Here, the extra electron density in the double bonds cancels out the extra repulsion from the lone pair, so you still get 120°.

4 ELECTRON PAIRS ON CENTRAL ATOM —

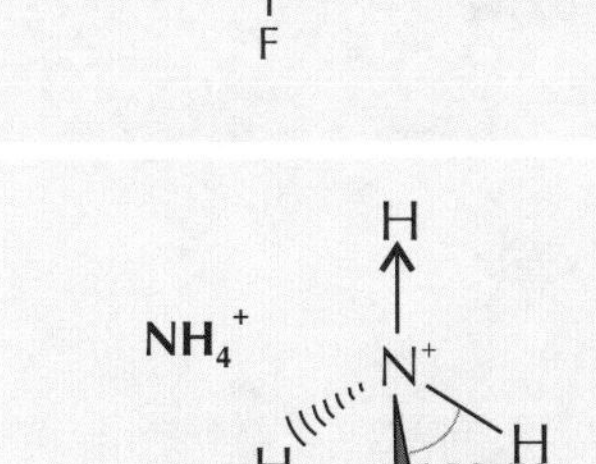
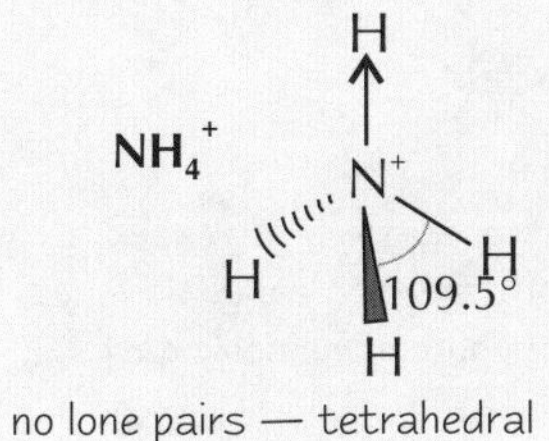

no lone pairs — tetrahedral

NH_3 107° SO_3^{2-} 107°

1 lone pair — trigonal pyramidal

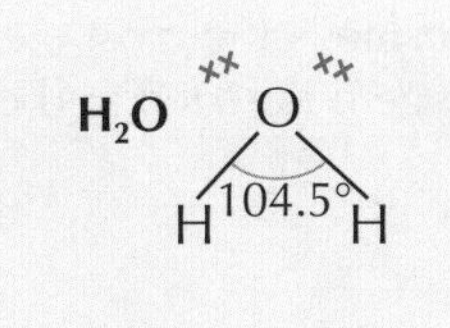

2 lone pairs — non-linear or 'bent'

Some central atoms can use d orbitals and can 'expand the octet' — which means they can have more than eight bonding electrons. E.g. In PCl_5, phosphorus has 10 electrons in its outermost shell, while in SF_6, sulphur has 12.

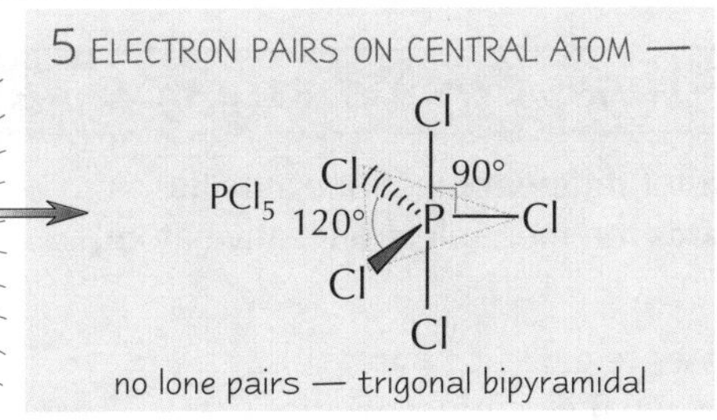

no lone pairs — trigonal bipyramidal

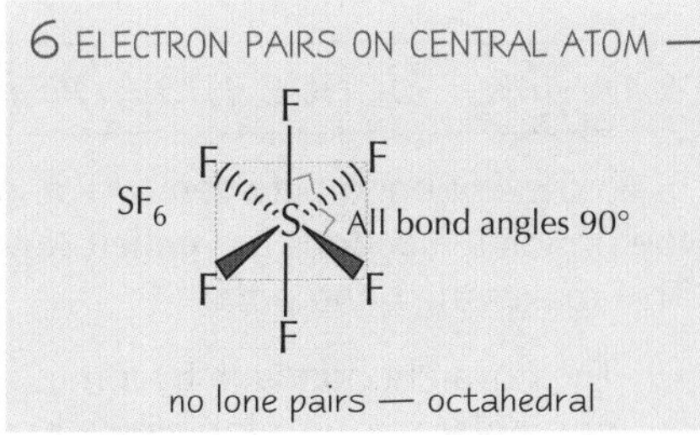

no lone pairs — octahedral

Practice Questions

Q1 What is a lone pair of electrons?

Q2 What is a charge cloud?

Q3 What shape is the charge cloud for a bonding pair of electrons?

Q4 Write down the order of repulsion between different kinds of electron pairs.

Q5 Draw a tetrahedral molecule.

Exam Questions

Q1 Nitrogen and boron can form the chlorides NCl_3 and BCl_3.

a) Draw 'dot and cross' diagrams to show the bonding in NCl_3 and BCl_3. [2 marks]

b) Draw the shapes of the molecules NCl_3 and BCl_3.
Show the approximate values of the bond angles on the diagrams and name each shape. [6 marks]

c) Explain why the shapes of NCl_3 and BCl_3 are different. [3 marks]

These molecules ain't square...

In the exam, those evil Examiners might try to throw you by asking you to predict the shape of an unfamiliar molecule. Don't panic — it'll be just like one you do know, e.g. PH_3 is the same shape as NH_3. Make sure you can draw every single molecule on this page. Yep, that's right — from memory. And you need to know what the shapes are called too.

Polarisation of Molecules and Ions

Opposites attract — like Jordan and Gareth Gates, that's all you need to know. Well OK that's not true, so get learnin'...

There's a Gradual **Transition** from Ionic to Covalent Bonding

1) Very few compounds come even close to being **purely ionic**.
2) Only bonds between atoms of a **single** element, like diatomic gases such as hydrogen (H_2) or oxygen (O_2), can be **purely covalent**.
3) So really, most compounds come somewhere **in between** the two extremes — meaning they've often got ionic **and** covalent properties, e.g. covalent hydrogen chloride gas molecules dissolve to form hydrochloric acid, which is an ionic solution.

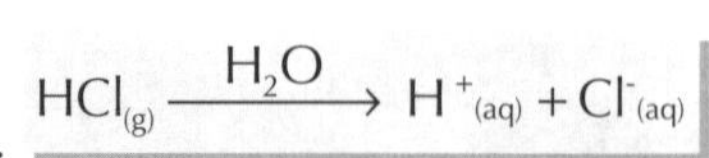

Some Atoms **Attract** Bonding Electrons More than Other Atoms

The ability to attract the bonding electrons in a covalent bond is called **electronegativity**.

1) Electronegativity is usually measured using the **Pauling scale**.
2) **Fluorine** is the most electronegative element — it's given a value of **4.0** on the Pauling scale. Oxygen, nitrogen and chlorine are also very strongly electronegative.

Element	H	C	N	Cl	O	F
Electronegativity	2.1	2.5	3.0	3.0	3.5	4.0

Electronegativity increases across periods and decreases down groups (ignoring the noble gases).

Covalent Bonds may be Polarised by **Differences** in **Electronegativity**

In a covalent bond between two atoms of **different** electronegativities, the bonding electrons are **pulled towards** the more electronegative atom. This makes the bond **polar**.

1) The covalent bonds in diatomic gases (e.g. H_2, Cl_2) are **non-polar** because the atoms have **equal** electronegativities and so the electrons are equally attracted to both nuclei.

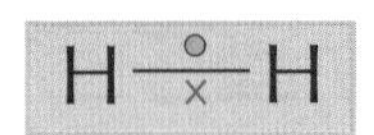

2) Some elements, like carbon and hydrogen, have pretty **similar** electronegativities, so bonds between them are essentially **non-polar**.
3) In a **polar bond**, the difference in electronegativity between the two atoms causes a **dipole**. A dipole is a **difference in charge** between the two atoms caused by a shift in **electron density** in the bond.
4) So what you need to **remember** is that the greater the **difference** in electronegativity, the **more polar** the bond.

Permanent polar bonding

Polar Bonds **don't** always make **Polar Molecules**

Whether a molecule has a **permanent dipole** depends on its **shape** and the **polarity** of its bonds.

1) So in a simple molecule, such as **hydrogen chloride**, the polar bond gives the whole molecule a permanent dipole — it's a **polar molecule**.

$\overset{\delta+}{H}—\overset{\delta-}{Cl}$ polar

'δ' (delta) means 'slightly', so 'δ+' means 'slightly positive'.

2) A more complicated molecule may have **several polar bonds**. If the polar bonds are arranged so they point in opposite directions, they'll **cancel each other out** — the molecule is **non-polar** overall.

No dipole overall.

$\overset{\delta-}{O}=\overset{\delta+}{C}=\overset{\delta-}{O}$

3) If the polar bonds all point in roughly the **same direction**, then the molecule will be **polar**.

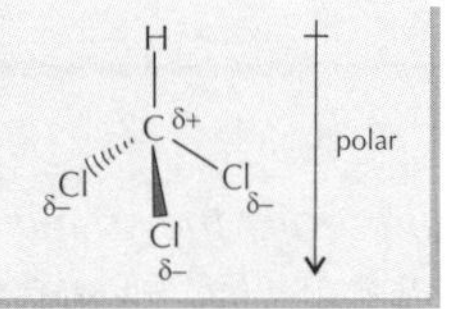

4) **Lone pairs of electrons** on the central atom also have an effect on the overall polarity and may **cancel out** the dipole created by the bonding pairs.

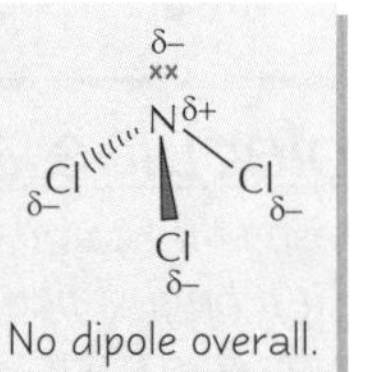

Polarisation of Molecules and Ions

Ions can be *Polarised* too

What normally happens in ionic compounds is that the **positive charge** on the **cation** attracts electrons towards it from the **anion** — this is **polarisation** again.

A cation is just a positive ion, an anion is a negative ion and an onion is the edible bulb of the Allium cepa plant.

1) **Small** cations with a **large charge** are **very polarising** because they have a **high charge density** — the positive charge is concentrated in the ion.
2) Large anions which have a **small charge** are **easily polarised** because they have a **low charge density** — the negative charge is more spread out in the ion.
3) If a compound contains a cation with a **high polarising ability** and an anion which is **easily polarised**, some of the anion's electron charge cloud will be dragged towards the positive cation.
4) If the compound is polarised enough, a **covalent bond** with a **dipole** is formed. It's now a **polar molecule**.

How much an ionic compound is polarised depends on the charge density of its ions. The charge density is just the charge/volume ratio.

$$\text{Charge density} = \frac{\text{charge}}{\text{volume}}$$

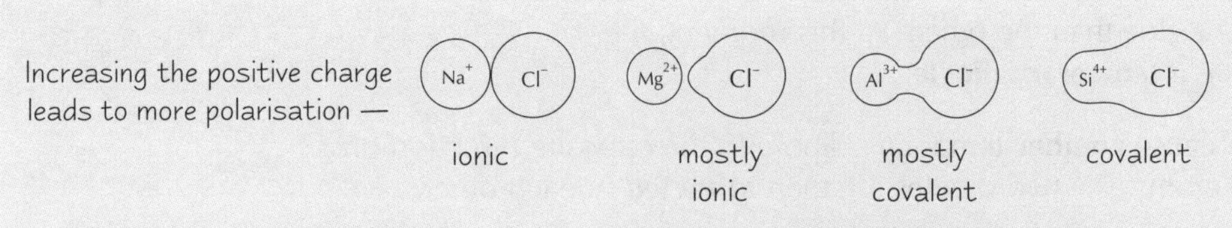

- The more a **covalent bond** is polarised, the more **ionic character** it gains.
- The more an **ionic bond** is polarised, the more **covalent character** it gains.
- You can work out why some compounds have **weird properties** by thinking about how **polarised** the compound is.

Practice Questions

Q1 What are the only bonds which can be purely covalent?

Q2 What is the most electronegative element?

Q3 What is a dipole?

Q4 What sort of ion is easily polarised?

Exam Questions

Q1 Many covalent molecules have a permanent dipole, due to differences in electronegativities.

a) Define the term electronegativity. [2 marks]

b) Draw the shapes and predict the overall polarity of the following molecules, marking any bond polarities clearly on your diagram:
(i) Br_2 (ii) H_2O (iii) CCl_4 (iv) NH_3 [8 marks]

c) Fluorine is the most electronegative element.
NF_3 is the same shape as NH_3, yet it has no permanent dipole. Why is this? [2 marks]

Q2 Metal/non-metal compounds are usually ionic, yet solid aluminium chloride exhibits many covalent characteristics. Explain why. [4 marks]

Enough of this chemistry rubbish. Here's some interesting facts...

If you chop the head off a beetle, it wouldn't die of being beheaded, but actually starvation. It's true. If you ate 14 lbs of almonds, you'd die of cyanide poisoning. It's true! Daddy-long-legs are actually the most poisonous insects in the world, but they can't pierce the skin... it's TRUE. Every night, the human body sweats enough to fill a swimming pool. It's true...

Intermolecular Forces

Intermolecular forces hold molecules together. They're pretty important, cos we'd all be gassy clouds without them.

Intermolecular Forces are *Very Weak*

Intermolecular forces are forces **between** molecules. They're much **weaker** than covalent, ionic or metallic bonds. There are three types you need to know about:

1) **Temporary dipole-induced dipole** or **van der Waals** forces (this is the weakest type)
2) **Permanent dipole-dipole interactions**
3) **Hydrogen bonding** (this is the strongest type)

Van der Waals Forces are Found Between *All* Atoms and Molecules

Van der Waals forces cause **all** atoms and molecules to be **attracted** to each other.

1) **Electrons** in charge clouds are always **moving** really quickly. At any particular moment, the electrons in an atom are likely to be more to one side than the other. At this moment, the atom would have a **temporary dipole**.

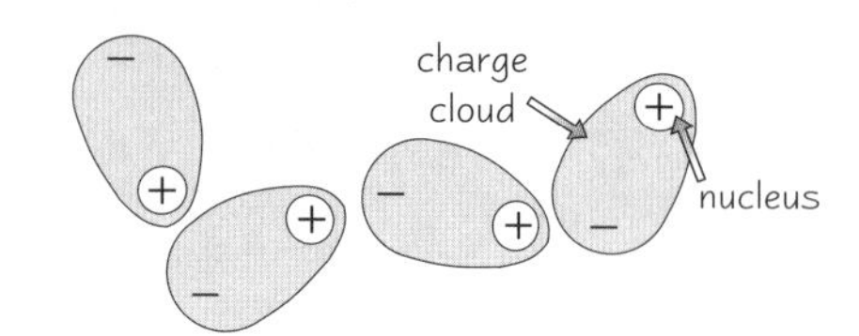

2) This dipole can cause **another** temporary dipole in the opposite direction on a neighbouring atom. The two dipoles are then **attracted** to each other.
3) The second dipole can cause yet another dipole in a **third atom**. It's kind of like a domino rally.
4) Because the electrons are constantly moving, the dipoles are being **created** and **destroyed** all the time. Even though the dipoles keep changing, the **overall effect** is for the atoms to be **attracted** to each another.

Stronger *Van der Waals Forces* mean *Higher Boiling Points*

1) Not all van der Waals forces are the same strength — larger molecules have **larger electron clouds**, meaning **stronger** van der Waals forces. Molecules with greater **surface areas** also have stronger van der Waals forces because they have a **bigger exposed electron cloud**.
2) When you **boil** a liquid, you need to **overcome** the intermolecular forces, so that the particles can **escape** from the liquid surface. It stands to reason that you need **more energy** to overcome **stronger** intermolecular forces, so liquids with stronger van der Waals forces will have **higher boiling points**.

Van der Waals forces affect other physical properties, such as melting point and viscosity, too.

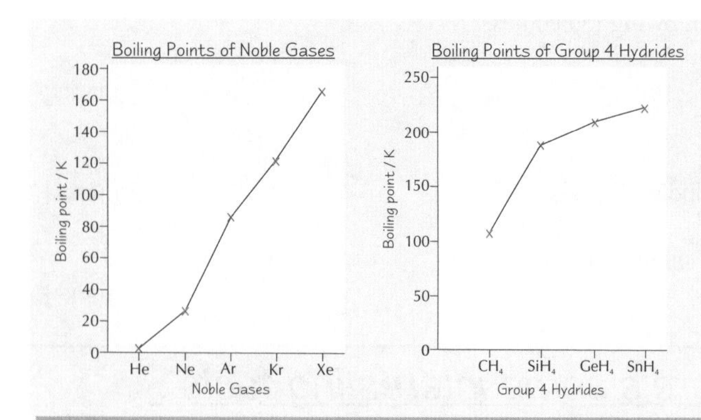

As you go **down** these groups:
1) the atomic/molecular **size** increases.
2) and the number of **shells** of electrons increases.

These both result in bigger **van der Waals forces**, meaning **higher boiling points**.

Intermolecular Forces

Polar Molecules have *Permanent Dipole-Dipole* Forces

The **δ+** and **δ-** charges on **polar molecules** cause **weak electrostatic forces** of attraction **between** molecules.

E.g. Hydrogen chloride gas has polar molecules. $\overset{\delta+}{H}-\overset{\delta-}{Cl}\cdots\cdots\overset{\delta+}{H}-\overset{\delta-}{Cl}\cdots\cdots\overset{\delta+}{H}-\overset{\delta-}{Cl}$

Even though they're weak, the forces are still much stronger than van der Waals forces.

Now this bit's pretty cool:
If you put an **electrostatically charged rod** next to a polar liquid, like water, it'll **move** towards the rod. I wouldn't believe me either, but it's true. It's because **polar liquids** contain molecules with **permanent dipoles**. It doesn't matter if the rod is **positively** or **negatively** charged. The polar molecules in the liquid can **turn around** so the oppositely charged end is attracted towards the rod.

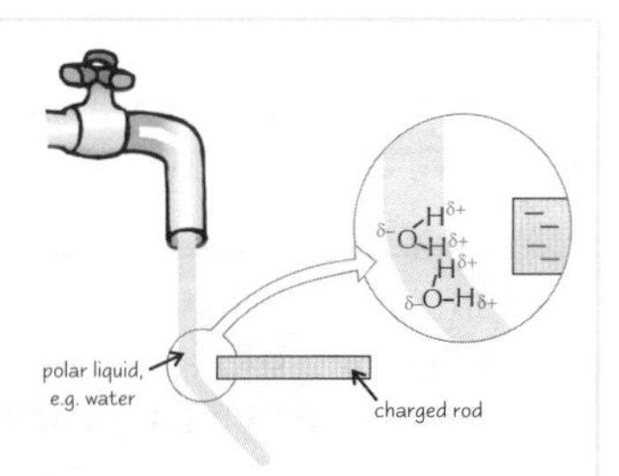

Hydrogen Bonding is the *Strongest* Intermolecular Force

1) Hydrogen bonding can **only** happen when **hydrogen** is covalently bonded to **fluorine**, **nitrogen** or **oxygen**. Hydrogen has a **high charge density** because it's so small and fluorine, nitrogen and oxygen are very **electronegative**. The bond is so **polarised** that the hydrogen of one molecule forms a weak bond with the fluorine, nitrogen or oxygen of **another molecule**.
2) Molecules which have hydrogen bonding are usually **organic**, containing **-OH** or **-NH** groups.
3) Hydrogen bonding has a huge effect on the properties of substances. They are **soluble** in water and have **higher boiling and freezing points** than non-polar molecules of a similar size.

A lone pair of electrons on the oxygen is attracted to the hydrogen.

Water, ammonia and hydrogen fluoride generally have the highest boiling points if you compare them with other hydrides in their groups, because of the extra energy needed to break the H bonds.

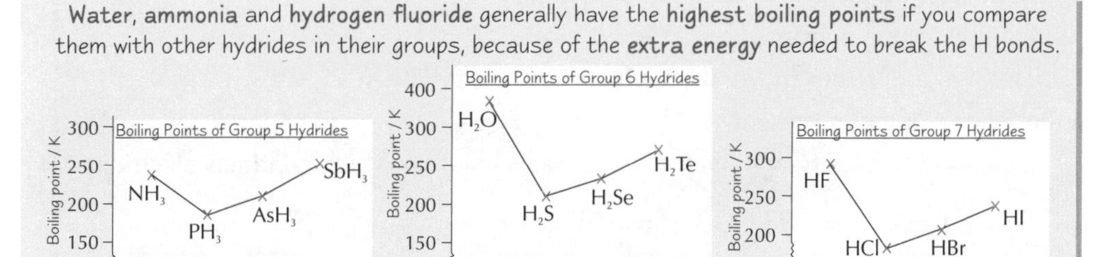

Water and ammonia both have hydrogen bonding.

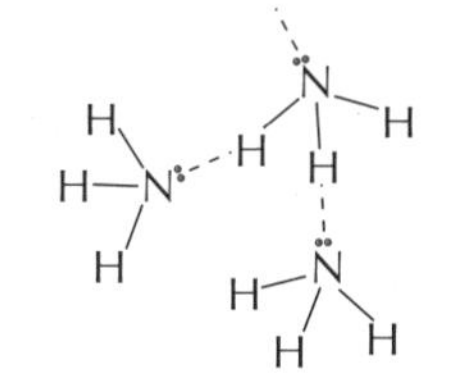

4) Ice is **less dense** than liquid water. This is because hydrogen bonds are relatively **long**.

Practice Questions

Q1 What's the strongest type of intermolecular force?

Q2 Which noble gas has the highest boiling point and why?

Q3 What is an H bond?

Exam Question

Q1 a) Name three types of intermolecular force. [3 marks]

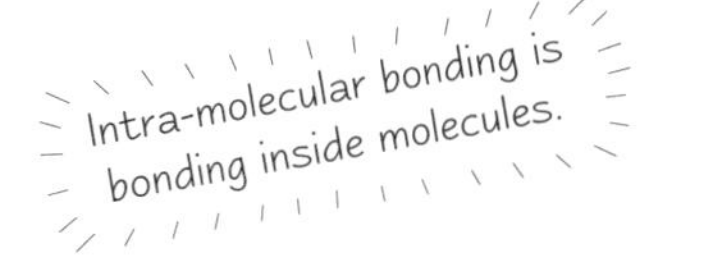

b) Water, H_2O, boils at 373 K.
Draw a clearly labelled diagram to show all the forms of intra- and intermolecular bonding in water. [4 marks]

c) State and explain the overall trend in boiling points for Group 6 hydrides.
Why is water's boiling point higher than expected in comparison to other Group 6 hydrides? [5 marks]

Van der Waal — a German hit for Oasis...

Just because intermolecular forces are a bit wimpy and weak, don't forget they're there. It'd all fall apart without them. Learn the 3 types — van der Waals, permanent dipole-dipole forces and hydrogen bonds. I bet fish are glad that water forms hydrogen bonds. If it didn't, their water would boil. (And they wouldn't have evolved in the first place).

Properties of Structures

Lots of this stuff you should already be able to recite in your sleep, but just in case it's fallen out of your brain, here it is...

The **Physical Properties** of Solids, Liquids and Gases Depend on **Particles**

1) A typical **solid** has its particles very **close** together. This gives it a high density and makes it **incompressible**. The particles **vibrate** about a **fixed point** and can't move about freely.

2) A typical **liquid** has a similar density to a solid and is virtually **incompressible**. The particles move about **freely** and **randomly** within the liquid, allowing it to flow.

3) In **gases**, the particles have **loads more** energy and are much **further apart**. So the density is generally pretty low and it's **very compressible**. The particles move about **freely**, with not a lot of attraction between them, so they'll quickly **diffuse** to fill a container.

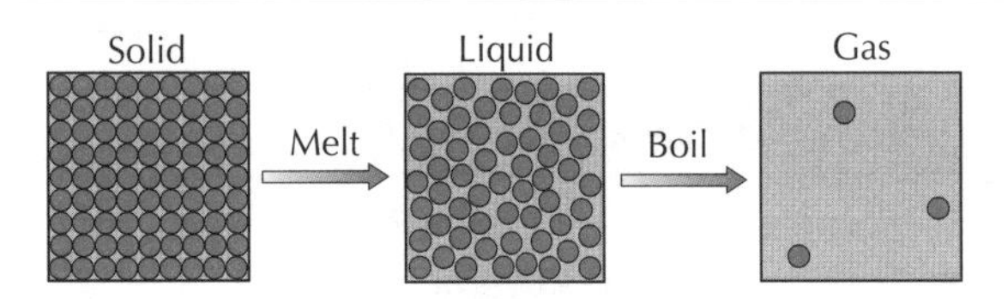

Edexcel only:

The jelly state* occurs in solids when the particles start feeling a bit tired and achy.

*Don't write this in the exam, cos I just made it up, like...

The Physical Properties of a **Solid** Depend on the **Nature** of its Particles

Here's some handy points that'll make AS chemistry a little less painful —

1) **Melting** and **boiling** points depend on **attraction** between particles.
2) The **closer** the particles, the **greater** the density.
3) If there are **charged** particles that are **free** to move, then it'll conduct electricity.
4) Solubility depends on the **type** of particles present.
5) Some substances (e.g. CO_2) **react chemically** with water, producing a solution which conducts electricity.

$$CO_{2(g)} + H_2O_{(l)} \rightleftharpoons H_2CO_{3(aq)} \rightleftharpoons 2H^+_{(aq)} + CO_3^{2-}{}_{(aq)}$$

freely moving ions

6) If a solid has a regular structure, it's called a **crystal**. The structure is a **crystal lattice**.

Covalent Bonds **Don't** Break during **Melting** and **Boiling***

This is something that confuses loads of people — prepare to be enlightened...

1) To **melt** or **boil** a simple covalent compound you only have to overcome the **van der Waals forces** or **hydrogen bonds** that hold the molecules together.
2) You **don't** need to break the much stronger covalent bonds that hold the atoms together in the molecules.
3) That's why simple covalent compounds have relatively **low melting** and **boiling points**. For example

When you boil water, you don't get hydrogen and oxygen.

Chlorine, Cl_2, has **stronger** covalent bonds than bromine, Br_2.
But under normal conditions, chlorine is a **gas** and bromine a **liquid**.
Bromine has the higher boiling point because its molecules are **bigger**, giving stronger van der Waals forces.

**Except for giant molecular substances, like silicon dioxide.*

Properties of Structures

Learn the **Properties** of the Main Substance Types

Make sure you know this stuff like the back of your spam —

Bonding	Examples	Melting and boiling points	Typical state at STP	Does solid conduct electricity?	Does liquid conduct electricity?	Is it soluble in water?
Ionic	NaCl $MgCl_2$	High	Solid	No (ions are held firmly in place)	Yes (ions are free to move)	Yes
Simple molecular (covalent)	CO_2 I_2 H_2O	Low (have to overcome van der Waals forces or hydrogen bonds, not covalent bonds)	Liquid or gas (water is liquid because it has hydrogen bonds)	No	No	Depends on how polarised the molecule is
Giant molecular (covalent)	Diamond Graphite SiO_2	High	Solid	No (except graphite)	— (will generally sublime)	No
Metallic	Fe Mg Al	High	Solid	Yes (delocalised electrons)	Yes (delocalised electrons	No

Practice Questions

Q1 Describe the motion of particles in solids, liquids and gases.

Q2 Why do gases diffuse to fill the space available?

Q3 What is a solid with a regular structure called?

Q4 What types of bonds must be overcome in order for a substance to boil or melt?

Q5 Do ionic compounds conduct electricity?

Q6 Why can metals conduct electricity?

Exam Questions

Q1

Substance	Melting point	Electrical conductivity of solid	Electrical conductivity of liquid	Solubility in water
A	High	Poor	Good	Soluble
B	Low	Poor	Poor	Insoluble
C	High	Good	Good	Insoluble
D	Very High	Poor	Poor	Insoluble

a) Identify the type of crystal structure present in each substance, A to D. [4 marks]

b) Which substance is most likely to be:
(i) diamond, (ii) aluminium, (iii) sodium chloride and (iv) iodine? [4 marks]

Q2 Explain the electrical conductivity of magnesium, sodium chloride and graphite.
In your answer you should consider the structure and bonding of each of these materials. [14 marks]

Gases — like flies in jam jars...

You need to learn the info in the table above. With a quick glance in my crystal ball, I can almost guarantee you'll need a bit of it in your exam...let me look a bit closer and tell you which bit....mmm....nah. It's clouded over. You'll have to learn the lot. Sorry. Tell you what — close the book and see how much of the table you can scribble out from memory.

The Periodic Table

The first 2 subsections are just for people doing OCR Salters (but they're a great read anyway...)

As far as Chemistry topics go, the periodic table is a bit of a biggie. So much so that they even want you to know the history of it. So make yourself comfortable and I'll tell you a story that began... oh, about 200 years ago...

In the **1800s**, they could only group elements by **Atomic Mass**

1) In the early 1800s, there was only 2 ways to categorise elements — by their **physical and chemical properties** and by their **relative atomic mass**. (The modern periodic table is arranged by proton number, but back then, they knew nothing about protons or electrons. The only thing they could measure was relative atomic mass.)
2) An English chemist called **John Newlands** had the first good stab at arranging the elements in 1863 — he noticed that if he arranged the elements in order of **mass**, similar elements appeared at regular intervals. So, he listed some known elements in rows of seven. He called this the **Law of Octaves**.

Li	Be	B	C	N	O	F
Na	Mg	Al	Si	P	S	Cl

3) The problem was, the pattern broke down on the third row, with many transition metals like Fe, Cu and Zn messing it up completely.

Dmitri Mendeleyev Created the **First Accepted Version**

1) In 1869, Russian chemist **Dmitri Mendeleyev** produced a much better table which wasn't far off the one we have today.
2) He arranged all the known elements by atomic mass (like Newlands did), but the clever thing he did was to leave **gaps** in the table where the next element didn't seem to fit. By putting in gaps, he could keep elements with similar chemical properties in the same group.
3) He also predicted the properties of **undiscovered elements** that would go in the gaps.
4) When elements were **later discovered** (e.g. germanium, scandium and gallium) with properties that matched Mendeleyev's predictions, it showed that clever old Mendeleyev had got it right.

	Group I	Group II	Group III	Group IV	Group V	Group VI	Group VII
Period 1	H						
Period 2	Li	Be	B	C	N	O	F
Period 3	Na	Mg	Al	Si	P	S	Cl
Period 4	K Cu	Ca Zn	* *	Ti *	V As	Cr Se	Mn Br
Period 5	Rb Ag	Sr Cd	Y In	Zr Sn	Nb Sb	Mo Te	* I

The **Modern Periodic Table** arranges Elements by **Proton Number**

The modern periodic table is pretty much the one produced by Henry Moseley in 1914.

	Group I	Group II											Group III	Group IV	Group V	Group VI	Group VII	Group O
								1 H Hydrogen 1										4 He 2
2	7 Li 3	9 Be 4											11 B 5	12 C 6	14 N 7	16 O 8	19 F 9	20 Ne 10
3	23 Na 11	24 Mg 12											27 Al 13	28 Si 14	31 P 15	32 S 16	35.5 Cl 17	40 Ar 18
4	39 K 19	40 Ca 20	45 Sc 21	48 Ti 22	51 V 23	52 Cr 24	55 Mn	56 Fe 26	59 Co 27	59 Ni 28	64 Cu 29	65 Zn 30	70 Ga 31	73 Ge 32	75 As 33	79 Se 34	80 Br 35	84 Kr 36
5	86 Rb 37	88 Sr 38	89 Y 39	91 Zr 40	93 Nb 41	96 Mo 42	99 Tc 43	101 Ru 44	103 Rh 45	106 Pd 46	108 Ag 47	112 Cd 48	115 In 49	119 Sn 50	122 Sb 51	128 Te 52	127 I 53	131 Xe 54
6	133 Cs 55	137 Ba 56	57-71 Lanthanides	179 Hf 72	181 Ta 73	184 W 74	186 Re 75	190 Os 76	192 Ir 77	195 Pt 78	197 Au 79	201 Hg 80	204 Tl 81	207 Pb 82	209 Bi 83	210 Po 84	210 At 85	222 Rn 86
7	223 Fr 87	226 Ra 88	89-103 Actinides															

1) He arranged the elements according to **atomic number** rather than by mass.
2) This fixed a few elements that Mendeleyev had put out of place using atomic mass.
3) He also added the **noble gases** (Group 0) which had been discovered in the 1890s.

1) The modern periodic table is arranged into **periods** (rows) and **groups** (columns).
2) All the elements **within a period** have the same number of **electron shells** (if you don't worry about s and p sub-shells)
— the elements of Period 1 (hydrogen and helium) both have 1 electron shell.
— the elements in Period 2 have 2 electron shells. And so on down the table...
3) All the elements **within a group** have the same number of **electrons in their outer shell**. This means they have similar physical and chemical properties. The group number tells you the number of electrons in the outer shell, e.g. Group I elements have 1 electron in their outer shell, Group IV elements have 4 electrons and so on...

The Periodic Table

You can use the Periodic Table to work out **Electron Configurations**

The periodic table can be split into an **s block**, **d block** and **p block** like this. Doing this shows you which sub-shells all the electrons go into.

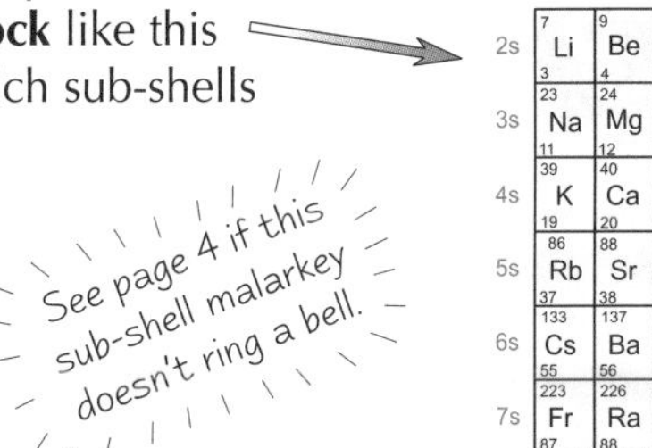

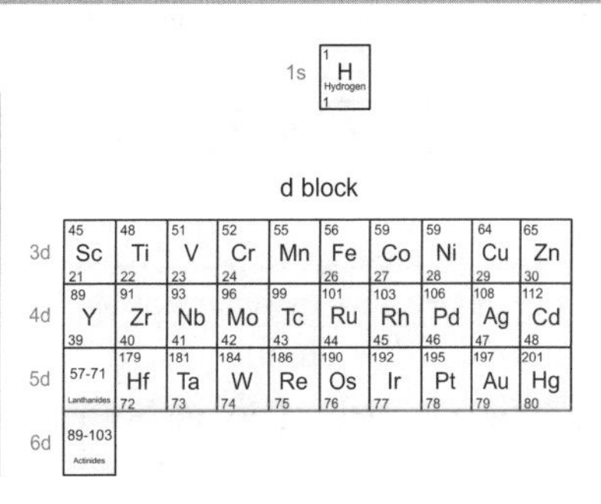

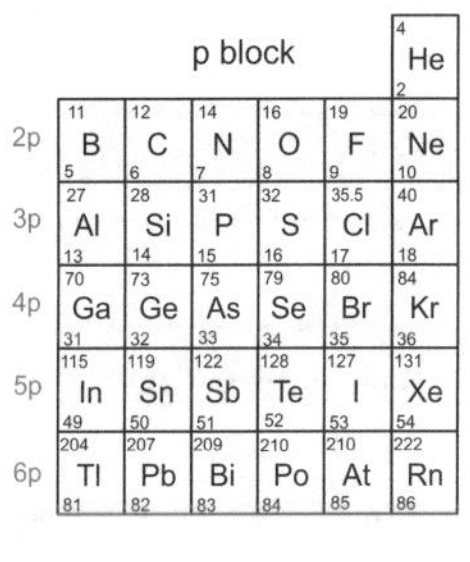

1) The **s-block** elements have an outer shell electron configuration of s^1 or s^2.

Example: Lithium ($1s^2$ $2s^1$) and Magnesium ($1s^2$ $2s^2$ $2p^6$ $3s^2$)

2) The **p-block** elements have an outer shell configuration of s^2p^1 to s^2p^6.

Example: Chlorine ($1s^2$ $2s^2$ $2p^6$ $3s^2$ $3p^5$)

3) The **d-block** elements have outer shell electron configurations in which d sub-shells are being filled.

Example: Cobalt ($1s^2$ $2s^2$ $2p^6$ $3s^2$ $3p^6$ $3d^7$ $4s^2$)

Even though the 3d sub-shell fills last in cobalt, it's not written at the end of the line.

When you've got the periodic table **labelled** with the **shells** and **sub-shells** like the one up there, it's pretty easy to read off the electron structure of any element by starting at the top and working your way across and down until you get to your element.

Example

Electron structure of Phosphorus (P):

Period 1 — $1s^2$
Period 2 — $2s^2$ $2p^6$ ← Complete sub-shells
Period 3 — $3s^2$ $3p^3$ ← Incomplete outer sub-shell

A wee apology...
This bit's really hard to explain clearly in words. If you're confused, just look at the examples until you get it...

Practice Questions

Q1 In what ways is Newlands' 'periodic table' not as good as Mendeleyev's?

Q2 In what order did Mendeleyev originally set out the elements?

Q3 In what order are the elements set out in the modern periodic table? Who was the first to do this?

Q4 What is the name given to the columns in the periodic table?

Q5 What is the name given to the rows in the periodic table? *(Err, hello — easy questions alert.)*

Q6 Why are elements classified as s-block, p-block and d-block?

Exam Question

Q1 a) Complete the electronic configuration of sodium: $1s^2$ ______________________

b) State the block in the Periodic Table to which sodium belongs.

c) Complete the electronic configuration of bromine: $1s^2$ ______________________

d) State the block in the Periodic Table to which bromine belongs. [4 marks]

Periodic — probably the best table in the world...*

Dropped History for AS Chemistry, did you... Ha, bet you're regretting that now, aren't you. If so, you'll enjoy the free History lesson that you get here with the periodic table. Make sure you learn all the key details and particularly how to spell Mendeleyev. This stuff's not here for fun — it's here because you're gonna get questions on it.

*Excluding Dinner and the Round, of course.

Periodic Trends

Periodicity is one of those words you hear a lot in Chemistry without ever really knowing what it means.
Well it basically means trends that occur (in physical and chemical properties) as you move across the periods.
E.g. Metal to non-metal is a trend that occurs going left to right in each period...

Atomic Radius **Decreases** across a Period

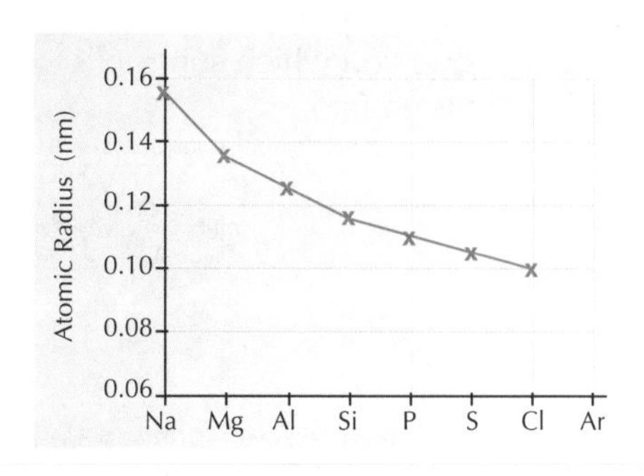

1) As the number of protons increases, the **positive charge** of the nucleus increases. This means electrons are **pulled closer** to the nucleus, making the atomic radius smaller.
2) The extra electrons that the elements gain across a period are added to the **outer energy level** so they don't really provide any shielding effect (shielding works with inner shells mainly).

Electronegativity **increases** across a Period

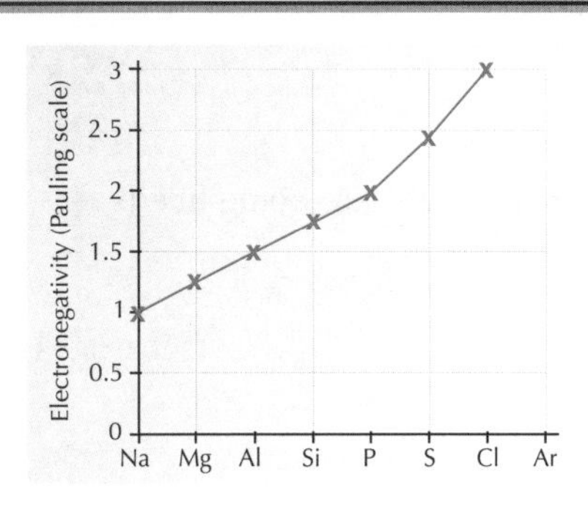

1) **Electronegativity** measures how strongly an **atom** attracts **electrons** in a chemical bond (see page 28 for a fuller explanation).
2) The **higher** the electronegativity of an atom, the greater its attraction for **bonding electrons**.
3) Elements on the **left** of the periodic table have 1 or 2 outer electrons and would rather **give these away** (to achieve a full shell in a lower energy level) than grab another atom's electrons. This means that they have **low** electronegativity.
4) Elements on the **right** side of the periodic table only need a few electrons to complete their outer shell, so they have a strong desire to **grab** another atom's electrons. These have a **high** electronegativity.

Metals are **Conductors** and Non-metals are **Insulators**

1) Sodium, magnesium and aluminium are good electrical conductors because they have **metallic** bonds, which means **delocalised electrons** are free to move through the structure, carrying an electric current.
2) Silicon, phosphorus, sulphur and chlorine have **covalent bonds**, so their electrons are **localised** — they're not free to move from one atom to another. Their electrical conductivities are almost zero.
3) Argon only exists as **single atoms** with full outer shells of electrons tightly held in place, so it's completely uninterested in electricity. It's an **insulator**.

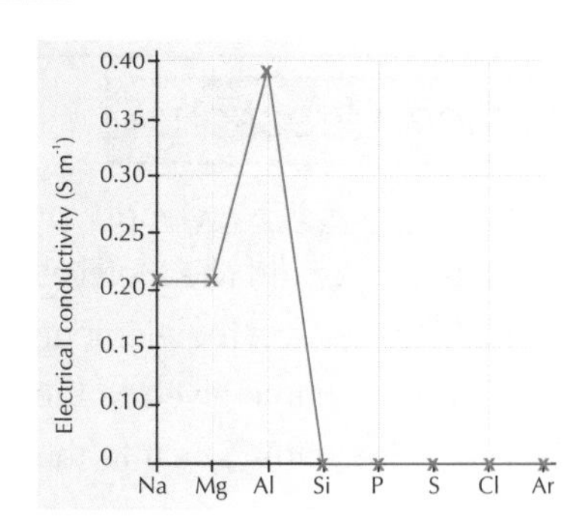

The **Atomic** and **Ionic** Radii of an Element are **Not** the Same Size

1) The atomic radius of a **metallic** element is **larger** than the **ionic radius**.
2) Metals **lose electrons** when they form **ions**, so the **positive charge** of the nucleus is **larger** than the **negative charge** in the electron cloud. This means that in an ion, the electrons are pulled closer. Also, when positive ions are formed, the outer electron shell is usually emptied, meaning there are fewer shells. The outer shell is now **closer** to the nucleus and there's less **electron shielding**. So, the outer electrons are attracted **more strongly** to the nucleus.
3) The atomic radius of a **non-metal** is **smaller** than the **ionic radius**.
4) Non-metals **gain electrons** when they form **ions**. So there's a bigger negative charge in the **electron cloud** of the ion, which means there's **greater repulsion** between the electrons and the electron cloud **expands** a bit.

Periodic Trends

Melting and Boiling Points are linked to Bond Strength and Structure

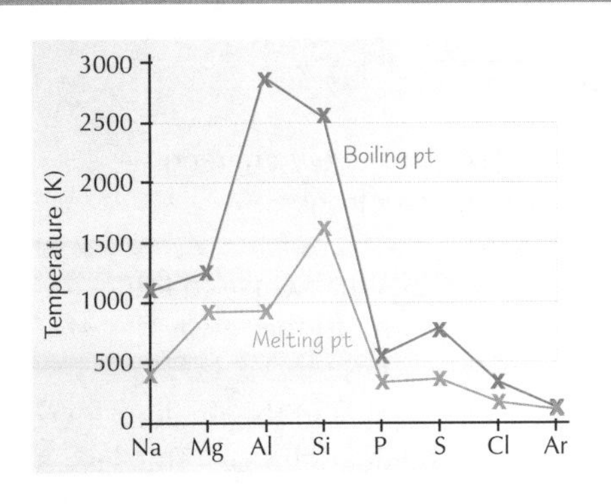

1) Sodium, magnesium and aluminium are **metals**. Their melting and boiling points **increase** across the period because the **metal-metal bonds** get stronger. The bonds get stronger because the metal ions have an increasing number of **delocalised electrons** and a decreasing **ionic radius**. This leads to a higher **charge density**, which attracts the ions together more strongly.

2) Silicon is **macromolecular**, with a tetrahedral structure — **strong covalent bonds** link all its atoms together. **A lot** of energy is needed to break these bonds, so silicon has **high** melting and boiling points.

3) Phosphorus (P_4), sulphur (S_8) and chlorine (Cl_2) are all **molecular substances**. Their melting and boiling points depend upon the strength of the **van der Waals forces** (see page 30) between their molecules. Van der Waals forces are weak and easily broken so these elements have **low** melting and boiling points.

4) More atoms in a molecule mean stronger van der Waals forces. Sulphur is the **biggest molecule** (S_8), so it's got higher melting and boiling points than phosphorus or chlorine.

5) Argon has **very low** melting and boiling points because it exists as **individual atoms** (monatomic) resulting in **very weak** van der Waals forces.

Sam is looking hot in the latest periodic trends.

Practice Questions

Q1 Which elements in Period 3 are found in the s block of the periodic table?

Q2 Which element has the lowest electronegativity in Period 3?

Q3 What type of bonding do most elements that are good electrical conductors have?

Q4 Which element in Period 3 has the highest melting point? Which has the highest boiling point?

Q5 How does the ionic radius of chlorine compare with its atomic radius?

Exam Questions

Q1 Explain the meaning of the term *periodicity* as applied to the properties of rows of elements in the periodic table. [2 marks]

Q2 Explain why the melting point of magnesium is higher than that of sodium. [3 marks]

Q3 This table shows the melting points for the Period 3 elements.

Element	Na	Mg	Al	Si	P	S	Cl	Ar
Melting point / K	371	923	933	1680	317	392	172	84

In terms of structure and bonding explain why:

a) silicon has a high melting point. [2 marks]

b) the melting point of sulphur is higher than phosphorus. [2 marks]

Q4 a) Define the term *electronegativity*. [1 mark]

b) State and explain the trend in electronegativity across Period 3. [3 marks]

Q5 State and explain the trend in atomic radius across Period 3. [4 marks]

Periodic trends — my mate Dom's always a decade behind...

*He still thinks Oasis, Blur and REM are the best bands around. The sad muppet. But not me. Oh no sirree, I'm up with the times — April Lavigne... Linkin' Pork... Christina Agorrilla. I'm hip, I'm with it. Da ga da ga da ga da ga.. ooaarrr ooup **

** Obscure reference to Austin Powers International Man of Mystery. You should watch it — it's better than doing Chemistry.*

Ionisation Energy Trends

Ionisation energy basically measures how much energy you need to remove electrons from atoms or ions. But I don't need to tell you this — you remember it all from page 6, don't you... *[long silence as tumbleweed rolls across the page]*

The **Factors** Affecting Ionisation Energy are...

Nuclear Charge

The **more protons** there are in the nucleus, the more positively charged the nucleus is and the **stronger the attraction** for the electrons.

Attraction falls off very **rapidly with distance**. An electron **close** to the nucleus will be **much more** strongly attracted than one further away.

As the number of electrons **between** the outer electrons and the nucleus **increases**, the outer electrons feel less attraction towards the nuclear charge. This lessening of the pull of the nucleus by inner shells of electrons is called **shielding (or screening)**.

A **high ionisation energy** means there's a **high attraction** between the **electron** and the **nucleus**.

Ionisation Energy **Decreases** Down a Group

As you **go down** a group in the Periodic Table, ionisation energies generally **fall**, i.e. it gets **easier** to remove outer electrons. The graph below shows the first ionisation energies of the first five elements of Group I.

1) Each element down a group has an **extra electron shell** compared to the one above.
2) The extra inner shells **shield** the outer electrons from the attraction of the nucleus.
3) Also, the extra shell means that the outer electrons are **further away** from the nucleus, which greatly reduces the nucleus's attraction.

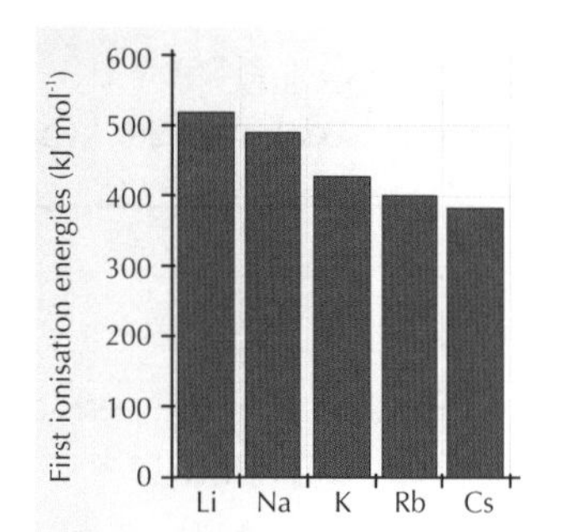

Mr Kelly has one final attempt at explaining electron shielding to his students...

Both of these factors make it **easier** to remove outer electrons, resulting in a **lower ionisation energy**.

The positive charge of the nucleus does increase as you go down a group (due to the extra protons), but this effect is overridden by the effect of the extra shells.

Ionisation Energy **Increases** Across a Period

The graph below shows the first ionisation energies of the elements in **Periods 2 and 3**.

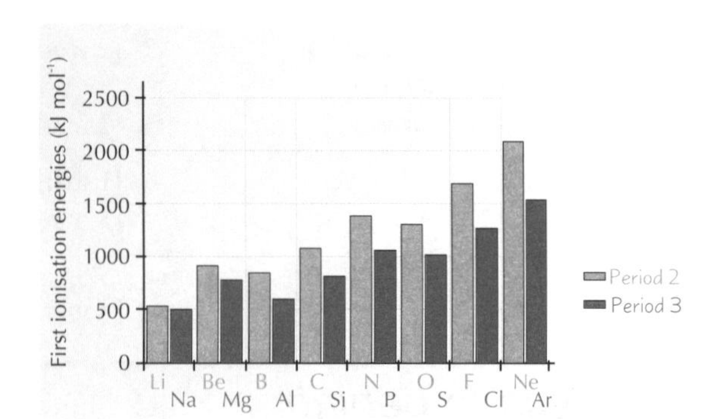

1) As you **move across** a period, the general trend is for the ionisation energies to **increase** — i.e. it gets harder to remove the outer electrons.
2) This is because the number of protons is increasing, which means a stronger **nuclear attraction**.
3) All the extra electrons are at **roughly the same** energy level, even if the outer electrons are in different orbital types.
4) This means there's generally little **extra shielding** effect or **extra distance** to lessen the attraction from the nucleus.
5) But, there are **small drops** between Groups II and III and V and VI. Tell me more, I hear you cry. Well, alright then...

Ionisation Energy Trends

Electronic Structure Explains the Drop between Groups II and III

Be	$1s^2 2s^2$	1st Ionisation energy = 900 kJ mol^{-1}
B	$1s^2 2s^2 2p_x^1$	1st Ionisation energy = 799 kJ mol^{-1}

1) Boron's outer electron is in a **2p orbital** rather than a 2s. The 2p orbital has a **slightly higher** energy than the 2s orbital, so the electron is, on average, to be found **further** from the nucleus.
2) The 2p orbital is screened not only by the $1s^2$ **electrons**, but also **partially** by the $2s^2$ **electrons**.
3) Both these factors together are strong enough to **override** the effect of the increased nuclear charge, resulting in the ionisation energy **dropping** slightly.

The explanation for the drop between magnesium and aluminium is the **same**, except that everything is happening in the **third** energy level: The **3p electron** in aluminium is slightly more distant from the nucleus than the 3s, and also **partially screened** by the $3s^2$ electrons. These two factors override the larger nuclear charge.

The Drop between Groups V and VI is due to **Electron Repulsion**

N	$1s^2 2s^2 2p_x^1 2p_y^1 2p_z^1$	1st Ionisation energy = 1400 kJ mol^{-1}
O	$1s^2 2s^2 2p_x^2 2p_y^1 2p_z^1$	1st Ionisation energy = 1310 kJ mol^{-1}

1) The **screening is identical** in the nitrogen and oxygen atoms (from the $1s^2$ and, to some extent, from the $2s^2$ electrons), and the electron is being removed from an identical orbital.
2) The difference is that in oxygen's case, the **electron** being **removed** is one of the $2p_x^2$ pair. The **repulsion** between the two electrons in the same orbital means that the electron is **easier to remove**.
3) The drop in ionisation energy at **sulphur** has the same explanation.

Practice Questions

Q1 Name three factors which affect the size of an ionisation energy.

Q2 What happens to the ionisation energy as you move down a group?

Q3 Which factors control the trend for ionisation energy in a group?

Q4 What happens to the ionisation energy as you move across a period?

Q5 Which factors control the trend for ionisation energy in a period?

Q6 Which two elements in Period 3 do not obey the general trend? Which groups do these elements belong to?

Exam Questions

Q1 The first ionisation energies of the elements lithium to neon are given below in kJ mol^{-1}:

Li	Be	B	C	N	O	F	Ne
519	900	799	1090	1400	1310	1680	2080

a) Explain why the ionisation energies show an overall tendency to increase across the period. [3 marks]

b) Explain the irregularities in this trend for:
i) Boron ii) Oxygen [4 marks]

Q2 The electronic configuration for sulphur is $1s^2 2s^2 2p^6 3s^2 3p_x^2 3p_y^1 3p_z^1$. State how the value of sulphur's first ionisation energy differs from the general trend in Period 3, and explain why. [3 marks]

Q3 Explain why the first ionisation energy of neon is greater than that of sodium. [2 marks]

Oops, I seem to have made a bit of a mess...

You need to really get your head round those electron orbital structure thingies. And it's not just so you can chat up the pretty ladies (or gents), it's so you can use it to explain things like ionisation energy in the exam. So... just make sure you're comfortable writing electron structures without getting stressed and pooing your pants.

Oxidation and Reduction

This double page has more occurences of "oxidation" than Robbie Williams has the word "me" in his songs. I don't suppose that helps you much, but it's something to fill the top of this page.

If Electrons are Transferred, it's a **Redox Reaction**

1) A **loss** of electrons is called **oxidation**. A **gain** in electrons is called **reduction**.
2) Reduction and oxidation happen **simultaneously** — hence the term "**redox**" reaction.
3) An **oxidising agent accepts** electrons and gets reduced.
4) A **reducing agent donates** electrons and gets oxidised.

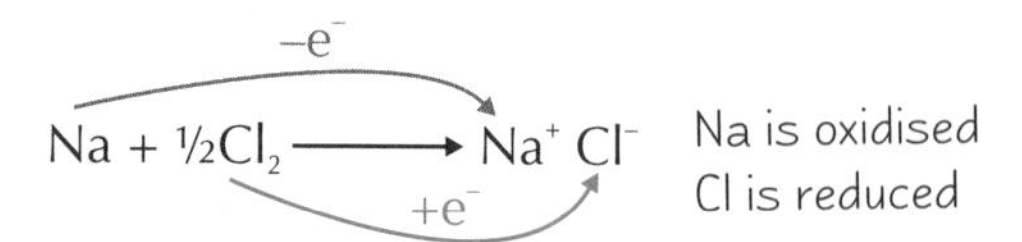

Sometimes it's easier to talk about **Oxidation States**

(It's also called oxidation <u>number</u>.)

There's lots of rules. Take a deep breath...

1) All atoms are treated as **ions** for this, even if they're covalently bonded.

2) Uncombined **elements** have an oxidation state of **0**.

3) Elements just bonded to **identical atoms**, like O_2 and H_2, also have an oxidation state of **0**.

4) The oxidation state of a simple **monatomic ion**, e.g. Na^+, is the same as its **charge**.

5) In **compounds** or **compound ions**, the **overall oxidation state** is just the ion charge.

SO_4^{2-} — **overall oxidation state = -2**,
oxidation state of **O = -2** (total = -8),
so oxidation state of **S = +6**

Within an ion, the most electronegative element has a negative oxidation state (equal to its ionic charge). Other elements have more positive oxidation states.

6) The sum of the oxidation states for a **neutral compound** is 0.

Fe_2O_3 — **overall oxidation state = 0**, oxidation state of **O = -2** (total = -6), so oxidation state of **Fe = +3**

7) Combined **oxygen** is -2, except in peroxides and F_2O, where it's -1 (and O_2 where it's 0).

In **H_2O**, oxidation state of **O = -2**, but in **H_2O_2**, oxidation state of **H** has to be **+1** (an H atom can only lose one electron), so oxidation state of **O = -1**

8) Combined **hydrogen** is +1, except in metal hydrides where it is -1 (and H_2 where it's 0).

In **HF**, oxidation state of **H = +1**, but in **NaH**, oxidation state of **H = -1**

If you see **roman numerals** in a chemical name, it's an **oxidation number**. E.g. copper has oxidation number **2** in **copper(II) sulphate**, and manganese has oxidation number **7** in a **manganate(VII) ion** (MnO_4^-).

Oxidation States go **Up** or **Down** as Electrons are **Lost** or **Gained**

1) The oxidation state for an atom will **increase by 1** for each **electron lost**.
2) The oxidation state will **decrease by 1** for each **electron gained**.
3) Elements can also be **oxidised and reduced** at the same time — this is called **disproportionation**.

$-e^-$
$Na + \frac{1}{2}Cl_2 \longrightarrow Na^+ Cl^-$
Oxidation No. 0 0 $+e^-$ +1 −1

Example:
Chlorine and its ions undergo disproportionation reactions:

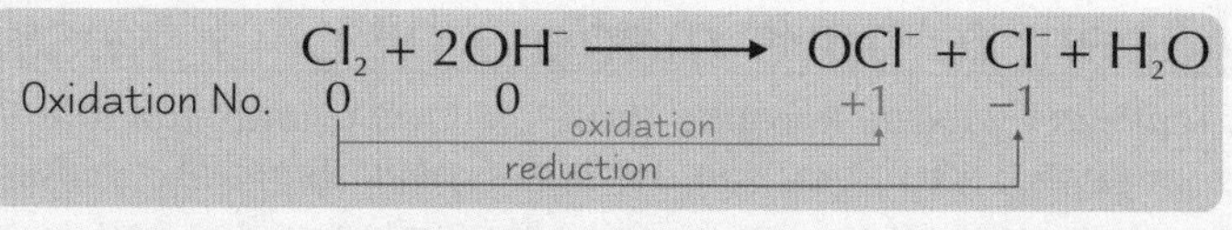

Oxidation and Reduction

You can separate Redox Reactions into Half-Equations

1) **Ionic half-equations** show oxidation or reduction.
2) You can **combine** half-equations for different oxidising or reducing agents together to make **full equations** for reactions.

Magnesium burns in oxygen to form magnesium oxide.
Magnesium is oxidised: $Mg \rightarrow Mg^{2+} + 2e^-$
Oxygen is reduced: $\frac{1}{2}O_2 + 2e^- \rightarrow O^{2-}$
Combining the half-equations makes: $Mg + \frac{1}{2}O_2 \rightarrow MgO$
The electrons aren't included in the full equation.

Some Oxidising or Reducing Agents are Stronger than Others

1) **Strong oxidising agents** will accept **lots of electrons.**
Transition metal ions with variable oxidation states make good oxidising agents.
E.g. acidified manganate(VII) and dichromate(VI) ions are strong oxidising agents:

$$MnO_4^- + 8H^+ + 5e^- \rightarrow Mn^{2+} + 4H_2O$$
$$Cr_2O_7^{2-} + 14H^+ + 6e^- \rightarrow 2Cr^{3+} + 7H_2O$$

2) A **strong reducing agent**, e.g. a reactive metal, will easily **donate electrons** and its oxidation state will **rise**.
3) The relative strength of metals as **reducing agents** is the basis of the **reactivity series**
4) More reactive metals or carbon will **reduce less reactive** metal ions to the element.

Potassium
Sodium
Calcium
Magnesium
Aluminium
(Carbon)
Zinc
Iron
Lead
(Hydrogen)
Copper
Silver
Gold

Most Reactive ↑ Least reactive

Strongest reducing agent ↑ Weakest reducing agent

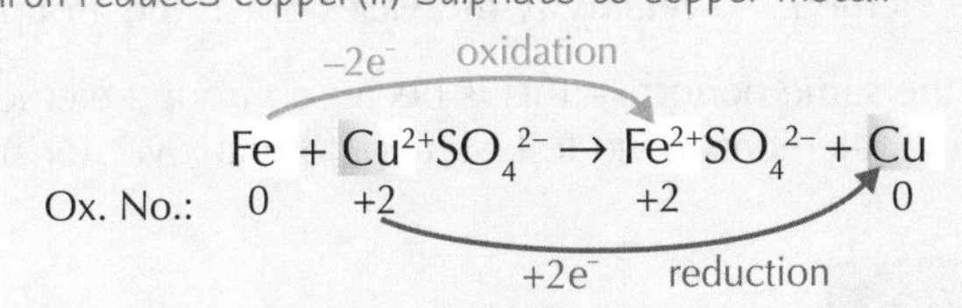

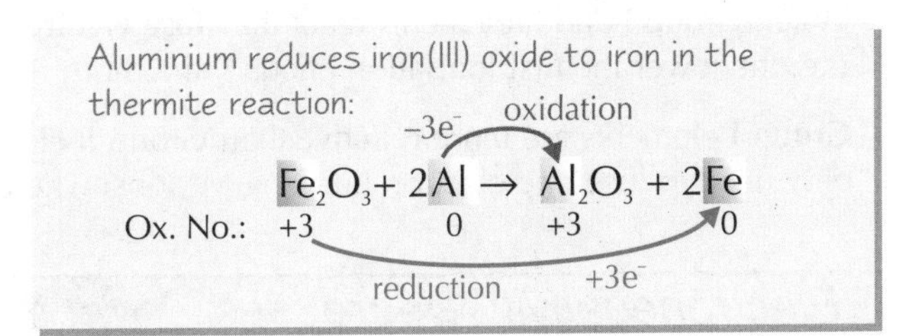

Aluminium reduces iron(III) oxide to iron in the thermite reaction:
−3e⁻ oxidation
Fe₂O₃+ 2Al → Al₂O₃ + 2Fe
Ox. No.: +3 0 +3 0
reduction +3e⁻

Practice Questions

Q1 What is a reducing agent?

Q2 What is the usual oxidation number for oxygen combined with another element?

Q3 What is disproportionation?

Q4 Name a good oxidising agent.

Q5 What is the role of aluminium in the thermite reaction?

Exam Question

Q1 When concentrated sulphuric acid is warmed with hydrogen iodide solution, hydrogen sulphide and iodine are produced.

a) Balance the equation below for the reaction. [1 mark]

$$H_2SO_{4(aq)} + HI_{(aq)} \rightarrow H_2S_{(g)} + I_{2(s)} + H_2O_{(l)}$$

b) State the oxidation number of sulphur in H_2SO_4 and in H_2S. [2 marks]

c) Write a half-equation to show the conversion of iodide, I^-, into iodine, I_2. [1 mark]

d) Write a half-equation to show the conversion of sulphuric acid into hydrogen sulphide. [2 marks]

e) In this reaction, which is the reducing agent? Give a reason. [2 marks]

Redox — relax in a lovely warm bubble bath...

Ionic equations are so evil even Satan wouldn't mess with them. But they're on the syllabus, so you can't ignore them. Have a flick back to p16 if they're freaking you out.

And while we're on the oxidation page, I suppose you ought to learn the most famous memory aid thingy in the world...

OIL RIG
- Oxidation Is Loss
- Reduction Is Gain
(of electrons)

S-Block Metals

The "s block" is Groups I and II of the periodic table. These metal groups are pretty similar in a lot of ways. They're basically the reactive metals of the periodic table. Anyway, we've got a lot to do, so let's get on...

1) Learn the **Electron Configurations**

Gp I	atom	ion	Gp II	atom	ion
Li	$1s^2\,2s^1$	$1s^2$	Be	$1s^2\,2s^2$	$1s^2$
Na	$1s^2\,2s^2\,2p^6\,3s^1$	$1s^2\,2s^2\,2p^6$	Mg	$1s^2\,2s^2\,2p^6\,3s^2$	$1s^2\,2s^2\,2p^6$
K	$1s^2\,2s^2\,2p^6\,3s^2\,3p^6\,4s^1$	$1s^2\,2s^1\,2p^6\,3s^2\,3p^6$	Ca	$1s^2\,2s^2\,2p^6\,3s^2\,3p^6\,4s^2$	$1s^2\,2s^1\,2p^6\,3s^2\,3p^6$

Group I elements have 1 electron in their outer sub-shell (s^1)

Group II elements have 2 electrons in their outer sub-shell (s^2)

The ions in the same period have the same electron configuration — that of a noble gas.

2) Atomic Radius and Ionic Radius **Increase** Down the Group

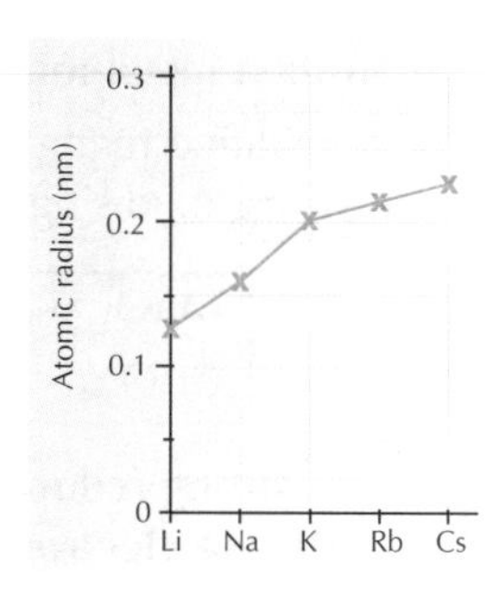

1) This is mainly because of the extra **electron shells** as you go down the group.
2) **Group II** atoms and ions are smaller than **Group I** elements in the same period because they have a stronger force of nuclear attraction (due to an extra proton).
3) Ionic radius is smaller than atomic radius for s-block elements because the loss of the outer electron(s) results in the loss of the **outer shell**.

3) Reactivity **Increases** Down the Group

1) As you go down the group, the **ionisation energy** decreases. This is due to the increasing atomic radius and shielding effect (see p38).
2) When Group I and II elements react they **lose electrons**, forming positive ions. The easier it is to lose electrons (i.e. the lower the first ionisation energy), the more reactive the element, so **reactivity increases** down the group.
3) **Group I** elements are **more reactive** than Group II elements in the same period — this is because Group I elements only need to lose one electron (forming M^+ ions) whereas Group II elements need to lose two (forming M^{2+} ions).

4) Electronegativity **Decreases** Down the Group

Electronegativity, in case you've forgotten already, measures how strongly an atom **attracts** the **bonding electrons** in a chemical bond.

1) Electronegativity is very **low** in s-block metals because they want to **lose** electrons, not attract them.
2) As atoms become larger, electronegativity **decreases** — shielding and distance reduce the positive attraction of the nucleus.

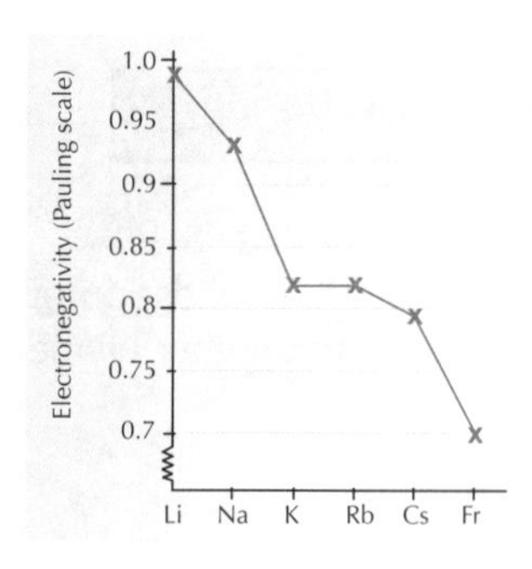

5) Melting Point and Boiling Point **Decrease** Down the Group

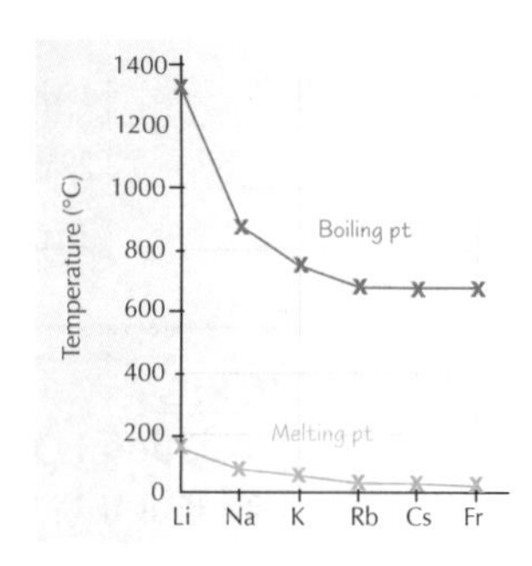

1) The s-block elements have typical **metallic structures**.
2) As the atoms get **bigger** down the group, the strength of the **bonding** decreases. This is due to the reduced attraction of the positive ions to the 'sea' of delocalised electrons. It's mainly because the ions are **bigger** and have a smaller **charge/volume ratio**. Also, the delocalised electrons are more **spread out**.
3) So it take **less energy** to break the bonds, meaning lower melting and boiling points.

S-Block Metals

This page is for Edexcel and Edexcel Nuffield only (except for the questions)...

S-Block Elements have Distinctive Flame Colours

...not all of them, but quite a few. For these elements, a flame test can be used to help **identify them**.

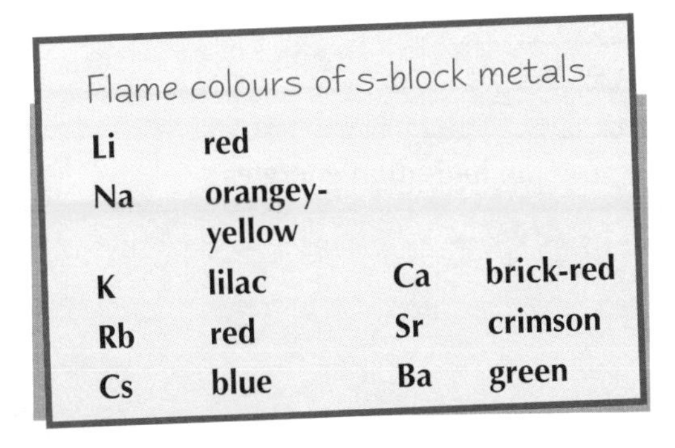

Flame colours of s-block metals

Li	red		
Na	orangey-yellow		
K	lilac	Ca	brick-red
Rb	red	Sr	crimson
Cs	blue	Ba	green

The explanation

The **energy** absorbed from the flame causes electrons to move to **higher energy levels**. The colours are seen as the electrons fall back down to lower energy levels, releasing energy in form of **light**. The **wavelengths** of light released determine the **colour**.

(It's never enough just to say "ooh that's nice." Oh no, chemists have to have an explanation for everything, even colour.)

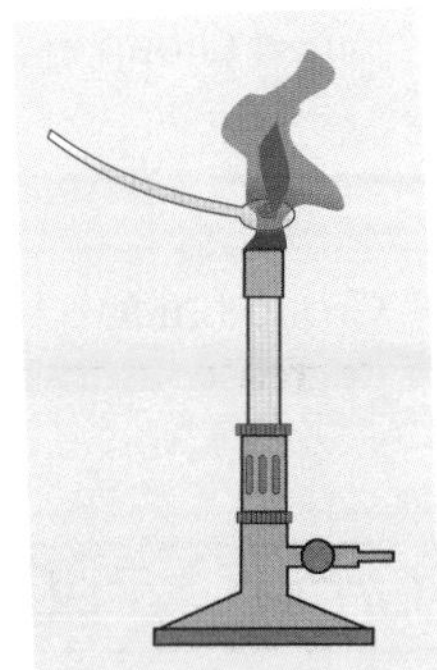

Viewing the Flame through a Spectroscope gives a Line Emission Spectrum

When viewed through a **spectroscope**, the light appears as a series of **coloured lines**. Each line is caused by a particular **wavelength** of light and provides **evidence** that electrons can only be found at particular **energy levels** (shells and sub-shells) within an atom.

The only movement possible is from one level to another. Each move to a lower level releases a specific amount of energy which corresponds to a particular **wavelength**, seen as one of the lines of light.

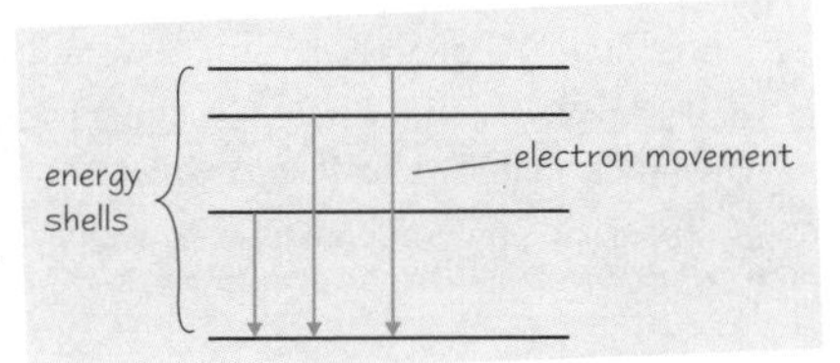

This line emission spectrum business was covered in more detail, way back on page 8. Have a flick back if this stuff tickles your hamster...

Practice Questions

Q1 Complete the electron configurations in the table.

Gp I	atom	ion	Gp II	atom	ion
Li	$1s^2\ 2s^1$		Be	$1s^2\ 2s^2$	$1s^2$
Na	$1s^2\ 2s^2\ 2p^6\ 3s^1$		Mg	$1s^2\ 2s^2\ 2p^6\ 3s^2$	$1s^2\ 2s^2\ 2p^6$
K		$1s^2\ 2s^2\ 2p^6\ 3s^2\ 3p^6$	Ca		$1s^2\ 2s^2\ 2p^6\ 3s^2\ 3p^6$

Q2 Which of the following increases in size down Group I?
ionic radius   first ionisation energy   boiling point

Q3 Which elements are indicated by the following flame colours?
a) lilac   b) brick-red   c) orangey-yellow

Q4 What piece of apparatus is used to view a line spectrum?

Exam Questions

Q1 Use the electron configurations of magnesium and calcium to help explain the difference in their first ionisation energies. [5 marks]

Q2 a) Place the following elements in order of decreasing reactivity: Cs Mg Na Rb [1 mark]
b) Explain your answer. [2 marks]

Q3 a) When a substance is heated, what changes occur within the atom that give rise to a coloured flame? [2 marks]
b) What evidence can be obtained from such a flame for the existence of energy levels? [2 marks]

"So that was lithium, now let's try..." "SCHTOP! — this flame is not reddy yet..."

Here at CGP, we like to test our flames slowly. So they burn real smooth with their characteristic colours...

[OK — s-block metals — that's Groups I and II. Lots of trends here. Just learn them. And learn the explanation for each one (not like a parrot – so you understand it). Then learn the flame colours and that explainy bit about line emission spectra and energy levels.] CGP — we only test flames when they're ready...

Reactions of the S-Block Metals

*S-block elements are **highly reactive** and undergo characteristic reactions with **oxygen, chlorine** and **water**. Don't know about you, but I'm excited already.* [long silence as tumbleweed from page 38 makes a reappearance]

Group I has the Most Reactive Metals

When Group I elements react, they are **oxidised** from a state of **0** to **+1**, forming M^+ ions.

	$M \rightarrow M^+ + e^-$	E.g.	$Na \rightarrow Na^+ + e^-$
Oxidation state:	0 +1		0 +1

Group I metals become **increasingly reactive** down the group. This is because the **ionisation energies decrease** (as the atoms become larger, it gets easier to lose an electron).

Group I metals...

Not Edexcel Nuffield.

1) **REACT WITH WATER TO PRODUCE HYDROXIDES**

$$2M_{(s)} + 2H_2O_{(l)} \rightarrow 2MOH_{(aq)} + H_{2\,(g)}$$

Oxidation state: 0 → +1

e.g. $2Na_{(s)} + 2H_2O_{(l)} \rightarrow 2NaOH_{(aq)} + H_{2\,(g)}$

Li	bubbles steadily
Na	moves rapidly around water surface as a molten ball
K	similar to Na but more vigorous — the hydrogen gas ignites and burns with the characteristic lilac flame colour of K
Rb	explodes violently on contact with water

(If you don't remember this one from GCSE, all I can say is... you're very naughty.)

The metal hydroxide produced dissolves to form a colourless solution that is **strongly alkaline**.
... which is why Group I elements are called the **alkali metals**. Amazing, eh.

2) **BURN IN OXYGEN WITH CHARACTERISTIC FLAME COLOURS** (see the previous page)

...and form solid white oxides.

$$4M_{(s)} + O_{2\,(g)} \rightarrow 2M_2O_{(s)}$$

Oxidation state of metal: 0 → +1
Oxidation state of oxygen: 0 → -2

E.g. $4Na_{(s)} + O_{2\,(g)} \rightarrow 2Na_2O_{(s)}$ — metal: **0** → **+1**; oxygen: **0** → **–2**

3) **REACT WITH CHLORINE**

...forming white solid chlorides.

$$2M_{(s)} + Cl_{2\,(g)} \rightarrow 2MCl_{(s)}$$

Ox. no. of metal: **0** → **+1**

E.g. $2K_{(s)} + Cl_{2\,(g)} \rightarrow 2KCl_{(s)}$ — **0** → **+1**

The formation of peroxides and superoxides is also possible as you go down the group:

$2Na_{(s)} + O_{2\,(g)} \rightarrow Na_2O_{2\,(s)}$ ⟸ sodium peroxide

Ox. no. of metal: **0** → **+1**
Ox. no. of oxygen: **0** → **–1**

$K_{(s)} + O_{2\,(g)} \rightarrow KO_{2\,(g)}$ (potassium superoxide)

Ox no. of metal: **0** → **+1**
Ox no. of oxygen: **0** → **–0.5**

Reactions of the S-Block Metals

The Group II Reactions are the Same as Group I but *Slower*

Group II elements (Be – Ra) react like those of Group I, but they're **less reactive** because they need to lose **two electrons** instead of one. The atoms contain 2 electrons in their outer shell and when they react they are **oxidised** from a state of 0 to +2, forming $\mathbf{M^{2+}}$ ions.

	$M \rightarrow M^{2+} + 2e^-$	E.g.	$Ca \rightarrow Ca^{2+} + 2e^-$
Oxidation state:	**0** **+2**		**0** **+2**

1) **REACTION WITH WATER**

It's the same reaction as for Group I, but with a slightly different equation. As with Group I, the metals get **increasingly** reactive down the group because the **ionisation energies** decrease.

$$M_{(s)} + 2H_2O_{(l)} \rightarrow M(OH)_{2\,(aq)} + H_{2\,(g)}$$

Oxidation state: **0** → **+2**

e.g. $Ca_{(s)} + 2H_2O_{(l)} \rightarrow Ca(OH)_{2\,(aq)} + H_{2\,(g)}$

Be	*doesn't react*
Mg	*VERY slowly*
Ca	*steadily*
Sr	*fairly quickly*
Ba	*rapidly*

2) **REACTION WITH OXYGEN**

Like Group I, the elements burn in oxygen to form white solid oxides. Magnesium burns with a brilliant white flame. Others burn with their characteristic **flame colours** (see p43).

$$2M_{(s)} + O_{2\,(g)} \rightarrow 2MO_{(s)}$$

Oxidation state of metal: 0 → +2

3) **REACTION WITH CHLORINE**

And like Group I, they burn in chlorine, forming white solid chlorides.

$$M_{(s)} + Cl_{2\,(g)} \rightarrow MCl_{2\,(s)}$$

Ox. no. of metal: **0** → **+2**

Practice Questions

Q1 Which is the least reactive metal in a) Group I b) Group II?

Q2 Why does reactivity with water increase down both groups?

Q3 What would be seen when magnesium burns in air?

Q4 What is the oxidation state of Na in a) NaCl b) Na_2O c) Na_2O_2?

Exam Questions

Q1 Use the periodic table to find the Group II element radium (Ra).

a) Predict what you would see if radium was added to water and write an equation for the reaction. [3 marks]

b) Predict what you would see if universal indicator was used to test the solution formed. [1 mark]

Q2 Calcium (Ca) can be burned in chlorine gas.

a) Write an equation for the reaction. [1 mark]

b) Show the change in oxidation state of calcium. [1 mark]

c) Predict the appearance of the product. [2 marks]

d) What type of bonding would the product have? [1 mark]

Q3 The table shows the atomic radii of three elements from Group II.

Element	Atomic radius/nm
X	0.089
Y	0.198
Z	0.176

a) Predict which element would react most rapidly with water. [1 mark]

b) Explain your answer. [2 marks]

.... *It's no use, I've got writer s-block...*

... .

.... *well, let's face it. It's a very dull page with some equations on it. Not much more to say, really...* *Nope.*

Compounds of S-Block Metals

If you're doing AQA, you can skip this double page, you jammy sausage...

Another page, and more juicy, squidgy facts about those jolly nice s-block fellas.
This time we're looking at their cuddly compounds... *(Sorry, just trying to liven things up a bit.)*

The Oxides and Hydroxides are **Bases**

1) THEY FORM ALKALINE SOLUTIONS IN WATER

Group I	Group II
$M_2O_{(s)} + H_2O_{(l)} \rightarrow 2MOH_{(aq)}$ oxide — hydroxide alkaline solution pH 13-14	$MO_{(s)} + H_2O_{(l)} \rightarrow M(OH)_{2\,(aq)}$ oxide — hydroxide alkaline solution pH 9-11
It's the hydroxide that causes the solution to be alkaline	
$M_2O_{(s)} + H_2O_{(l)} \rightarrow 2M^+_{(aq)} + 2OH^-_{(aq)}$	$MO_{(s)} + H_2O_{(l)} \rightarrow M^{2+}_{(aq)} + 2OH^-_{(aq)}$

2) THEY NEUTRALISE ACIDS

Group I	Group II
$M_2O_{(s)} + 2HCl_{(aq)} \rightarrow 2MCl_{(aq)} + H_2O_{(l)}$ oxide — salt	$MO_{(s)} + 2HCl_{(aq)} \rightarrow MCl_{2\,(aq)} + H_2O_{(l)}$ oxide — salt
$MOH_{(aq)} + HCl_{(aq)} \rightarrow MCl_{(aq)} + H_2O_{(l)}$ hydroxide — salt	$M(OH)_{2\,(aq)} + 2HCl_{(aq)} \rightarrow MCl_{2\,(aq)} + 2H_2O_{(l)}$ hydroxide — salt

Thermal Stability *of Carbonates and Nitrates* ***Changes*** *Down the Group*

Thermal decomposition is when a substance **breaks down** (decomposes) when **heated**.
The more thermally stable a substance is, the more heat it will take to break it down.

1) **Thermal stability increases down a group**

   The carbonate and nitrate ions are **large** and can be made **unstable** by the presence of a **positively charged ion** (a cation). The cation **polarises** the anion, distorting it. The greater the distortion, the less stable the anion.

   Large cations cause **less distortion** than small cations. So the further down the group, the larger the cations, the less distortion caused and the **more stable** the carbonate/nitrate anion. Phew... that was hard.

2) **Group II compounds are less thermally stable than Group I compounds**

   The greater the **charge** on the cation, the greater the **distortion** and the **less stable** the carbonate/nitrate ion becomes. Group II cations have a **2+** charge, compared to a **1+** charge for Group I cations.
   So Group II carbonates and nitrates are less stable than those of Group I.

Group I	Group II
Group I carbonates* are **thermally stable** — they don't decompose when heated. *except Li_2CO_3 which decomposes to Li_2O and CO_2 (there's always one...)	Group II carbonates decompose to form the **oxide** and **carbon dioxide**. $MCO_{3\,(s)} \rightarrow MO_{(s)} + CO_{2\,(g)}$ e.g. $CaCO_{3\,(s)} \rightarrow CaO_{(s)} + CO_{2\,(g)}$ calcium carbonate — calcium oxide
Group I nitrates* decompose to form the **nitrite** and **oxygen**. $2MNO_{3\,(s)} \rightarrow 2MNO_{2\,(s)} + O_{2\,(g)}$ e.g. $2KNO_{3\,(s)} \rightarrow 2KNO_{2\,(s)} + O_{2\,(g)}$ potassium nitrate — potassium nitrite *except $LiNO_3$ which decomposes to form Li_2O and NO_2.	Group II nitrates decompose to form the **oxide, nitrogen dioxide** and **oxygen**. $2M(NO_3)_2 \rightarrow 2MO_{(s)} + 4NO_{2\,(g)} + O_{2\,(g)}$ e.g. $2Ca(NO_3)_2 \rightarrow 2CaO_{(s)} + 4NO_{2\,(g)} + O_{2\,(g)}$ calcium nitrate — calcium oxide — nitrogen dioxide

Ease of decomposition of nitrates can be tested by measuring...
- how long it takes until oxygen is produced (i.e. to relight a glowing splint)

OR
- how long it takes until a brown gas (NO_2) is produced. This needs to be done in a fume cupboard because NO_2 is toxic.

Ease of decomposition of carbonates can be tested by timing how long it takes for carbon dioxide to be produced (using limewater — see next page).

Compounds of S-Block Metals

Limestone is a **Useful** Group II Compound

Limestone (calcium carbonate) is a commonly occurring sedimentary rock. One of its uses is to make **slaked lime** (calcium hydroxide), which is a white powder used to neutralise **acidity** in lakes and fields. To make slaked lime, limestone is **heated** causing it to decompose to **calcium oxide**. The calcium oxide is then reacted with water to form **calcium hydroxide**.

(1) $CaCO_3 \rightarrow CaO + CO_2$
(2) $CaO + H_2O \rightarrow Ca(OH)_2$

Limestone $CaCO_3$ (calcium carbonate) —①→ LIME CaO (calcium oxide) —②→ SLAKED LIME $Ca(OH)_2$ (calcium hydroxide)

Limewater is used to **Test for CO_2**

1) **Limewater** is a saturated aqueous solution of **calcium hydroxide**.
2) Calcium hydroxide is only **sparingly soluble** and forms an **alkaline** solution with a pH of about 9 – 10.
3) Limewater is used as a **test for carbon dioxide gas** — carbon dioxide turns limewater cloudy.
The cloudiness is due to a precipitate of calcium carbonate being formed.

$$Ca(OH)_{2\,(aq)} + CO_{2\,(g)} \rightarrow CaCO_{3\,(s)} + H_2O_{(l)}$$

white precipitate of calcium carbonate

4) If carbon dioxide is continually bubbled through, the precipitate dissolves and a clear solution of **calcium hydrogencarbonate** is seen.
$CaCO_{3\,(s)} + H_2O_{(l)} + CO_{2\,(g)} \rightarrow Ca(HCO_3)_{2\,(aq)}$
5) This reaction occurs naturally when rain containing dissolved carbon dioxide falls on limestone rock. This is one way you get **temporary hard water** (which is just water containing hydrogencarbonate ions).
6) Heating temporary hard water results in a **reversal** of the above reaction, and the precipitation of a **limestone 'scale'**.
$Ca(HCO_3)_{2\,(aq)} \rightarrow CaCO_{3\,(s)} + H_2O_{(l)} + CO_{2\,(g)}$ ← Reactions like these cause the ming in your kettle.

Practice Questions

Q1 Name two properties of a Group I oxide that show it to be a base.
Q2 Write an equation for the thermal decomposition of calcium carbonate.
Q3 What is the trend in the thermal stability of the nitrates of Group I elements?
Q4 What is the chemical name for slaked lime?

Exam Questions

Q1 When heated, a compound of calcium produces a gas **A** and a solid **B**.
The gas **A** is bubbled through a solution of limewater to give a cloudy precipitate of **C**.
Give the formulae of the substances **A**, **B** and **C**, and the formula of the original compound. [4 marks]

Q2 a) Write a balanced equation for the thermal decomposition of sodium nitrate. [1 mark]
b) How could you test for the gas produced in the thermal decomposition? [1 mark]
c) Place the following in order of ease of decomposition (easiest first).
magnesium nitrate   potassium nitrate   sodium nitrate
Explain your answer. [3 marks]

Q3 Explain with the help of an equation how calcium hydrogencarbonate gets into tap water.

Bored of s-block trends? Me too. Let's play noughts and crosses...

X | O |
X | O | X
O | O |

Noughts and crosses is pretty rubbish really, isn't it?
It's always a draw. Ho hum. Back to Chemistry then, I guess...

Solubilities and Uses of S-Block Compounds

Edexcel Nuffield people — you can miss this page out.

Oh, hello again. Welcome to the last double page about s-block elements, which to be honest, is bit of a random mish-mash of bits that wouldn't fit anywhere else. Never mind, it's got a great, catchy title, don't you think...

Solubility Trends Depend on the **Compound Anion**

Generally, compounds (of Group II elements) that contain **singly charged** negative ions (e.g. OH^-) **increase** in solubility down the group, whereas compounds that contain **doubly charged** negative ions (e.g. SO_4^{2-} and CO_3^{2-}) **decrease** in solubility down the group.

Group II element	hydroxide (OH^-)	sulphate (SO_4^{2-})	carbonate (CO_3^{2-})
magnesium	least soluble	most soluble	most soluble
calcium	↓	↑	↑
strontium	↓	↑	↑
barium	most soluble	least soluble	least soluble

Compounds like magnesium hydroxide which have **very low** solubilities are said to be **sparingly soluble**. The exact solubility can be found by **titrating** the solution with an acid and then calculating its concentration.

Most sulphates are soluble in water, but **barium sulphate** is **insoluble**.
The test for sulphate ions makes use of this property...

Test for sulphate ions

If a solution of a soluble barium compound, such as barium chloride or barium nitrate, is added to a solution containing sulphate ions then a white precipitate of barium sulphate is formed.

$$Ba^{2+}_{(aq)} + SO_4^{2-}{}_{(aq)} \rightarrow BaSO_{4\,(s)}$$

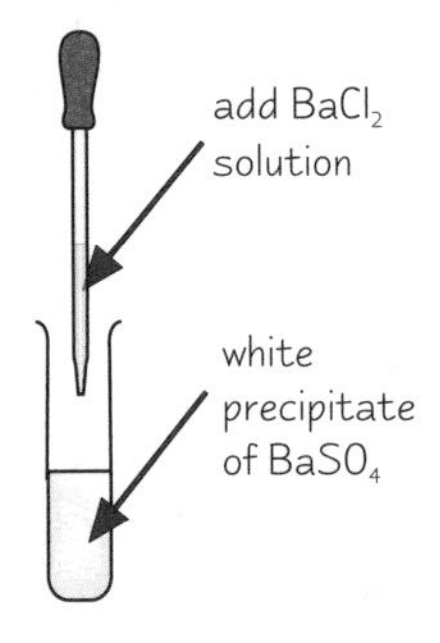

The First Element is **Different** from the Rest

The first member of a group in the periodic table often has **atypical** (different) properties compared to the rest of the group. The first element of a group is the **smallest** (it has the least number of shells), but still has the same **charge**. This gives it a high **charge/volume** ratio, which can make it behave differently.

Beryllium at the top of Group II has atypical properties. Here's some examples of its weirdness...

1) BERYLLIUM CHLORIDE IS COVALENT
(Group II compounds are usually ionic.)
This is because of its strong **polarising power** (see p28) resulting from its high **charge/volume ratio**... which means beryllium **isn't keen** on totally losing its bonding electrons to chlorine... so they end up **sharing them**. How nice.
Typical covalent properties of $BeCl_2$ are that it dissolves readily in **organic solvents** and it reacts with (is **'hydrolysed'** by) water to form an **acidic solution**.

2) BERYLLIUM HYDROXIDE IS AMPHOTERIC
...which means it will dissolve in and neutralise acids **AND** alkalis.

(The other hydroxides of Group II are bases (see page 46).)

$$Be(OH)_{2\,(s)} + \underset{\text{acid}}{2H^+_{(aq)}} \rightarrow Be^{2+}_{(aq)} + 2H_2O_{(l)}$$

$$Be(OH)_{2\,(s)} + \underset{\text{alkali}}{2OH^-_{(aq)}} \rightarrow Be(OH)_4^{2-}{}_{(aq)}$$

3) BERYLLIUM HAS A MAXIMUM COORDINATION NUMBER OF 4
When an ionic compound dissolves, each of its ions gets surrounded by water molecules. The number of water molecules that surround each **metal ion** is the called the **coordination number**. All the other Group II metals are surrounded by **six** water molecules, so have a coordination number of 6. But teeny-weeny beryllium can only fit four around it. Its aqueous ion is $[Be(H_2O)_4]^{2+}$ compared with $[M(H_2O)_6]^{2+}$ for the others.

Solubility and Uses of S-Block Compounds

Group II Compounds are used to Neutralise Acidity

Group II elements are known as the **alkaline earth metals**, and many of their common compounds are used for neutralising acids. Here's a couple of common examples:

1) Calcium hydroxide (slaked lime, $Ca(OH)_2$, see p47) is used in **agriculture** to neutralise acid soils.

Daisy the cow*

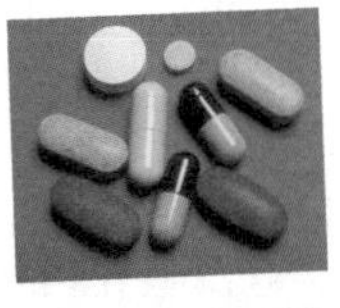

2) Magnesium hydroxide ($Mg(OH)_2$) is used in some indigestion tablets as an **antacid**.

In both cases, the ionic equation for the neutralisation is
$H^+_{(aq)} + OH^-_{(aq)} \rightarrow H_2O_{(l)}$

Practice Questions

Q1 Which is less soluble, barium sulphate or magnesium sulphate?

Q2 How is the solubility of magnesium hydroxide often described?

Q3 Name a use of magnesium hydroxide.

Q4 List three atypical properties of beryllium compounds.

Exam Questions

Q1 Hydrochloric acid can be produced in excess quantities in the stomach, causing indigestion. Antacid tablets often contain sodium hydrogencarbonate (bicarbonate of soda) which reacts with the acid to form a salt, carbon dioxide and water.

a) Write an equation for the neutralisation of hydrochloric acid with sodium hydrogencarbonate. [1 mark]

b) What discomfort could be caused by the carbon dioxide produced? [1 mark]

c) From your knowledge of Group II compounds, choose an alternative antacid that would not give this problem and write an equation for its reaction with hydrochloric acid. [2 marks]

Q2 Describe a chemical test to distinguish between solutions of zinc chloride and zinc sulphate. [1 mark]
Give the expected observations and the appropriate balanced equation(s) including state symbols. [3 marks]

Q3 Identify which of the following solutions would be most likely to give the results described for each test, A-C, below. Give an explanation for each of your answers.

Solutions: $BaCl_2(aq)$ $BeCl_2(aq)$ $MgCl_2(aq)$ $MgSO_4(aq)$

Test A No precipitate formed on addition of sodium hydroxide solution. [2 marks]

Test B White precipitate formed on addition of $BaCl_2(aq)$ [2 marks]

Test C Red colour seen when universal indicator added. [2 marks]

I'm not gonna make it. You've gotta get me out of here, Doc...

We're deep in the dense jungle of Inorganic Chemistry now. Those carefree days of Section Three are well behind us. It's now an endurance test and you've just got to keep going. By now, all the facts are probably blurring into one, all the compounds looking the same. It's tough, but you've got to stay awake, stay focused and keep learning. That's all you can do.

*She wanted to be in the book. I said OK.

Group VII — The Halogens

Finally we can wave goodbye to those pesky s-block elements. Here come the halogens.

Halogens are the **Highly Reactive Non-Metals** of Group 7

The table below gives some of the main properties of the first 4 halogens.

halogen	formula	colour	physical state	electronic structure	electronegativity
fluorine	F_2	pale yellow	gas	$1s^2\ 2s^2\ 2p^5$	increases
chlorine	Cl_2	green	gas	$1s^2\ 2s^2\ 2p^6\ 3s^2\ 3p^5$	up
bromine	Br_2	red-brown	liquid	$1s^2\ 2s^2\ 2p^6\ 3s^2\ 3p^6\ 3d^{10}\ 4s^2\ 4p^5$	the
iodine	I_2	grey	solid	$1s^2\ 2s^2\ 2p^6\ 3s^2\ 3p^6\ 3d^{10}\ 4s^2\ 4p^6\ 4d^{10}\ 5s^2\ 5p^5$	group

The word halogen should be used when describing the atom (X) or molecule (X_2), but the word halide is used to describe the negative ion (X^-)

1) **Their boiling points increase down the group**
This is due to the increasing strength of the **van der Waals forces** as the size and relative mass of the atoms increases. This trend is shown in the changes of **physical state** from chlorine (gas) to iodine (solid).
(A substance is said to be **volatile** if it has a low boiling point. So volatility **decreases** down the group.)
2) **Electronegativity decreases down the group.**
Electronegativity, remember, is the tendency of an atom to **attract** a bonding pair of **electrons**. The halogens are all highly electronegative elements. But larger atoms attract electrons **less** than smaller ones. So, going down the group, as the atoms become **larger**, the electronegativity **decreases**.

Fluorine is the most electronegative element.

There's **Various Tests** to Identify Halogens

Halogens in their natural state exist as covalent diatomic molecules (e.g. Br_2, Cl_2). Because they're covalent, they have **low solubility in water**.
But they do dissolve easily in **organic compounds** such as hexane. Some of these resulting solutions have distinctive colours which can be used to identify them.

	colour in water	colour in hexane
chlorine	virtually colourless	virtually colourless
bromine	orange	red
iodine	brown	violet

That's not much help with chlorine, but luckily there are some other ways of identifying chlorine and iodine.

1) The reaction of iodine with starch.
In Biology, you use iodine solution to test for the presence of starch.
Chemists do it the other way round — they use starch solution to test for iodine.
The result's the same — you get a **blue-black colour**.
2) Damp litmus paper is bleached white by chlorine gas (or by chlorine dissolved in water)
...it goes from **blue** to **pink** to **white**.

Halogens undergo **Disproportionation** with Alkalis

The halogens react with hot and cold alkali solutions. In these reactions, the halogen is simultaneously oxidised and reduced (called **disproportionation**)...

COLD

$$X_2 + 2NaOH \rightarrow NaXO + NaX + H_2O$$

Ion equation: $X_2 + 2OH^- \rightarrow XO^- + X^- + H_2O$

Ox. state of X: 0 (in X_2), +1 (in XO^-), -1 (in X^-)

HOT

$$3X_2 + 6NaOH \rightarrow NaXO_3 + 5NaX + 3H_2O$$

Ion equation: $3X_2 + 6OH^- \rightarrow XO_3^- + 5X^- + 3H_2O$

Ox. state of X: 0 (in X_2), +5 (in XO_3^-), -1 (in X^-)

The halogens (except fluorine) can exist in a wide range of oxidation states e.g.

-1	0	+1	+1	+3	+5	+7
Cl^-	Cl_2	ClO^-	BrO^-	BrO_2^-	IO_3^-	IO_4^-
chloride	chlorine	Chlorate(I)	bromate(I)	bromate(III)	iodate(V)	iodate(VII)

All the **halogen -ate ions** have a **single halogen atom** and a charge of **–1**
— so if you forget the formula you should be able to work it out from the **oxidation number**.

Group VII — The Halogens

Halogens get **Less Reactive** Down the Group

When the halogens react, they **gain an electron** to achieve a full outer shell. This means they're **reduced**.

$X + e^- \rightarrow X^-$
ox. state: 0 → -1

1) The halogens are **strong oxidising agents** (electron acceptors), but this strength **decreases** down the group as the atoms become larger (and less electronegative).

2) Their **relative oxidising strengths** can be seen in their **displacement reactions** with the halide ions:

	Potassium chloride solution $KCl_{(aq)}$ - colourless	Potassium bromide solution $KBr_{(aq)}$ - colourless	Potassium iodide solution $KI_{(aq)}$ - colourless
Chlorine water $Cl_{2(aq)}$ - colourless	no reaction	orange solution (Br_2) formed	brown solution (I_2) formed
Bromine water $Br_{2(aq)}$ - orange	no reaction	no reaction	brown solution (I_2) formed
Iodine solution $I_{2(aq)}$ - brown	no reaction	no reaction	no reaction

3) These displacement reactions can be used to help **identify** which halogen (or halide) is present in solution.

A **halogen** will **displace a halide** from solution if the halide is **below it** in the periodic table, e.g.

Periodic table	Displacement reaction	Ionic equation
Cl	chlorine (Cl_2) will displace bromide (Br^-) and iodide (I^-)	$Cl_{2(aq)} + 2Br^-_{(aq)} \rightarrow 2Cl^-_{(aq)} + Br_{2(aq)}$ $Cl_{2(aq)} + 2I^-_{(aq)} \rightarrow 2Cl^-_{(aq)} + I_{2(aq)}$
Br	bromine (Br_2) will displace iodide (I^-)	$Br_{2(aq)} + 2I^-_{(aq)} \rightarrow 2Br^-_{(aq)} + I_{2(aq)}$
I	no reaction with F^-, Cl^-, Br^-	

These are **redox reactions** so you can also say a halogen will **oxidise** a halide if the halide is below it in the periodic table.

$Cl_{2(aq)} + 2Br^-_{(aq)} \rightarrow 2Cl^-_{(aq)} + Br_{2(aq)}$

ox. state of Cl: **0** → **-1** reduction
ox. state of Br: **-1** → **0** oxidation

Practice Questions

Q1 Place the halogens F, Cl, Br and I in order of increasing (a) boiling point (b) volatility (c) electronegativity

Q2 What would be seen when chlorine water reacts with potassium iodide solution?

Q3 What does disproportionation mean?

Q4 Describe simple tests for iodine solution and chlorine gas.

Exam Questions

Q1 a) Write an ionic equation for the reaction between iodine solution and sodium astatide (NaAt). [1 mark]

b) For the equation in (a), deduce which substance is oxidised. [1 mark]

Q2 Iodide ions react with chlorate(I) ions and water to form iodine, chloride ions and hydroxide ions.

a) Write a balanced equation for this reaction. [2 marks]

b) Show by use of oxidation states which substance has been oxidised and which has been reduced. [2 marks]

c) Predict the colour change for the reaction. [1 mark]

Q3 Write formulae for the following compounds

a) magnesium fluoride [1 mark]

b) potassium bromate(I) [1 mark]

c) sodium chlorate(V) [1 mark]

Don't skip this page — it could cost you £31 000...

Let me explain... the other night I was watching Who Wants to Be a Millionaire, and this question was on for £32000:

Which of the these elements is a halogen?
A Argon B Nitrogen
C Fluorine D Sodium

Bet Mr Redmond from Wiltshire wishes he paid more attention in Chemistry now, eh. Ha sucker...

Sources of the Halogens

You can skip this whole double page if you're doing AQA...

This page is like a really good trip to the dentist — lots of extractions...

Iodine can be Extracted from Seaweed

This bit is for Edexcel Nuffield only...

Today, iodine is mainly extracted from **caliche** mineral deposits in Chile, but it was originally **isolated from seaweed**:

1) **Iodide** ions are taken in from **seawater** and concentrated in the **seaweed**.
2) ***Laminaria*** seaweeds have the **highest concentrations** of iodine.

Extraction of Iodine from seaweed

1) You can release iodine from dried *Laminaria* seaweed by oxidation and then use solvent extraction to concentrate it.
2) Burn the dried seaweed to ash on a tin lid in a fume cupboard.
3) Boil the ash with water for a few minutes to dissolve the iodide ions.
4) Filter the mixture and add dilute sulphuric acid and hydrogen peroxide to the filtrate to oxidise the iodide ions to iodine.
5) Extract the iodine from the mixture by shaking it with some hydrocarbon solvent in a separating funnel. Then discard the lower aqueous layer and run the iodine extract into a flask, (the iodine will dissolve in the hydrocarbon solvent, because it is a non-polar molecule).

We've got a new dentist starting today. Bob...

Dentist Bob started out in the construction industry.

Bromine is Extracted from Seawater by Oxidation

This bit is for Edexcel Nuffield or OCR Salters only...

1) Chlorine is a **stronger oxidising agent** than bromine and bromine is a **stronger** oxidising agent than iodine (see P51).
2) So you can use **chlorine** to **oxidise bromide ions** dissolved in **seawater**.

There are four stages in the extraction of bromine from seawater...

You need to be able to give the oxidation states in all the equations.

Extraction of bromine from seawater

1) **The bromide is oxidised to bromine.**
   First, the seawater is filtered, concentrated by evaporation and sulphuric acid is added to minimise the reactions of bromine or chlorine with water.
   Then, chlorine is bubbled through the seawater to oxidise and displace the bromine.

$$Cl_{2\,(g)} + 2Br^-_{(aq)} \rightarrow 2Cl^-_{(aq)} + Br_{2\,(aq)}$$

Ox. state: 0, −1, −1, 0

2) The bromine is vaporised and extracted by blowing air through the mixture.

3) The bromine vapour is reduced to hydrobromic acid. (The air / bromine mixture is mixed with sulphur dioxide gas and water and then condensed. This forms a concentrated solution of hydrobromic acid.)

$$Br_{2\,(g)} + SO_{2\,(g)} + 2H_2O_{(l)} \rightarrow 2HBr_{(aq)} + H_2SO_{4\,(aq)}$$

Ox. state: 0, +4, −1, +6

4) The hydrobromic acid is oxidised to bromine again. (Chlorine is blown through the acid solution, forming a hot vapour mixture of hydrochloric acid and bromine.)

$$Cl_{2\,(g)} + 2HBr_{(aq)} \rightarrow 2HCl_{(aq)} + Br_{2\,(aq)}$$

Ox. state: 0, −1, −1, 0

5) When this is condensed, it separates into an aqueous layer floating on top of a denser layer of wet bromine. The bromine is dried using concentrated sulphuric acid.

6) Finally, sulphur dioxide is mixed with the used seawater to remove traces of toxic chlorine or bromine before returning it to the sea.

Sources of the Halogens

The bits on this page are for Edexcel (but not the Nuffield syllabus)...

Chlorine is Extracted from Brine by **Electrolysis**

You probably did this old chestnut at GCSE.
Well you still need to know it for AS, so here we go again...

Electrolysing sodium chloride solution (brine) gives you **chlorine**, **hydrogen** and **sodium hydroxide**.

Extraction of Chlorine by Electrolysis

1) There's four ions in solution: Na^+, Cl^-, H^+ and OH^-.
2) Chloride ions get <u>oxidised</u> to chlorine gas at the <u>anode</u>.

$$2Cl^-_{(aq)} \rightarrow Cl_{2\,(g)} + 2e^-$$

3) Hydrogen ions are <u>reduced</u> to hydrogen gas at the <u>cathode</u>.

$$2H^+_{(aq)} + 2e^- \rightarrow H_{2\,(g)}$$

4) The Na^+ and OH^- ions left behind form NaOH solution (with a bit of NaCl thrown in for good measure).
5) The overall equation is:

$$2NaCl_{(aq)} + 2H_2O_{(l)} \rightarrow 2NaOH_{(aq)} + H_{2\,(g)} + Cl_{2\,(g)}$$

As well as admiring the immense beauty of this diagram, learn it...

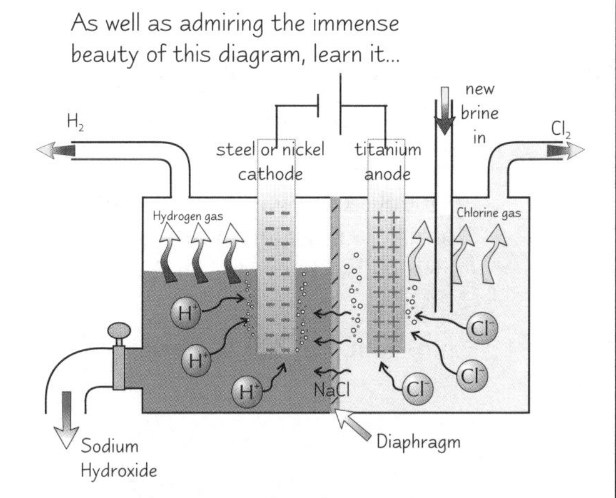

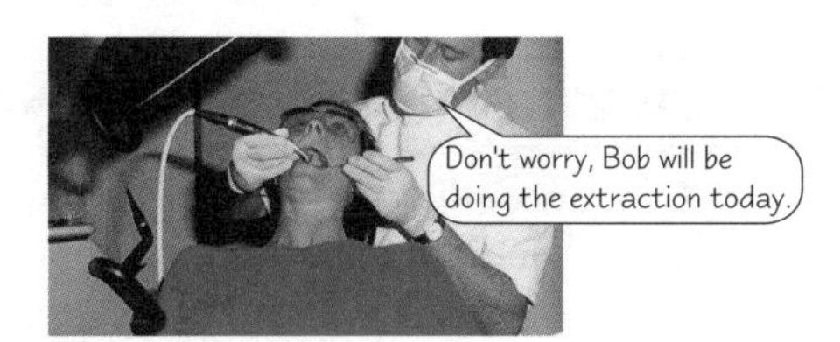

Practice Questions

Q1 What kind of seaweed has the highest concentration of iodine?

Q2 Why will iodine dissolve in a hydrocarbon solvent?

Q3 Which halogen is the strongest oxidising agent?

Q4 What are the main stages in the extraction of bromine from seawater?

Q5 What are the four ions in solution in the electrolysis of brine?

Exam Question

Q1 The chlor-alkali industry is based on the electrolysis of brine (sodium chloride solution), producing chlorine gas, hydrogen gas and sodium hydroxide.

a) Write an ionic half-equation for the reaction occurring at the negative electrode. [1 mark]

b) Write an ionic half-equation for the reaction occurring at the positive electrode. [1 mark]

c) Give the overall equation for the reaction, including state symbols. [2 marks]

Just take a look at these pages... you know what you've got to do...

Never in all my years have I seen an AS Chemistry page so screaming out with the words — "learn me, learn me, learn ALL OF ME, up a bit, across a bit, oh yes that's it, learn me..." ahem, you get the idea. It's quite nice to learn about some real chemical processes after all of that theory stuff about periodic trends, don't you think? No? Just me then. Again.

Uses of the Halogens

Miss out this double page if you're doing OCR Salters or the main Edexcel syllabus (i.e. not Nuffield)...

Here's comes another page jam-packed with golden nuggets of halogen fun. Oh yes, I kid you not. This page is the Alton Towers of AS Chemistry... white-knuckle excitement all the way...

Chlorine is used to kill bacteria in water

When you mix chlorine with water, it undergoes disproportionation.

You end up with a mixture of hydrochloric acid and **chloric(I) acid** (also called hypochlorous acid).

Aqueous chloric(I) acid **ionises** to make **chlorate(I) ions** (also called hypochlorite ions).

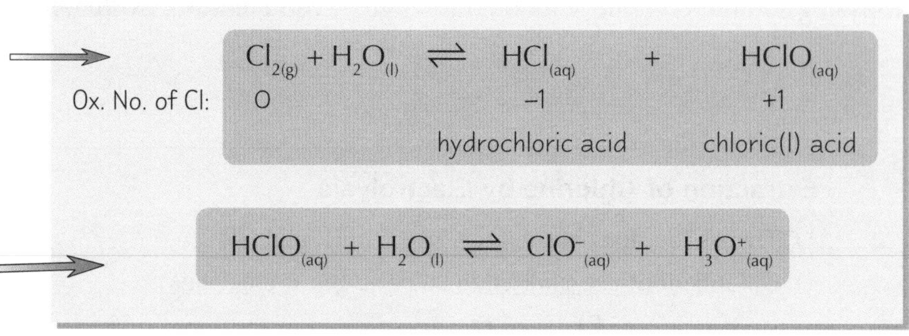

Chlorate(I) ions **kill bacteria**.

So, **adding chlorine** (or a compound containing chlorate(I) ions) to water can make it safe to **drink** or **swim** in.

Chlorine and Sodium Hydroxide make Bleach

If you mix chlorine gas with sodium hydroxide (products of the electrolysis of brine – see p53) at **room temperature**, you get **sodium chlorate(I) solution**, $NaOCl_{(aq)}$, which just happens to be common household **bleach**.

$$2NaOH_{(aq)} + Cl_{2\,(aq)} \rightarrow NaOCl_{(aq)} + NaCl_{(aq)} + H_2O_{(l)}$$

Ox. state: Cl in Cl_2: **0**; Cl in $NaOCl$: **+1**; Cl in $NaCl$: **−1**

The oxidation state of Cl goes up and down so, you guessed it, it's another disproportionation. Hurray.

The sodium chlorate(I) solution (bleach) has loads of uses — it's used in **water treatment**, to bleach **paper** and **textiles**... and it's good for **cleaning toilets**, too. Handy...

1) Bleach contains sodium chloride left over from the electrolysis process. This isn't a problem unless the bleach is mixed with acid. Then the chlorate(I) would oxidise chloride ions to liberate toxic chlorine gas.
2) As some other chemicals in cleaning agents are acidic, e.g. sodium hydrogen sulphate, all bleach bottles carry a warning not to mix bleach with other cleaning agents.

Bleaches react with Potassium Iodide to give Iodine

Chlorate(I) ions react with potassium iodide to make iodine.

Here's the equation for the reaction...

$$2I^-_{(aq)} + ClO^-_{(aq)} + 2H^+_{(aq)} \rightarrow I_{2(aq)} + Cl^-_{(aq)} + H_2O_{(l)}$$

- $2I^-_{(aq)}$: Iodide ions from KI.
- $ClO^-_{(aq)}$: Chlorate(I) ions from sodium chlorate (bleach)
- $I_{2(aq)}$: Iodine solution formed.

Chlorine atoms are reduced (from +1 to 0), iodine is oxidised (from −1 to 0).

The solution changes from **colourless** to **brown**.

Uses of the Halogens

Find the Concentration of Iodine Solution by **Titration**

Iodine reacts with **thiosulphate ions** like this:

$$I_2 + 2S_2O_3^{2-} \rightarrow 2I^- + S_4O_6^{2-}$$

If you want to find the **concentration** of iodine in a solution, **titrate it** with sodium thiosulphate.
You need to set up the titration apparatus like this:

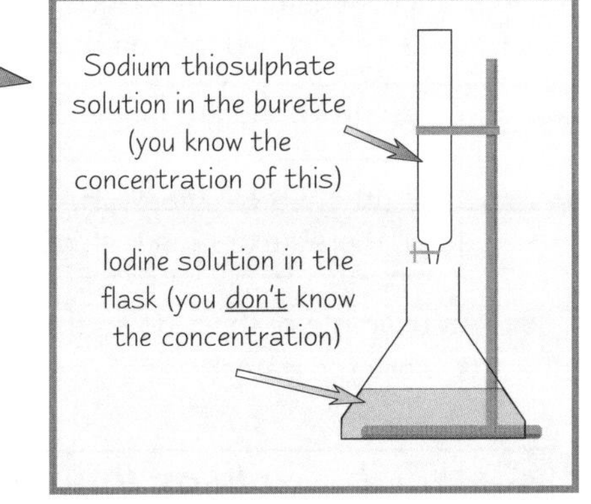

Sodium thiosulphate solution in the burette (you know the concentration of this)
Iodine solution in the flask (you don't know the concentration)

Titration of Iodine with Sodium Thiosulphate

1) From the burette, add sodium thiosulphate solution to the iodine solution.
2) When the iodine colour fades to pale yellow, add 2 cm^3 starch solution (to detect the presence of iodine). The solution in the conical flask will go dark blue to show there's still some iodine there.
3) Add sodium thiosulphate one drop at a time until the blue colour disappears.
4) When this happens, it means all the iodine has just been reacted.
5) Now you can calculate the concentration of the iodine solution.

Here's the titration calculation: (It's basic titration stuff – see p18).

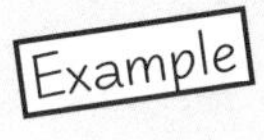
Example

10 cm^3 of iodine solution reacts with 11.1 cm^3 of 0.12 mol dm^{-3} thiosulphate solution.
Calculate the concentration of the iodine solution.

Number of moles of thiosulphate = $\frac{11.1}{1000} \times 0.12$ = **1.33×10^{-3} moles**

1 mole of iodine reacts with **2 moles** of thiosulphate ⟸ See the equation up at the top.

So number of **moles of iodine in 10 cm^3** of solution = $1.33 \times 10^{-3} \div 2$ = **6.66×10^{-4} moles**

So number of **moles of iodine in 1 dm^3** of solution = $\frac{1000}{10} \times 6.66 \times 10^{-4}$ = **0.0666 moles**

Therefore, concentration of iodine = **0.0666 mol dm^{-3}**

Practice Questions

Q1 Write the equation for the reaction of chlorine with water. State underneath the oxidation number of the chlorine.

Q2 How is common household bleach formed?

Q3 Write an equation to show how sodium chlorate(I) reacts with potassium iodide.

Exam Questions

Q1 If chlorine gas and sodium hydroxide are allowed to mix at room temperature, sodium chlorate(I) is formed.

a) This is a disproportionation reaction. Give the ionic equation for the reaction and use it to explain what is meant by disproportionation. [4 marks]

b) Sodium chlorate(I) is used in bleach. Bleach also contains sodium chloride ions. Why is it dangerous to mix bleach with acids? [3 marks]

Q2 25 cm^3 of iodine solution reacts with 21.6 cm^3 of 0.1 mol dm^{-3} sodium thiosulphate solution. What is the concentration of the iodine solution? [3 marks]

Remain seated until the page comes to a halt. Please exit to the right...

Oooh, what a lovely page, if I do say so myself. I bet the question of how bleach is made and how it would react with potassium iodide has plagued your mind since childhood. Well now you know. There's nothing too taxing here. The only bit that might upset you is the titration. If you're at all rusty on those calculations, have a look back to page 18...

Halide Ions

OK, basics first. Halides are compounds with the –1 halogen ion (e.g. Cl^-, Br^-, I^-) like KI, HCl, NaBr. They all end in "-ide" — chloride, bromide, iodide. Got that? Good. Now, you're ready to go in...

The **Reducing Power** of Halides **Increases** Down the Group...

To reduce something, the halide ion needs to lose an electron from its outer shell. How easy this is depends on the **attraction** between the **nucleus** and outer **electron**.

As you go down the group, the attraction gets **weaker** because:

1) the ions get bigger, so the electrons are **further** away from the positive nucleus
2) there's extra inner electron shells, so there's a greater **shielding** effect.

An example of them doing this is the good old halogen / halide displacement reaction (the one you learned on p51... yes, that one). And here comes some more examples to learn...

...which Explains their Reactions with **Sulphuric Acid**

You don't need this section for OCR or OCR Salters...

All the halides react with sulphuric acid to give a **hydrogen halide** as a product to start with. But what happens next depends on which halide you've got...

Reaction of NaCl with H_2SO_4

$$NaCl_{(s)} + H_2SO_{4(aq)} \rightarrow NaHSO_{4(s)} + HCl_{(g)}$$

1) Hydrogen chloride gas (HCl) is formed.
2) But HCl isn't strong enough to reduce the sulphuric acid, so the reaction stops there.
3) It's not a redox reaction — the oxidation states of the chlorine and sulphur stay the same (–1 and +6).

Reaction of NaBr with H_2SO_4

$$NaBr_{(s)} + H_2SO_{4(aq)} \rightarrow NaHSO_{4(s)} + HBr_{(g)}$$

$$2HBr_{(aq)} + H_2SO_{4(aq)} \rightarrow Br_{2(g)} + SO_{2(g)} + 2H_2O_{(l)}$$

ox. state of S: +6 → +4 reduction

ox. state of Br: -1 → 0 oxidation

1) The first reaction gives misty fumes of hydrogen bromide gas (HBr).
2) But the HBr is a stronger reducing agent than HCl and reacts with the H_2SO_4 in a redox reaction.
3) The reaction produces choking fumes of SO_2 and orange fumes of Br_2.

Reaction of NaI with H_2SO_4

$$NaI_{(s)} + H_2SO_{4(aq)} \rightarrow NaHSO_{4(s)} + HI_{(g)}$$

$$2HI_{(g)} + H_2SO_{4(aq)} \rightarrow I_{2(s)} + SO_{2(g)} + 2H_2O_{(l)}$$

ox. state of S: +6 → +4 reduction

ox. state of I: -1 → 0 oxidation

1) Same initial reaction giving HI gas.
2) The HI then reduces H_2SO_4 like above.
3) But HI (being well 'ard as far as reducing agents go) keeps going and reduces the SO_2 to H_2S.

$$6HI_{(g)} + SO_{2(g)} \rightarrow H_2S_{(g)} + 3I_{2(s)} + 2H_2O_{(l)}$$

ox. state of S: +4 → –2 reduction

ox. state of I: -1 → 0 oxidation

H_2S gas is toxic and smells of bad eggs. A bit like my mate Andy at times...

Halide Ions

Silver Nitrate Solution is used to *Test for Halides*

The test for halides is dead easy. First you add **dilute nitric acid** to remove ions which might interfere with the test. Then you just add **silver nitrate solution** ($AgNO_{3\ (aq)}$). A **precipitate** is formed (of the silver halide).

$$Ag^{+}_{(aq)} + X^{-}_{(aq)} \rightarrow AgX_{(s)}$$ ...where X is Cl, Br or I

1) The **colour** of the precipitate identifies the halide.
2) Then to be extra sure, you can test your results by adding **ammonia solution**. (They have different solubilities in ammonia.)

SILVER NITRATE TEST FOR HALIDE IONS...	
Chloride Cl^-:	white precipitate, dissolves in dilute $NH_{3(aq)}$
Bromide Br^-:	cream precipitate, dissolves in conc. $NH_{3(aq)}$
Iodide I^-:	yellow precipitate, insoluble in conc. $NH_{3(aq)}$

Hydrogen Halides are *Acidic Gases*

Before I go, a few final words about the **hydrogen halides**...

1) They're all **colourless gases**.
2) They're **very soluble**, dissolving in water to make **strong acids**. ⟹ $HCl_{(g)} \rightarrow H^{+}_{(aq)} + Cl^{-}_{(aq)}$
   (They'll happily turn blue litmus paper red.)
3) Hydrogen chloride forms **hydrochloric** acid, hydrogen bromide forms **hydrobromic** acid and hydrogen iodide gives **hydroiodic** acid. (You don't hear of this last one much — that's because its name is too silly.)
4) They react with **ammonia gas** to give **white fumes**. ⟹ $NH_{3(g)} + HCl_{(g)} \rightarrow NH_4Cl_{(s)}$
   Hydrogen chloride gives ammonium chloride.
   (It's an acid-base reaction.)

Practice Questions

Q1 Give two reasons why a bromide ion is a more powerful reducing agent than a chloride ion.

Q2 Name the gaseous products formed when sodium bromide reacts with concentrated sulphuric acid.

Q3 What do you see when potassium iodide reacts with concentrated sulphuric acid?

Q4 What type of substance is formed when a hydrogen halide is passed through water?

Q5 How would you test to show that an aqueous solution contained chloride ions?

Exam Questions

Q1 Describe the tests you would carry out in order to distinguish between solid samples of sodium chloride and sodium bromide using:
a) silver nitrate solution and aqueous ammonia,
b) concentrated sulphuric acid.

For each test, state your observations and write an equation for the reaction which occurs. [12 marks]

Q2 The halogen below iodine in Group 7 is astatine (At). Predict, giving an explanation, whether or not:
a) hydrogen sulphide gas would be evolved when concentrated sulphuric acid is added to a solid sample of sodium astatide,
b) silver astatide will dissolve in concentrated ammonia solution. [7 marks]

[Sing along with me] "Why won't this section end... Why won't this section end..."

AS Chemistry. What a bummer, eh... No one ever said it was going to be easy. Not even your teacher would be that cruel. There's plenty more equations on this page to learn. As well as that, make sure you really understand everything... what exactly reducing agents do... how you work out oxidation states for reactions... And no, you can't swap to English. Sorry.

Extracting Iron

This page is for AQA and OCR Salters only...

Ted?... Yes, Dougal?... Well, I was just wondering... What is it, Dougal? Well, err... where does all the metal come from?

Iron is Extracted in the **Blast Furnace**

Iron is normally found as its major ore — **haematite**. This is a mineral containing **iron(III) oxide (Fe_2O_3)**. To get rid of the oxygen, the haematite is **reduced** by carbon (in the form of coke) in a **blast furnace**.

Extracting iron in a blast furnace is a **continuous process** — it runs 24 hours a day, 7 days a week without stopping. **Haematite, coke** and **limestone** are ground up and fed in to the top of the furnace and **hot air** is blasted in at the bottom. Read the rest of the page to find out the nitty-gritty of what goes in the blast furnace — it's hot stuff.

Carbon and Carbon Monoxide act as **Reducing Agents**

1) The hot coke **burns**, producing carbon dioxide:
$$C_{(s)} + O_{2\,(g)} \rightarrow CO_{2\,(g)}$$
2) The CO_2 is reduced to **carbon monoxide** by unburnt coke:
$$CO_{2\,(g)} + C_{(s)} \rightarrow 2CO_{(g)}$$
3) The carbon monoxide then reduces the iron ore to **metallic iron**:
$$Fe_2O_{3\,(s)} + 3CO_{(g)} \rightarrow 2Fe_{(l)} + 3CO_{2\,(g)}$$
4) In the **really hot** middle bits, the coke reduces the iron ore **directly**:
$$2Fe_2O_{3\,(s)} + 3C_{(s)} \rightarrow 4Fe_{(l)} + 3CO_{2\,(g)}$$
5) Being rather hot in there, the iron is **molten**, so it runs down to the bottom where it's 'tapped off'.
6) The waste carbon dioxide goes **out the top**. But it's not allowed to escape — it's a bit hot from its experience, so it's used in a **heat exchanger** to heat air going into the furnace.

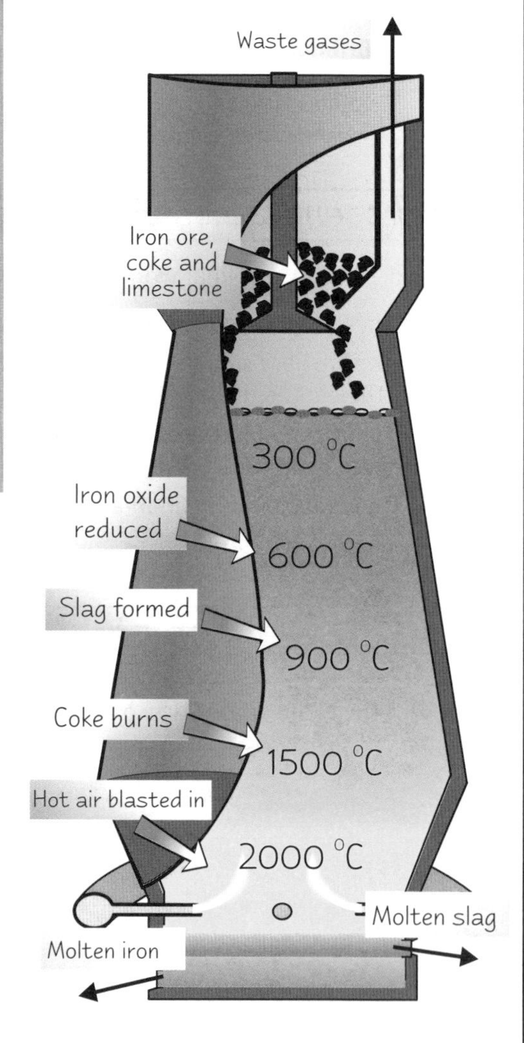

Limestone Removes the **Impurities**

1) The limestone decomposes to produce calcium oxide.
$$CaCO_{3\,(s)} \rightarrow CaO_{(s)} + CO_{2\,(g)}$$
2) This then reacts with **silicon oxide** (from sand and clay) and other acidic impurities to produce a **molten slag** (which is mainly **calcium silicate**).
$$SiO_{2\,(s)} + CaO_{(s)} \rightarrow CaSiO_{3\,(l)}$$
3) The **slag** isn't wasted. It cools and solidifies and is used in road building.

Most of the Iron produced gets made into **Steel**

Iron from the blast furnace (pig iron or cast iron) is **impure** and **brittle**. The impurities in a typical sample are: 4 – 5% carbon, 1% silicon, and smaller amounts of phosphorus and sulphur. Basically, it's not much use like this.

Most iron gets made into various types of steel:
A **steel** contains **mainly iron**, **carbon**, and **carefully controlled amounts of other elements** added to give the desired physical properties suitable for its use.

1) Steel-making begins with the removal of **sulphur impurities** from the molten iron using **magnesium powder**.
2) The **magnesium sulphide** formed is scraped from the surface as a slag.
$$Mg_{(s)} + S_{(s)} \rightarrow MgS_{(s)}$$

Extracting Iron

This page is just for AQA.

Steel is made in the **Basic Oxygen Converter**

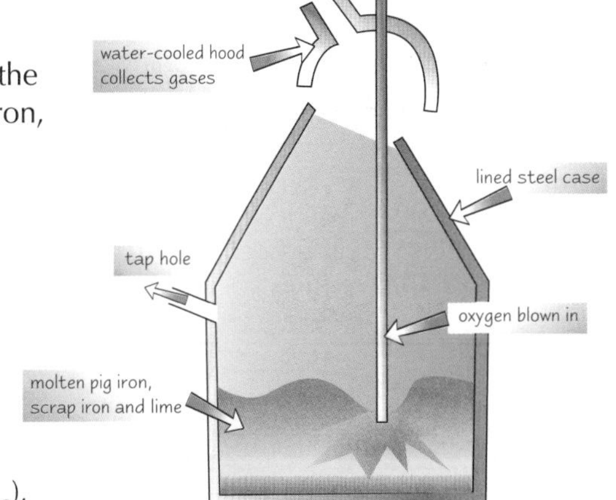

The **basic oxygen converter** gets rid of the other main impurities from the iron. High pressure **oxygen** gets blown onto a mixture of molten pig iron, scrap iron, and a base, **calcium oxide** (**lime**). **Carbon**, **silicon** and **phosphorus** in the iron react with the oxygen to form their **oxides**.

$$2C_{(s)} + O_{2\,(g)} \rightarrow 2CO_{(g)}$$
$$Si_{(s)} + O_{2\,(g)} \rightarrow SiO_{2\,(s)}$$
$$4P_{(s)} + 5O_{2\,(g)} \rightarrow P_4O_{10\,(s)}$$

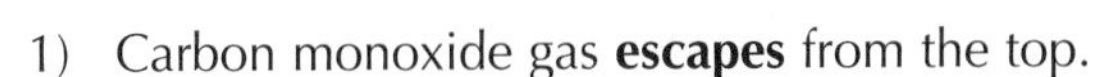

1) Carbon monoxide gas **escapes** from the top.
2) The lime reacts with the acidic non-metal oxides (SiO_2 and P_4O_{10}), converting them into a **molten slag** that floats to the surface and is tapped off.
3) The last stage is a big one — small amounts of other **transition metals** are added to make the steel you want. E.g. to make stainless steel, you usually add **chromium** and **nickel** in the right amounts.

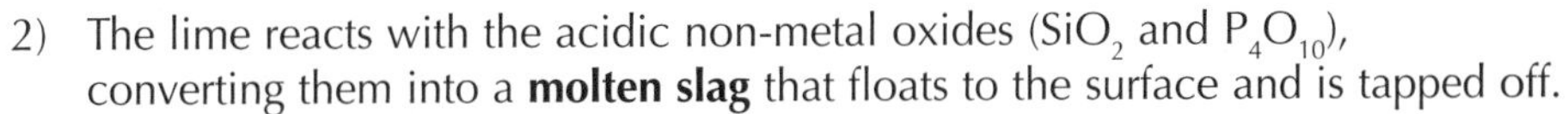

But Reduction with Carbon does have its **Limitations**

1) Carbon reduction **can't** extract metals more **reactive** than zinc from their ores. For these ones, you need to use **electrolysis** of the molten ore.
2) Even with some less reactive metals, like titanium and tungsten, carbon reduction doesn't really work because you get **metal carbides** forming, which make the metal **too brittle**.

E.g. $TiO_{2\,(s)} + 3C_{(s)} \rightarrow TiC_{(s)} + 2CO_{(g)}$

Carbon reduction also poses **environmental problems**:
1) Carbon dioxide released into the atmosphere contributes to **global warming**.
2) Roasting sulphide ores can release sulphur dioxide into the air, contributing to **acid rain**.

and general smelliness...

Oh right, yeah. Brilliant Ted.

Practice Questions

Q1 List the raw materials that are fed into a blast furnace for producing iron.

Q2 What are the equations for the following important processes in the blast furnace?
(a) The reduction of iron(III) oxide by carbon monoxide.
(b) The removal of silicon dioxide as a molten slag.

Q3 Which elements are always present in stainless steel?

Q4 Why is carbon reduction not used to extract titanium or tungsten from their ores?

Q5 Give two environmental problems associated with extracting metals by carbon reduction.

Exam Question

Q1 a) What type of reaction is always involved in the extraction of a metal from its ore? [1 mark]
b) Which element is most likely to be combined with a metal in its ore? [1 mark]
c) Outline the essential chemistry of the process for converting crude iron into carbon steel. [2 marks]

The blast furnace — don't worry, it's OK to slag it off...

...not that you'd dream of slagging off this topic. Because surely after the pain... the torture... the sorrows... the brief highs ... then the monumental lows of this eternal section, you must have quite enjoyed this easy page. There's nothing hard here, even the equations are dead simple. So just make sure you learn it all (and don't forget the pretty diagrams too).

Extracting Aluminium and Titanium

You can skip this double page if you're doing OCR, OCR Salters or Edexcel Nuffield...

Aluminium and titanium are cool metals — they're used in planes, and planes are cool because they fly. But I suppose by that argument, pigeons would be cool... Anyway, enough of this nonsense, here's how they're extracted...

Aluminium is Extracted by Electrolysis

Aluminium's ore is called **bauxite** and it's basically aluminium oxide, Al_2O_3, with various impurities. First of all, these impurities are removed. Next, it's dissolved in **molten cryolite** (sodium aluminium fluoride, Na_3AlF_6), which lowers its **melting point** from a scorching 2050 °C, to a cool **970 °C**. This reduces the operating costs.

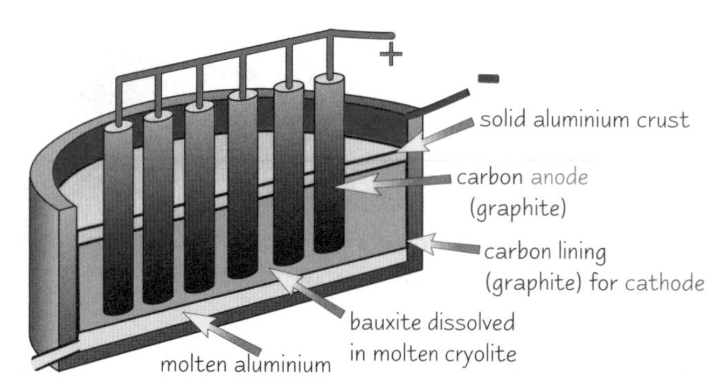

Electrolysis takes place in carbon-lined steel tanks. The graphite lining is the cathode of the cell. The anodes are blocks of graphite. The current used is high (200 000 A), so the process is carried out where cheap electricity is available, often near hydroelectric power stations.

ELECTROLYSIS OF ALUMINIUM

1) Aluminium is produced at the **cathode** and collects as the molten liquid at the bottom of the cell.

   $$Al^{3+} + 3e^- \rightarrow Al$$

2) Oxygen is produced at the **anode**.

   $$2O^{2-} \rightarrow O_2 + 4e^-$$

3) Much of the oxygen reacts with the carbon anodes to form **carbon dioxide**. The anodes slowly burn away and have to be **replaced** regularly.
4) The waste gases from the cell contain fluorides, so they need to be **cleaned** thoroughly to avoid local pollution effects.

Titanium is Great but a bit too Expensive

This bit is AQA only...

Titanium is a pretty **abundant** metal in the Earth's crust. In its pure form, titanium is a **strong**, **light** metal that is highly resistant to **corrosion**. Pretty much perfect really, so how come it's not used more... Well basically, it's just a bit too **difficult** and **expensive** to produce.

The main ore is rutile (titanium(IV) oxide, TiO_2). You can't extract it by carbon reduction because you get titanium carbide which ruins it... $TiO_{2\,(s)} + 3C_{(s)} \rightarrow TiC_{(s)} + 2CO_{(g)}$

THE EXTRACTION OF TITANIUM

...is a **batch** process with several stages.

1) The ore is converted to **titanium(IV) chloride** by heating it with carbon in a stream of chlorine gas.

   $$TiO_{2\,(s)} + 2Cl_{2\,(g)} + 2C_{(s)} \rightarrow TiCl_{4\,(g)} + 2CO_{(g)}$$

2) The titanium chloride is purified by **fractional distillation** under an inert atmosphere of argon or nitrogen.
3) Then the chloride gets reduced in a **furnace** by heating it with a **more reactive** metal such as sodium or magnesium. An inert atmosphere is used to prevent side reactions.

   $$TiCl_{4\,(g)} + 4Na_{(l)} \rightarrow Ti_{(s)} + 4NaCl_{(s)}$$
   $$TiCl_{4\,(g)} + 2Mg_{(l)} \rightarrow Ti_{(s)} + 2MgCl_{2\,(l)}$$

The high costs of the process have meant that titanium hasn't been used as widely as it deserves. 50 – 80% of the metal produced is used in the aerospace industry.

EXTRACTION IS EXPENSIVE BECAUSE...

1) Chlorine, sodium and magnesium are all expensive (they're produced by **electrolysis**).
2) The reactions need **high temperatures**.
3) Handling of $TiCl_4$ requires special care as it's **highly reactive** with water.
4) The process needs an **inert atmosphere** to prevent oxidation of the titanium.

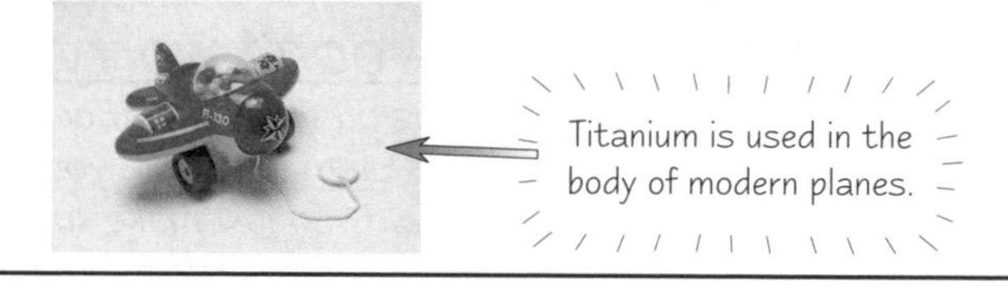

Extracting Aluminium and Titanium

The Main Factors affecting the Choice of Metal Extraction are...

1) **The Reactivity of the Metal**
The most reactive metals are usually produced by **electrolysis** because there's nothing available to use as a reducing agent.

2) **The cost of the reducing agent**
A naturally available reducing agent such as **carbon** (from coal) is cheaper than one which needs to be extracted itself, like sodium.

3) **The energy costs of the process**
The lower the **temperature** of the process, the lower the **energy** costs. Electrolysis of molten ores is generally expensive.

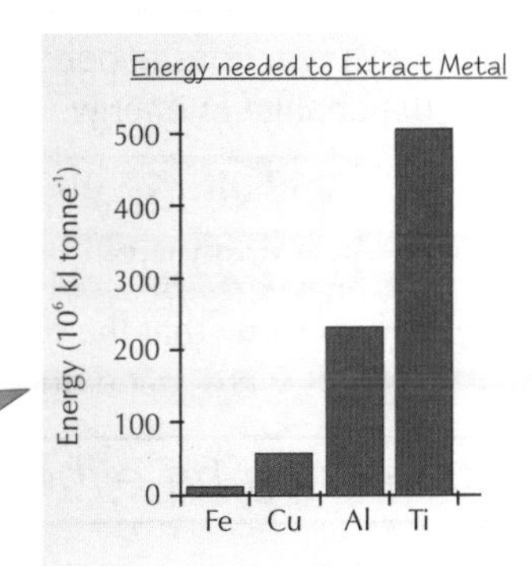

4) **The required purity of the metal**
Very high purity is **expensive**. For copper, purity is often really important because it affects electrical conductivity. So copper has to be purified expensively by electrolysis.

5) **The environmental costs of production**
Mining and careless disposal of industrial waste can **scar** the landscape. Avoiding atmospheric and water **pollution** has to be considered too in the costing.

Recycling Metals is Good for Costs and the Environment

Recycling metals, particularly iron (and steel) and aluminium, is becoming increasingly important...

1) Recycling conserves the Earth's resources
of iron ore and bauxite. It also reduces some of the environmental costs of producing new metal.

2) Recycling is much cheaper than Extracting metals
This is especially true for aluminium — recycling scrap aluminium costs only 5% as much as making the pure metal. Now there's a handy saving...

Practice Questions

Q1 Name the major ore of aluminium.

Q2 What is the molten aluminium oxide mixed with in the electrolysis cell? Why is this done?

Q3 What properties of titanium make it a very useful metal?

Q4 Write the equation for the displacement of titanium from titanium chloride using sodium.

Q5 What type of reaction is this?

Exam Questions

Q1 Aluminium is extracted from its purified ore by electrolysis.

a) What important step is taken to reduce the cost of extracting aluminium? [2 marks]

b) Write equations for the reactions occurring at each electrode. [2 marks]

c) Explain why aluminium is more expensive to extract than iron. [1 mark]

Q2 a) Industrially, titanium is produced by the reduction of titanium(IV) chloride.
Give the name of one possible reducing agent and write an equation for the process. [2 marks]

b) Why is titanium manufactured by this method rather than reduction of titanium(IV) oxide with carbon? [2 marks]

Al and Ti — finally, some real manly metals, not like those weedy s-blockers...

Oh yes indeed, these are fine metals that you'd be proud to take home to meet your parents. As with the last page, there's nothing hard here at all. But there is plenty to get stuck into with your revision shovel. Remember when your teacher said "Chemistry is all experiments and fun, hardly any learning"? Well now can see what a big fat liar he or she was, eh...

Enthalpy Changes

A whole new section to enjoy — but don't forget, Big Brother is watching...

Chemical Reactions Often Have Enthalpy Changes

When chemical reactions happen, some bonds are **broken** and some bonds are **made**. More often than not, this'll cause a **change in energy**. The souped-up chemistry term for this is **enthalpy change** —

Enthalpy change, ΔH (delta H), is the heat energy transferred in a reaction at **constant pressure**. The units of ΔH are **kJ mol**$^{-1}$.

You write $\Delta H^{\ominus}$ to show that the elements were in their **standard states** and that the measurements were made under **standard conditions**.

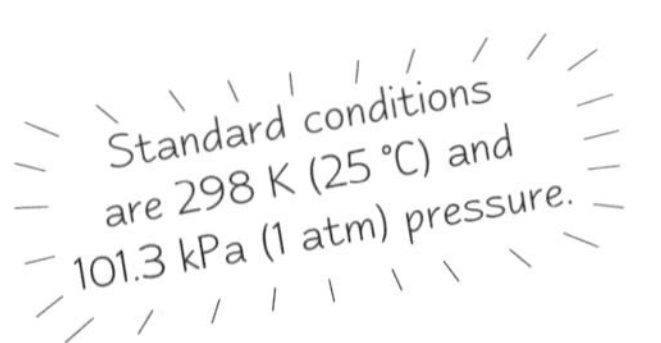

Standard conditions are 298 K (25 °C) and 101.3 kPa (1 atm) pressure.

Reactions can be either Exothermic or Endothermic

1) **Exothermic** reactions **give out** energy — ΔH is **negative**. In exothermic reactions, the temperature often goes **up**.

Oxidation is exothermic. Here's 2 examples —
- The **combustion** of fuels like methane ⟹ $CH_{4(g)} + 2O_{2(g)} \rightarrow CO_{2(g)} + 2H_2O_{(l)}$ $\Delta H_c^{\ominus} = -890\ \text{kJ mol}^{-1}$ **exothermic**
- The oxidation of **carbohydrates**, such as glucose, $C_6H_{12}O_6$, in respiration.

2) **Endothermic** reactions **absorb** energy — ΔH is **positive**. In these reactions, temperature often **falls**.

The **thermal decomposition** of calcium carbonate is endothermic. $CaCO_{3(s)} \rightarrow CaO_{(s)} + CO_{2(g)}$ $\Delta H_r^{\ominus} = +178\ \text{kJ mol}^{-1}$ **endothermic**

The main reactions of **photosynthesis** are also endothermic — sunlight supplies the energy.

Enthalpy Profile Diagrams show you how the enthalpy (energy) changes during reactions —

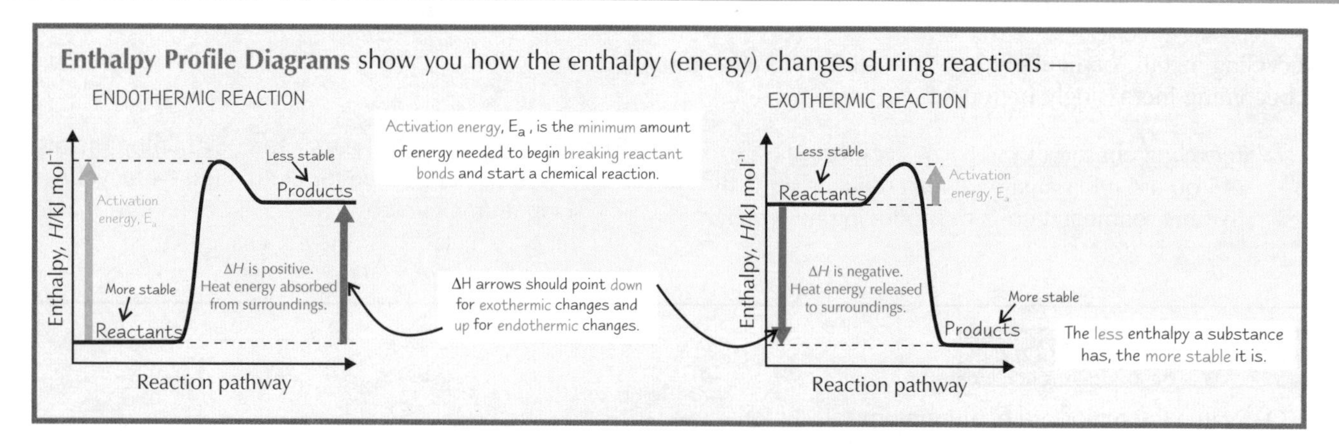

Enthalpy, H/kJ mol⁻¹

ΔH is positive. Heat energy absorbed from surroundings.

Activation energy, Eₐ, is the minimum amount of energy needed to begin breaking reactant bonds and start a chemical reaction.
ΔH arrows should point down for exothermic changes and up for endothermic changes.

Enthalpy, H/kJ mol⁻¹

ΔH is negative. Heat energy released to surroundings.

The less enthalpy a substance has, the more stable it is.

Exothermic Reactions are NOT always Spontaneous

Edexcel only.

Once a **spontaneous reaction** is started, it'll just **carry on** going. Like if you leave the handbrake off on a steep hill.

1) Many **exothermic** reactions are spontaneous — after all, the **products** are more stable than the reactants.
2) Most **endothermic** reactions are **not** spontaneous under standard conditions — because the **reactants** are more stable.

BUT —

1) Endothermic reactions **might** become spontaneous under **non-standard conditions**, like high temperatures.
2) Some exothermic reactions have such **slow rates** that they just don't happen. E.g. diamond changes to graphite **REALLY** slowly (this is just as well, or the diamonds in your ring would be black and brittle before you knew it).
3) Some endothermic reactions are **spontaneous**, even under standard conditions.

So...the basic rule seems to be...there's no basic rule.

Thermodynamic and Kinetic Stability are NOT the same

Edexcel only.

1) When ethyne, C_2H_2, is made, energy needs to be put in — it's **endothermic**. This makes it **thermodynamically unstable** compared to its elements.
2) But it can be stored for ages without decomposing, so it's **kinetically stable**. Because the activation energy's so high, it decomposes very **slowly**. $2C_{(s)} + H_{2(g)} \rightarrow C_2H_{2(g)}$ $\Delta H_f^{\ominus} = +227\ \text{kJ mol}^{-1}$

Enthalpy Changes

There's **Loads** of Different Types of ΔH Depending On the **Reaction**

1) **Standard enthalpy change of reaction, ΔH_r°,** is the enthalpy change when the reaction occurs in the **molar quantities** shown in the **chemical equation**, under standard conditions in their standard states.
2) **Standard enthalpy change of formation, ΔH_f°,** is the enthalpy change when **1 mole** of a **compound** is formed from its **elements** in their standard states under standard conditions, e.g. $2C_{(s)} + 3H_{2(g)} + \frac{1}{2}O_{2(g)} \longrightarrow C_2H_5OH_{(l)}$
3) **Standard enthalpy change of combustion, ΔH_c°,** is the enthalpy change when **1 mole** of a substance is completely **burned in oxygen** under standard conditions.
4) **Standard enthalpy of neutralisation, ΔH_{neut}°,** is the enthalpy change when **1 mole** of **water** is formed from the neutralisation of **hydrogen ions** by **hydroxide ions** under standard conditions, e.g. $H^+_{(aq)} + OH^-_{(aq)} \longrightarrow H_2O_{(l)}$
5) **Standard enthalpy change of atomisation, ΔH_{at}°,** is the enthalpy change when **1 mole** of **gaseous atoms** is formed from the element in its **standard state**, e.g. $\frac{1}{2}Cl_{2(g)} \longrightarrow Cl_{(g)}$
6) **First electron affinity, ΔH_{e1}°,** is the enthalpy change when **1 mole** of gaseous **–1 ions** are made from **1 mole** of gaseous **atoms**, e.g. $O_{(g)} + e^- \longrightarrow O^-_{(g)}$
7) **Second electron affinity, ΔH_{e2}°,** is the enthalpy change when **1 mole** of gaseous **–2 ions** are made from **1 mole** of gaseous **–1 ions**, e.g. $O^-_{(g)} + e^- \longrightarrow O^{2-}_{(g)}$

The second electron affinity is always endothermic. Energy has to be supplied to overcome the repulsion between the negative ion and the negative incoming electron.

Practice Questions

Q1 Explain the terms exothermic and endothermic, giving an example reaction in each case.

Q2 Draw and label enthalpy profile diagrams for an exothermic and an endothermic reaction.

Q3 Define standard enthalpy of formation and standard enthalpy of combustion.

Exam Questions

Q1 Hydrogen peroxide, H_2O_2, can decompose into water and oxygen. $2H_2O_{2(l)} \longrightarrow 2H_2O_{(l)} + O_{2(g)}$ $\Delta H_r^\circ = -98 \text{ kJ mol}^{-1}$

a) Draw an enthalpy profile diagram for this reaction. Mark on the activation energy and ΔH. [3 marks]

b) Hydrogen peroxide can be stored for long periods of time, without decomposing.

i) What does this tell you about the stability of the reactants and products? [2 marks]

ii) Suggest one reason why the reaction is not spontaneous. [1 mark]

Q2 Methanol, CH_3OH, when blended with petrol, can be used as a fuel. $\Delta H_c^\circ[CH_3OH] = -726 \text{ kJ mol}^{-1}$.

a) Write an equation, including state symbols, for the standard enthalpy change of combustion of methanol. [2 marks]

b) Write an equation, including state symbols, for the standard enthalpy change of formation of methanol. [2 marks]

c) Liquid petroleum gas is a fuel that contains propane, C_3H_8.
Give two reasons why the following equation does not represent a standard enthalpy change of combustion. [2 marks]

$$2C_3H_{8(g)} + 10O_{2(g)} \longrightarrow 8H_2O_{(g)} + 6CO_{2(g)} \quad \Delta H_r = -4113 \text{ kJ mol}^{-1}$$

It's getting hot in here, so take off all your bonds...

What a lotta definitions. And you need to know them all. If you're going to bother learning them, you might as well do it properly and learn all the pernickety details. They probably seem about as useful as a dead fly in your custard right now, but all will be revealed over the next few pages. Learn them now, so you've got a bit of a head start.

Calculating Enthalpy Changes

Now you know what enthalpy changes are, here's how to calculate them...

You can find out **Enthalpy Changes** in the Lab

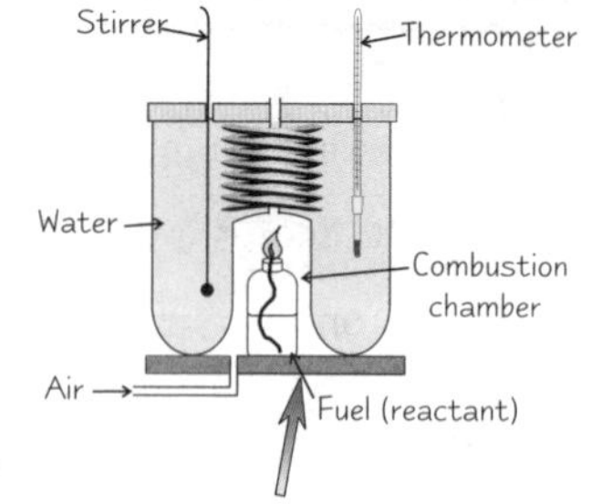

This top bit's just for Edexcel and Edexcel Nuffield.

1) To measure the **enthalpy change** for a reaction you only need to know **two things** —
   - The **number of moles** of the stuff that's reacting.
   - The change in **temperature**.
2) How you go about doing the experiment depends on what type of reaction it is. Some reactions will quite happily take place in a **container** and you can just stick a **thermometer** in to find out the temperature change. It's best to use a **polystyrene beaker**, so that you don't lose or gain much heat through the sides.
3) **Combustion reactions** are trickier because the reactant is burned in air. A **copper calorimeter** containing a **known mass of water** is often used. You burn a **known mass of the reactant** and record the **temperature change** of the water.

Calculate **Enthalpy Changes** Using the **Equation $q = mc\Delta T$**

It seems there's a snazzy equation for everything these days, and enthalpy change is no exception —

$q = mc\Delta T$ where, q = heat lost or gained (in joules). This is the same as the enthalpy change if the pressure is constant.

m = mass of water in the calorimeter, or solution in the polystyrene beaker (in grams)

c = specific heat capacity of water (4.18 J $g^{-1}K^{-1}$)

ΔT = the change in temperature of the water or solution

Example —

In a laboratory experiment, 1.16 g of an organic liquid fuel was completely burned in oxygen.
The heat formed during this combustion raised the temperature of 100 g of water from 295.3 K to 357.8 K.

Calculate the molar enthalpy of combustion, ΔH_c, of the fuel. Its M_r is 58.

Remember — m is the mass of water, NOT the mass of fuel.

1. First off, you need to calculate the **amount of heat** given out by the fuel using $q = mc\Delta T$.

$q = mc\Delta T$

$q = 100 \times 4.18 \times (357.8 - 295.3) = 26\,125 \text{ J} = 26.125 \text{ kJ}$

Change the amount of heat from J to kJ.

2. Next you need to find out **how many moles** of fuel produced this heat. It's back to the old $n = \frac{\text{mass}}{M}$ equation.

$n = \frac{1.16}{58} = 0.02$ moles of fuel

3. The molar enthalpy of combustion involves 1 mole of fuel.

It's negative because combustion is an exothermic reaction.

So, the heat produced by 1 mole of fuel $= \frac{-26.125}{0.02}$

$\approx$ **-1306 kJ mol^{-1}**. This is the molar enthalpy change of combustion.

The actual ΔH_c of this compound is -1615 kJ mol^{-1} — loads of heat has been **lost** and not measured. E.g. it's likely a fair bit would escape through the **copper calorimeter** and also the fuel might not **combust completely**.

Hess's Law — the Total Enthalpy Change is **Independent** of the Route Taken

Hess's Law says that —

The **total enthalpy change** of a reaction is always **the same**, no matter **which route** is taken.

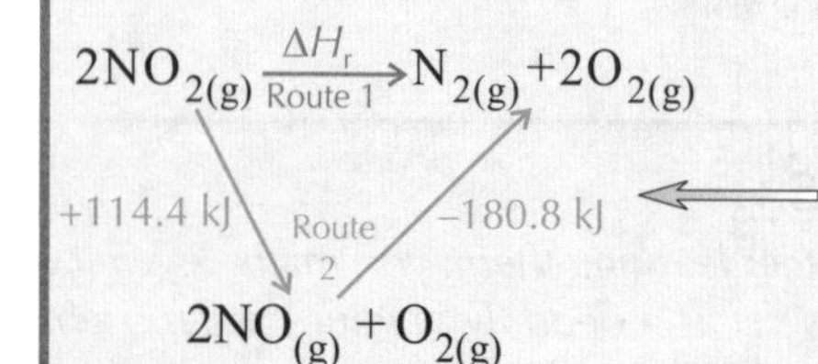

This law is handy for working out enthalpy changes that you **can't find directly** by doing an experiment.

Here's an example —

The **total enthalpy change** for route 1 is the **same as for route 2**.

So, $\Delta H_r = +114.4 + (-180.8) = -66.4$ kJ mol^{-1}.

Calculating Enthalpy Changes

Enthalpy Changes Can be **Worked Out Indirectly**

The element's being formed from the element, so there's no change

Enthalpy changes of formation are useful for calculating enthalpy changes you can't find directly.
You need to know $\Delta H_f^\ominus$ for **all** the reactants and products which are **compounds** — the value of $\Delta H_f^\ominus$ for elements is **zero**.

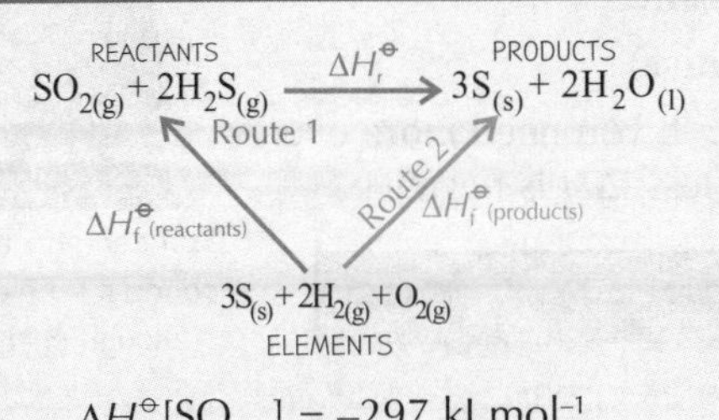

Here's how to calculate $\Delta H_r^\ominus$ for the reaction shown...

Using **Hess's Law**: Route 1 = Route 2

$\Delta H_r^\ominus$ + the sum of $\Delta H_f^\ominus$ (reactants) = the sum of $\Delta H_f^\ominus$ (products)

So, **$\Delta H_r^\ominus$ = the sum of $\Delta H_f^\ominus$ (products) – the sum of $\Delta H_f^\ominus$ (reactants)**

$\Delta H_f^\ominus[SO_{2(g)}] = -297 \text{ kJ mol}^{-1}$

$\Delta H_f^\ominus[H_2S_{(g)}] = -20.2 \text{ kJ mol}^{-1}$

$\Delta H_f^\ominus[H_2O_{(l)}] = -286 \text{ kJ mol}^{-1}$

To find $\Delta H_r^\ominus$ of this reaction: $SO_{2(g)} + 2H_2S_{(g)} \rightarrow 3S_{(s)} + 2H_2O_{(l)}$

Just plug the numbers into the equation above:

$$\Delta H_r^\ominus = [0 + (-286 \times 2)] - [-297 + (-20.2 \times 2)] = \mathbf{+234.6 \text{ kJ mol}^{-1}}$$

$\Delta H_f^\ominus$ of sulphur is zero — it's an element.

There's 2 moles of H_2O and 2 moles of H_2S.

You can use a similar method to find **enthalpy changes of formation** from enthalpy changes of combustion.

Here's how to calculate $\Delta H_f^\ominus$ of **ethanol**...

Using Hess's Law: Route 1 = Route 2

$\Delta H_f^\ominus[\text{ethanol}] + \Delta H_c^\ominus[\text{ethanol}] = 2\Delta H_c^\ominus[C] + 3\Delta H_c^\ominus[H_2]$

$\Delta H_f^\ominus[\text{ethanol}] + (-1367) = (2 \times -394) + (3 \times -286)$

$\Delta H_f^\ominus[\text{ethanol}] = -788 + -858 - (-1367)$

$= \mathbf{-279 \text{ kJ mol}^{-1}}$.

REACTANTS $\Delta H_f^\ominus$ PRODUCTS

$2C_{(s)} + 3H_{2(g)} + \frac{1}{2}O_{2(g)} \rightarrow C_2H_5OH_{(1)}$

Route 1

Route 2

$4\frac{1}{2}O_{2(g)}$

$2O_{2(g)}$

$2CO_{(g)} + 3H_2O_{(l)}$

COMBUSTION PRODUCTS

$\Delta H_c^\ominus[C] = -394 \text{ kJ mol}^{-1}$

$\Delta H_c^\ominus[H_2] = -286 \text{ kJ mol}^{-1}$

$\Delta H_c^\ominus[\text{ethanol}] = -1367 \text{ kJ mol}^{-1}$

Practice Questions

Q1 Briefly describe an experiment that could be carried out to find the enthalpy change of a reaction.

Q2 Why is the enthalpy change determined in a laboratory likely to be lower than the value shown in a data book?

Q3 What equation is used to calculate the heat change in a chemical reaction?

Q4 What does Hess's Law state?

Q5 What is the standard enthalpy change of formation of any element?

Exam Questions

Q1 Using the facts that the standard enthalpy change of formation of $Al_2O_{3(s)}$ is $-1676 \text{ kJ mol}^{-1}$ and the standard enthalpy change of formation of $MgO_{(s)}$ is -602 kJ mol^{-1}, calculate the enthalpy change of the following reaction.

$$Al_2O_{3(s)} + 3Mg_{(s)} \rightarrow 2Al_{(s)} + 3MgO_{(s)}$$

[3 marks]

Q2 A 50 cm^3 sample of 0.200 M copper(II) sulphate solution placed in a polystyrene beaker gave a temperature increase of 2.6 K when excess zinc powder was added and stirred. Calculate the enthalpy change when 1 mole of zinc reacts. Assume that the specific heat capacity for the solution is 4.18 $J\ g^{-1}K^{-1}$.

The equation for the reaction is: $Zn_{(s)} + CuSO_{4(aq)} \rightarrow Cu_{(s)} + ZnSO_{4(aq)}$

[8 marks]

To understand this lot, you're gonna need a bar of chocolate. Or two...

To get your head around those Hess diagrams, you're going to have to do more the skim them. It'll also help if you know the definitions for those standard enthalpy thingumabobs on page 63. If you didn't bother learning them, have a quick flick back and remind yourself about them — especially the standard enthalpy changes of combustion and formation.

Bond Enthalpy and Entropy Changes

I bonded with my friend. Now we're on the waiting list to be surgically separated.

Reactions are all about **Breaking** and **Making** Bonds

When reactions happen, **reactant bonds** are **broken** and **product bonds** are **formed**.

1) You **need** energy to break bonds, so bond breaking is **endothermic** (ΔH is **positive**).
2) Energy is **released** when bonds are formed, so this is **exothermic** (ΔH is **negative**).
3) The **enthalpy change** for a reaction is the **overall effect** of these two changes. If you need **more** energy to **break** bonds than is released when bonds are made, ΔH is **positive**. If it's less, ΔH is negative.

You can only break bonds if you've got enough energy.

You need **Energy** to **Break** the **Attraction** between **Atoms** and **Ions**

1) In covalent molecules, the **positive nuclei** are attracted to the **negative** shared electrons. In ionic bonding, **positive** and **negative ions** are attracted to each other.
2) You need energy to **break** this attraction — **stronger** bonds take more energy to break. The **amount of energy** you need per mole is called the **bond dissociation enthalpy**. (Of course it's got a fancy name — this is Chemistry.)
3) Bond dissociation enthalpies always involve bond breaking in **gaseous compounds**. This makes comparisons fair.

The **Length** of a Bond depends on its **Strength**

OCR Salters and Edexcel Nuffield only.

1) In covalent bonds, there isn't just an **attraction** between the nuclei and the shared electrons. The two **positively charged nuclei** also **repel** each other, as do the **electrons**.
2) The distance between the **two nuclei** is the distance where the **attractive** and **repulsive** forces balance each other. This distance is the **bond length**.
3) The **stronger** the attraction between the atoms, the higher the **bond dissociation enthalpy** and the **shorter** the bond length. It makes sense really. If there's more attraction, the nuclei will pull **closer** together.

A C=C bond has a greater bond dissociation enthalpy and is shorter than a C–C bond. Four electrons are shared in C=C and only two in C–C, so the electron density between the two carbon atoms is greater. C≡C has an even higher bond dissociation enthalphy and is shorter than C=C — six electrons are shared here.

Bond	C–C	C=C	C≡C
Average Bond Dissociation Enthalpy (kJ mol^{-1})	+347	+612	+838
Bond length (nm)	0.154	0.134	0.120

Average Bond Dissociation Enthalpies are **not Exact**

Water (H_2O) has got **two O–H bonds**. You'd think it'd take the same amount of energy to break them both...but it **doesn't**.

The **first** bond, $H\text{–}OH_{(g)}$: $E(\text{H–OH}) = +492$ kJ mol^{-1}

The **second** bond, $H\text{–}O_{(g)}$: $E(\text{H–O}) = +428$ kJ mol^{-1}

(OH^- is a bit easier to break apart because of the extra electron repulsion.)

So, the **average** bond dissociation enthalpy is $\frac{492+428}{2}$ = **+460 kJ mol^{-1}**.

The data book says the bond enthalpy for O–H is +463 kJ mol^{-1}. It's a bit different because it's the average for a much bigger range of molecules, not just water. For example, it includes the O-H bond in alcohols and carboxylic acids too.

Bond Enthalpies are Calculated using **Hess's Law**

Here's another amazing example of what you can do with Hess's Law. It's hard to calculate **bond enthalpies** directly, but you can work them out from standard enthalpy changes of **atomisation**, $\Delta H^{\ominus}_{at}$, and **formation**, $\Delta H^{\ominus}_{f}$.
So, here's how to calculate the bond enthalpy of **C–H in methane** using a Hess's law energy cycle —

$$C_{(graphite)} + 2H_{2(g)} \xrightarrow{\Delta H_1} CH_{4(g)}$$

Route 1: ΔH_1 then ΔH_2 (from $CH_{4(g)}$ to $C_{(g)} + 4H_{(g)}$); Route 2: ΔH_3 (from $C_{(graphite)} + 2H_{2(g)}$ to $C_{(g)} + 4H_{(g)}$)

$\Delta H_1 = \Delta H^{\ominus}_f \, CH_{4(g)} = -74.8$ kJ mol^{-1}

ΔH_2 = four times the bond enthalpy of the C-H bond in $CH_{4(g)}$.
You need to find the bond enthalpy of 1 C-H bond in methane.

$\Delta H_3 = \Delta H^{\ominus}_{at} \, C_{(g)}$ (+716.7 kJ mol^{-1}) + four times $\Delta H^{\ominus}_{at} \, H_{(g)}$ (4 × 218.0 kJ mol^{-1}).

Route 1 = Route 2

$\Delta H_1 + \Delta H_2 = \Delta H_3$

$\Delta H_2 = [+716.7 + (4 \times 218.0)] - (-74.8) = +1663.5$ kJ mol^{-1}

This is the bond enthalpy of four C–H bonds. Just divide by 4 to find the bond enthalpy of 1 C–H bond.

E(C–H) in methane = $\frac{1663.5}{4} \approx$ **416 kJ mol^{-1}**

Bond Enthalpy and Entropy Changes

Entropy Tells you How Much Disorder there is

Only learn this bit if you're doing OCR Salters.

To explain **entropy** we need to go back to the good old **solid-liquid-gas** particle explanation thingies...

1) So... in **solids**, everything's nice and orderly. The particles don't move about freely — they just wobble about a fixed point. This means it's pretty easy to **predict** where a particle's going to be.
2) In **liquids**, the particles are still close together, but they can move about freely. So it's not quite so orderly and it's harder to **predict** the position of a particle.
3) In **gases**, the particles are very far apart, whizzing around wherever they like. There's **no order** — in fact, it's absolute **chaos** (that's a technical term). The position of a particle is totally **unpredictable**.

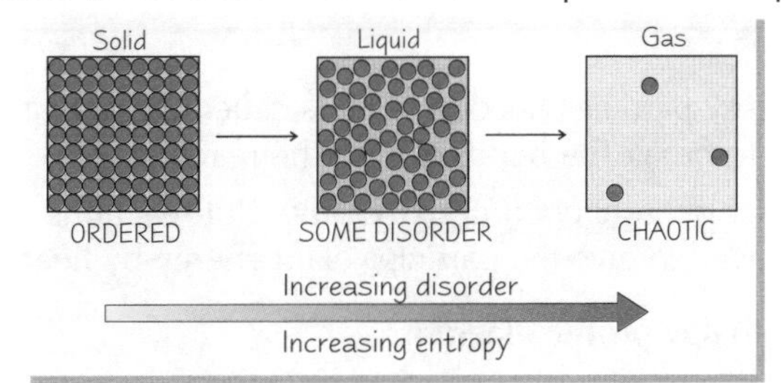

Looks like someone else has been reading the energetics section...

Entropy is a measure of the **number of ways** the particles can be **arranged** — but it's basically just a measure of disorder. Now get this: substances **like** disorder. Particles will naturally move to give a substance the **maximum possible entropy**...

- Gases diffuse to fill all the available space because there's more ways of arranging particles in a bigger space.
- When something dissolves, the **solute** particles spread out in the **solvent**, and entropy increases.

Practice Questions

Q1 Is energy taken in or released when bonds are broken?

Q2 What state must compounds be in when bond dissociation enthalpies are measured?

Q3 Which is shorter — a single C–C bond or a double C=C bond?

Q4 In terms of entropy, why do gases diffuse to fill all the available space?

Exam Questions

Q1

Bond	Compound	Bond length (nm)	Bond enthalpy (kJ mol^{-1})
C–O	alcohols	0.143	336
C=O	ketones	0.122	749

Explain why the bond energy of C=O in ketones is greater than the C–O bond energy in alcohols and the bond length of C=O is less than that of C–O. [6 marks]

Q2 a) Construct a Hess's law energy cycle to show the standard enthalpy change of formation of ammonia and the standard enthalpy changes of atomisation of its elements. [3 marks]

b) Use the cycle and the enthalpy changes given below to calculate the bond enthalpy of N–H in ammonia.

$$\tfrac{1}{2}N_{2(g)} + 1\tfrac{1}{2}H_{2(g)} \rightarrow NH_{3(g)} \quad \Delta H^{\ominus} = -46.2 \text{ kJ mol}^{-1}$$
$$\tfrac{1}{2}N_{2(g)} \rightarrow N_{(g)} \quad \Delta H^{\ominus} = +473 \text{ kJ mol}^{-1}$$
$$\tfrac{1}{2}H_{2(g)} \rightarrow H_{(g)} \quad \Delta H^{\ominus} = +218 \text{ kJ mol}^{-1}$$

[3 marks]

c) The data book value for the average bond enthalpy of N–H is +388 kJ mol^{-1}. Why is there a discrepancy between this value and the calculated value? [2 marks]

My bedroom has the maximum possible entropy...

Reactions are like pulling your Lego spaceship apart and building something new. Sometimes the bits get stuck together and you need to use loads of energy to pull 'em apart. Okay, so energy's not really released when you stick them together, but you can't have everything — and it wasn't that bad an analogy up till now. Ah, well...you best get on and learn this stuff.

Reaction Rates

The rate of a reaction is just how quickly it happens. Lots of things can make it go faster or slower.

Particles Must Collide to React

1) Particles in liquids and gases are **always moving** and **colliding** with **each other**. They **don't** react every time though — only when the **conditions** are right. A reaction **won't** take place between two particles **unless** —

- They collide in the **right direction**. They need to be **facing** each other the right way.
- They collide with at least a certain **minimum** amount of kinetic (movement) **energy**.

This stuff's called **Collision Theory**.

2) The **minimum amount of kinetic energy** particles need to react is called the **activation energy**. The particles need this much energy to **break the bonds** to start the reaction.
3) Reactions with **low activation energies** often happen **pretty easily**. But reactions with **high activation energies** don't. You need to give the particles extra energy by **heating** them.

To make this a bit clearer, here's another **enthalpy profile diagram**.

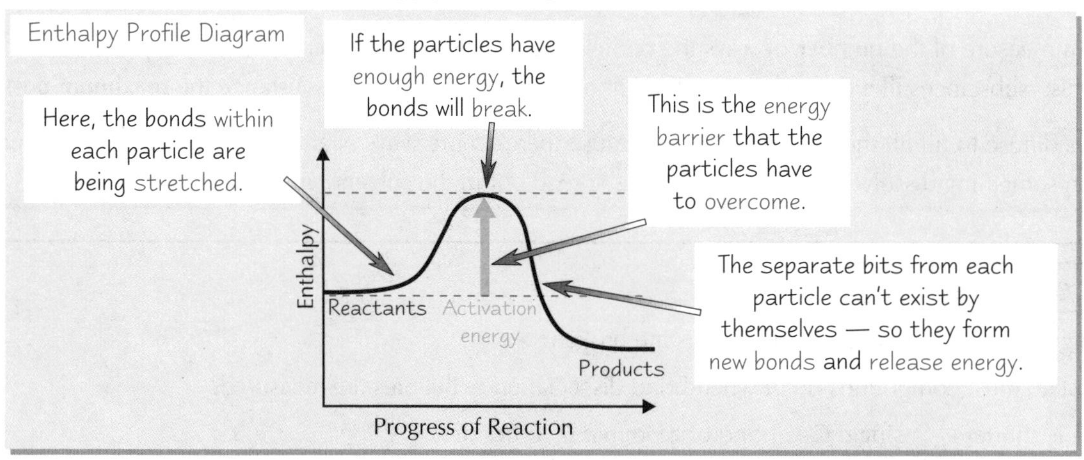

Molecules in a Gas Don't all have the Same Amount of Energy

Imagine looking down on **Oxford Street** when it's teeming with people. You'll see some people ambling along **slowly**, some hurrying **quickly**, but most of them will be walking with a **moderate speed**. It's the same with the **molecules** in a **gas**. Some **don't have much kinetic energy** and move **slowly**. Others have **loads of kinetic energy** and **whizz** along. But most molecules are somewhere **in between**.

If you plot a **graph** of the **numbers of molecules** in a **gas** with different **kinetic energies** you get a **Maxwell-Boltzmann distribution**. It looks like this —

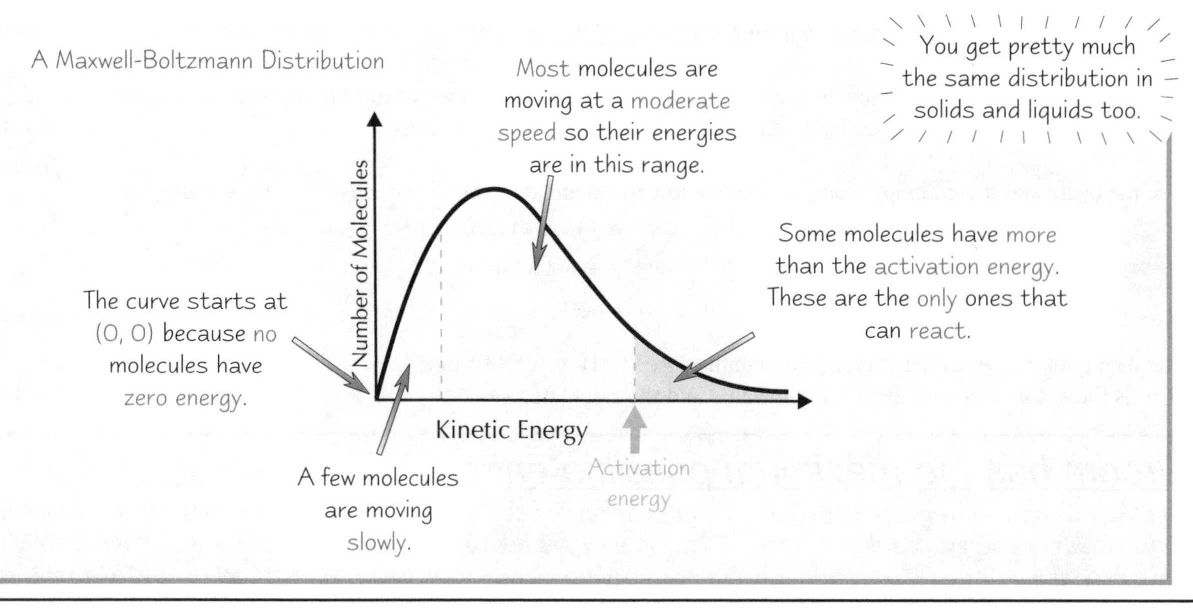

Reaction Rates

Increasing the *Temperature* makes Reactions *Faster*

1) If you increase the **temperature**, the particles will on average have more **kinetic energy** and will move **faster**.
2) So, a **greater proportion** of molecules will have the **activation energy** and be able to **react**.
This changes the **shape** of the **Maxwell-Boltzmann distribution curve** — it pushes it over to the **right**.

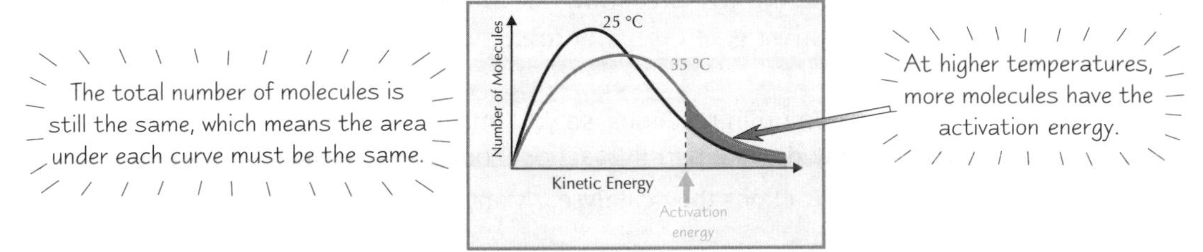
The total number of molecules is still the same, which means the area under each curve must be the same.
25 °C
35 °C
Number of Molecules
Kinetic Energy
Activation energy
At higher temperatures, more molecules have the activation energy.

3) Because the molecules are flying about **faster**, they'll **collide more often**.
This is **another reason** why increasing the temperature makes a reaction faster.

Concentration, *Surface Area* and *Catalysts* also Affect the *Reaction Rate*

Increasing Concentration Speeds Up Reactions

If you increase the **concentration** of reactants in a **solution** or the **pressure** of a **gas**, the particles will on average be **closer together**. If they're closer, they'll **collide more often**. If there's **more collisions**, they'll have **more chances** to react.

Increasing Surface Area Speeds Up Reactions

If one reactant is in a **big lump** then most of the particles won't collide with other reactants.
You need to **crush** these lumps so that more of the particles can come in **contact** with the other **reactants**.
A **smaller particle size** means a **larger surface area**. This leads to a **speedier** reaction.

Catalysts Can Speed Up Reactions

Catalysts are really useful. They **lower the activation energy** by providing a **different way** for the bonds to be broken and remade. If the activation energy's **lower**, more particles will have **enough energy** to react. There's heaps of information about catalysts on **pages 70-73**.

Practice Questions

Q1 Explain the term 'activation energy'.

Q2 What is a Maxwell-Boltzmann distribution?

Q3 Name the four factors that affect the rate of a reaction.

Exam Questions

Q1 Nitrogen oxide (NO) and ozone (O_3) sometimes react to produce nitrogen dioxide (NO_2) and oxygen (O_2).
The collision between the two molecules does not always lead to a reaction. Explain why. [2 marks]

Q2 Use the collision theory to explain why the reaction between a solid and a liquid is generally faster than that between two solids. [2 marks]

Reaction Rates — cheaper than water rates

This page isn't too hard to learn — no equations, no formulas...what more could you ask for. The only tricky thing might be the Maxwell-Boltzmann thingymajiggle. Remember, increasing concentration and pressure do exactly the same thing. The only difference is you increase the concentration of a ***solution*** *and the pressure of a* ***gas****. Don't get them muddled.*

Catalysts

Catalysts were tantalisingly mentioned on the last page — here's the full story...

Catalysts Increase the Rate of Reactions

You can use **catalysts** to make chemical reactions happen **faster**. Learn this definition:

> A **catalyst** increases the **rate** of a reaction by providing an **alternative reaction pathway** with a **lower activation energy**. The catalyst is **chemically unchanged** at the end of the reaction.

1) Catalysts are **great**. They **don't** get used up in reactions, so you only need a **tiny bit** of catalyst to catalyse a **huge** amount of stuff. Many **do** take part in reactions, but they're **remade** at the end.
2) Catalysts are **very fussy** about which reactions they catalyse. Many will usually **only** work on a single reaction.

An example of a catalyst is **iron**. It's used in the **Haber process** to make ammonia.

$$N_{2(g)} + 3H_{2(g)} \xrightleftharpoons{Fe_{(s)}} 2NH_{3(g)}$$

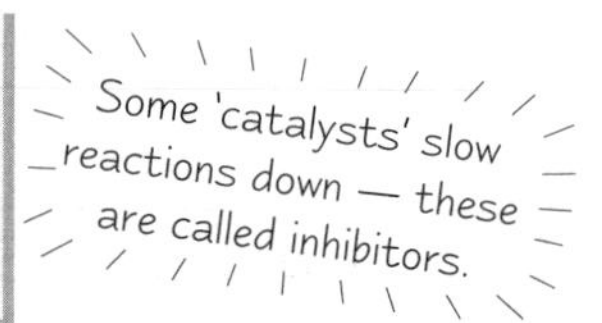

Some 'catalysts' slow reactions down — these are called inhibitors.

Enthalpy Profiles and Boltzmann Distributions Show Why Catalysts Work

If you look at an **enthalpy profile** together with a **Maxwell-Boltzmann Distribution**, you can see **why** catalysts work.

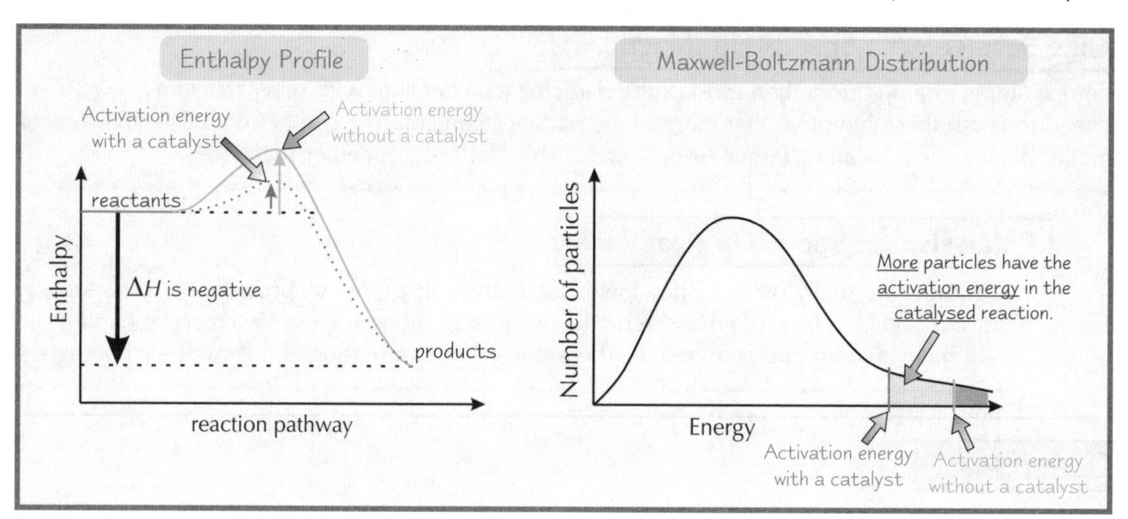

The catalyst **lowers the activation energy**, meaning there's **more particles** with **enough energy** to react when they collide. So, in a certain amount of time, **more particles react**.

Catalysts Can Be Poisoned

Catalysts can be **poisoned** so they don't work any more. For instance:

1) **Carbon monoxide**, CO, poisons the solid **iron catalyst** used in the **Haber process**.
2) A **platinum catalyst** is sometimes used in the **contact process** for making sulphuric acid. A tiny bit of **arsenic** in the starting materials can poison the catalyst.
3) **Lead** poisons **catalytic converters**, which are used to remove pollutants from car exhausts. This **was** a problem when lead was added to **all** petrol, but it's OK now there's **unleaded petrol**.

Heterogeneous catalysts (have a peep at **pages 72 and 73**) often get poisoned because the **poison** clings to the catalyst's surface **more strongly** than the reactant does. So, the catalyst is **prevented** from getting involved in the reaction it's meant to be **speeding up**.

Catalysts

Catalysts Make Heaps of **Money for Industries**

Loads of industries rely on **catalysts**. Here's a few examples —

Iron is used as a catalyst in the **Haber process**. This is a really important **industrial process**.
It produces **ammonia** which is needed to make **fertilisers, nylon** and **nitric acid** (which is used to make explosives).
If it wasn't for the catalyst, they'd have to raise the **temperature** loads to make the reaction happen **quick enough**.
Not only would this be bad for their fuel bills, it would **reduce the amount of ammonia** produced. This'll all become clear on **page 76**. This page tells you more than you ever wanted to know about the Haber process.

Catalysts are used **loads** in the **petroleum industry** (this'll make more sense when you read pages 88 and 89).

- Long chain alkanes are **cracked** into shorter, more useful molecules using **zeolite** catalysts.
- **Platinum** and **zeolite** catalysts are used in the **isomerisation** of straight chain alkanes.
- Catalysts made out of **platinum** and another metal are used in **reforming**.
  Reforming's where alkanes are converted to **cycloalkanes** and then to **arenes**.

Vegetable oil is turned into **margarine** by **hydrogenation**.
This process uses a **nickel catalyst**. (See pages 94 and 95.)

Practice Questions

Q1 Explain what a catalyst is.

Q2 Draw an enthalpy profile diagram and a Maxwell-Boltzmann distribution diagram to show how a catalyst works.

Q3 Describe **three** important industrial processes that use a catalyst.

Exam Questions

Q1 Sulphuric acid is manufactured by the contact process. In one of the stages, sulphur dioxide, SO_2, is converted into sulphur trioxide. A vanadium(V) oxide, V_2O_5, catalyst is used.

$$2SO_{2(g)} + O_{2(g)} \xrightleftharpoons{V_2O_{5(s)}} 2SO_{3(g)} \quad \Delta H = -197 \text{ kJ mol}^{-1}$$

a) Draw and label an enthalpy profile diagram for the catalysed reaction. Label the activation energy. [3 marks]

b) On your diagram from part a), draw a profile for the uncatalysed reaction. [1 mark]

c) Explain how catalysts work. [2 marks]

d) Although vanadium catalysts are less efficient than platinum, platinum is seldom used because it is susceptible to poisoning by arsenic. Explain the term poisoning and suggest how the poison might work. [2 marks]

Q2 The decomposition of hydrogen peroxide, H_2O_2, into water and oxygen is catalysed by manganese(IV) oxide, MnO_2.

a) Write an equation for the reaction. [2 marks]

b) Sketch a Maxwell-Boltzmann distribution for the reaction.
Mark on the activation energy for the catalysed and uncatalysed process. [3 marks]

c) Referring to your diagram from part b), explain how manganese(IV) oxide acts as a catalyst. [3 marks]

I'm a catalyst — I like to speed up arguments without getting too involved...

Whatever you do, do not confuse the Maxwell-Boltzmann diagram for catalysts with the one for a temperature change. Catalysts lower the activation energy without changing the shape of the curve. BUT, the shape of the curve does change with temperature. Get these mixed up and you'll be the laughing stock of the Examiners' tea room.

Homogeneous and Heterogeneous Catalysts

Skip these pages if you're doing AQA, Edexcel or Edexcel Nuffield.
There's two types of catalyst — homogeneous and heterogeneous. Both types'll make reactions hurry up though.

Homogeneous Catalysts are in the Same State as the Reactants

A **homogeneous catalyst** is in the **same state** as the **reactants**. So, if the reactants are **gases**, the catalyst must be a **gas** too. And if the reactants are **aqueous** (dissolved in water), the catalyst has to be **aqueous** too.

Enzymes are biological catalysts.

When **enzymes** catalyse reactions in your body **cells**, everything's **aqueous** — so it's **homogeneous catalysis**.

Homogeneous Catalysts Work by Forming Intermediates

1) If a reaction is speeded up by a **homogeneous catalyst**, its enthalpy profile will have **two humps** in it.

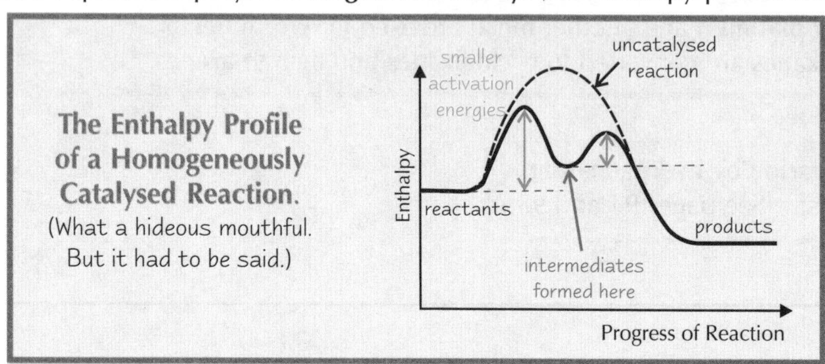

(What a hideous mouthful. But it had to be said.)

Mrs Watson tried everything to lower the camel's activation energy.

2) You get **this shape** because the **homogeneous catalyst** forms an **intermediate compound**.
3) The activation energy needed to form the **intermediates** (and to form the products from the intermediates) is **lower** than that needed to make the products directly from the reactants.
4) The catalyst is **reformed** again and carries on **catalysing** the reaction.

The Ozone Layer's being Destroyed by Homogeneous Catalysis

The ozone in the stratosphere acts as a **chemical sunscreen**. It absorbs a lot of the **ultraviolet radiation** which damages your skin, among other things. Ozone's **formed** when an **oxygen molecule** is **broken down** into **two free radicals** by **ultraviolet radiation**. The free radicals **attack** other oxygen molecules forming **ozone**. Just like this:

$$O\bullet_{(g)} + O_{2(g)} \rightarrow O_{3(g)}$$

Free radicals are formed when covalent bonds split in two — they've got an unpaired electron (shown by the dot), which makes them highly reactive.

You've heard of how the **ozone layer's** being destroyed by **CFCs**, right. Well, here's what's happening.

1) **Chlorine free radicals**, $Cl\bullet$, are formed when **CFCs** (chlorofluorocarbons) are broken down by **ultraviolet radiation**.

   E.g. $CCl_3F_{(g)} \rightarrow CCl_2F\bullet_{(g)} + Cl\bullet_{(g)}$

CFCs were very useful as propellant gases for aerosols, and in fridges. They've now been banned from use on a large scale.

2) These free radicals are **catalysts**. They react with **ozone** to form an **intermediate** ($ClO\bullet$), and an oxygen molecule.

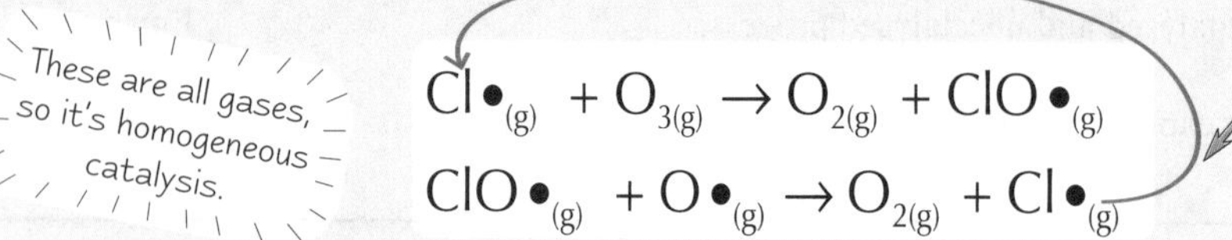

These are all gases, so it's homogeneous catalysis.

$$Cl\bullet_{(g)} + O_{3(g)} \rightarrow O_{2(g)} + ClO\bullet_{(g)}$$
$$ClO\bullet_{(g)} + O\bullet_{(g)} \rightarrow O_{2(g)} + Cl\bullet_{(g)}$$

The chlorine free radical is regenerated. It goes straight on to attack another ozone molecule. It only takes one little chlorine free radical to destroy loads of ozone molecules.

3) So the **overall reaction** is...

$$O_{3(g)} + O\bullet_{(g)} \rightarrow 2O_{2(g)}$$ ... and $Cl\bullet$ is the catalyst.

Homogeneous and Heterogeneous Catalysts

Heterogeneous Catalysts are in *Different States* from the *Reactants*

Heterogeneous catalysts are in a **different physical state** from the reactants.
So, if the catalyst is **solid**, the reactants will have to be **gases** or **liquids**. Here's two examples —

Iron's used as a **heterogeneous catalyst** in the **Haber process** to produce ammonia.
Iron's a **solid** and the reactants are hydrogen **gas** and nitrogen **gas**.

Platinum is used as a **heterogeneous catalyst** in **catalytic converters**.
Catalytic converters sit quietly in a car **exhaust** and stop some **pollutants** from coming out.

Without catalytic converters, cars spew out **lots** of bad stuff, like **carbon monoxide**, **oxides of nitrogen** and **unburnt hydrocarbons**. When the sun shines on nitrogen oxides and hydrocarbons, **low-level** (or ground level) **ozone** is produced. This **isn't** good ozone, like the stuff in the sky. This is **smog** — it makes you **cough** and **choke**, and generally doesn't do you much good. Have a look at **pages 90-91** to find out what else these nasty gases do.

Catalytic converters **get rid** of them by changing them to **harmless gases**, like **water vapour** and **nitrogen**, or to **less harmful** ones like **carbon dioxide**.

Reactions Happen **On** *Heterogeneous Catalysts*

Solid heterogeneous catalysts can provide a **surface** for a reaction to take place on.

Here's how it works —

1) **Reactant molecules** arrive at the **surface** and **bond** with the solid catalyst. This is called **ad**sorption.
2) The bonds between the **reactant's** atoms are **weakened** and **break up**. This forms **radicals**.
   These radicals then **get together** and make **new molecules**.

This example shows you how a catalytic converter changes the harmful gases nitric oxide, NO, and carbon monoxide, CO, to nitrogen and carbon dioxide.

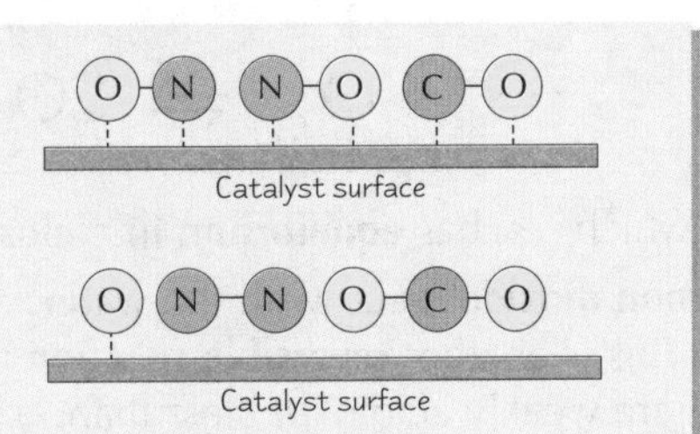

Remember — the adsorption **mustn't** be **too strong** or it won't **let go** of the atoms. The atoms need to be able to **detach** themselves, so that they can react with the **other atoms**. When the atoms detach themselves, it's called **desorption**.

Practice Questions

Q1 Give an example of a homogeneous catalyst and describe how it works.

Q2 Describe how ozone can be useful as well as harmful.

Q3 What do 'adsorption' and 'desorption' mean?

Exam Questions

Q1 Enzymes are proteins that catalyse specific biological reactions.
Draw a fully labelled enthalpy profile for an enzyme-catalysed reaction and an uncatalysed reaction. [4 marks]

Q2 Heterogeneous catalysts are more common than homogeneous catalysts. In the manufacture of ammonia, finely divided iron is used as the catalyst. Explain why the iron is finely divided. [2 marks]

Don't get the hump now — you've gotta learn it...

CFCs used to be everywhere — in McDonald's cups, in deodorant and hairspray, and in fridges. When people realised the crazy amount of damage it was doing, they really cracked down on it. You need to practise writing out the ozone equations, and don't forget to dot your Cl's and O's. Oh, and wear sunscreen...or you'll be wrinkly before you know it.

Reversible Reactions

There's a lot of to-ing and fro-ing on this page. Mind your head doesn't start spinning.

Reversible Reactions Can Reach Dynamic Equilibrium

1) Lots of chemical reactions are **reversible** — they go **both ways**. To show a reaction's reversible, you stick in a $\rightleftharpoons$. Here's an example:

$$H_{2(g)} + I_{2(g)} \rightleftharpoons 2HI_{(g)}$$

This reaction can go in **either direction** —

forwards $H_{2(g)} + I_{2(g)} \rightarrow 2HI_{(g)}$ ....or **backwards** $2HI_{(g)} \rightarrow H_{2(g)} + I_{2(g)}$.

2) As the **reactants** get used up, the **forward** reaction **slows down** — and as more **product** is formed, the **reverse** reaction **speeds up**.
3) After a while, the forward reaction will be going at exactly the **same rate** as the backward reaction. The amounts of reactants and products **won't be changing** any more, so it'll seem like **nothing's happening**. It's a bit like you're **digging a hole**, while someone else is **filling it in** at exactly the **same speed**. This is called a **dynamic equilibrium**.
4) A **dynamic equilibrium** can only happen in a **closed system**. This just means nothing can get in or out.
5) In a **homogeneous** equilibrium, **all** the reactants and products are in the **same state**. E.g. they might be **all gases**. In a **heterogeneous** equilibrium, **not** all the reactants and products are in the same state.

When Carbon Dioxide Dissolves in Water, you get a Dynamic Equilibrium

Carbon dioxide in water is a great example of a reversible reaction.

1) **Carbon dioxide gas** dissolves in water to form **aqueous carbon dioxide**.

$$CO_{2(g)} \rightleftharpoons CO_{2(aq)}$$

2) It's a **reversible reaction** which reaches **equilibrium** in a **closed system**, like a closed fizzy drink bottle.
3) Some of the **aqueous carbon dioxide** reacts with the **water**. It forms **hydrogencarbonate ions** (HCO_3^-) and **hydrogen ions** (H^+). This is another **reversible reaction** which'll also reach an **equilibrium**. Carbon dioxide solutions are weakly acidic (*p*H less than 7) because of the formation of the H^+ ions.

$$CO_{2(aq)} + H_2O_{(l)} \rightleftharpoons HCO_3^-{}_{(aq)} + H^+{}_{(aq)}$$

Le Chatelier's Principle Predicts what will happen if Conditions are Changed

If you **change** the **concentration**, **pressure** or **temperature** of a reversible reaction, you're going to **alter** the **position of equilibrium**. This just means you'll end up with **different amounts** of reactants and products at equilibrium.

If the position of equilibrium moves to the **left**, you'll get more **reactants**. $H_{2(g)} + I_{2(g)} \rightleftharpoons 2HI_{(g)}$

If the position of equilibrium moves to the **right**, you'll get more **products**. $H_{2(g)} + I_{2(g)} \rightleftharpoons 2HI_{(g)}$

Le Chatelier's principle tells you how the **position of equilibrium** will change if a **condition changes**:

> If there's a change in **concentration**, **pressure** or **temperature**, the equilibrium will move to help **counteract** the change.

So, basically, if you **raise the temperature**, the position of equilibrium will shift to try to **cool things down**.
And, if you **raise the pressure or concentration**, the position of equilibrium will shift to try to **reduce it again**.

Reversible Reactions

Here's Some Handy Rules for Using Le Chatelier's Principle

CONCENTRATION $2SO_{2(g)} + O_{2(g)} \rightleftharpoons 2SO_{3(g)}$

1) If you **increase** the **concentration** of a **reactant** (SO_2 or O_2), the equilibrium tries to **get rid** of the extra reactant. It does this by making **more product** (SO_3). So the equilibrium's shifted to the **right**.
2) If you **increase** the **concentration** of the **product** (SO_3), the equilibrium tries to remove the extra product. This makes the **reverse reaction** go faster. So the equilibrium shifts to the **left**.
3) **Decreasing** the concentrations has the **opposite effect**.

PRESSURE (changing this only affects **equilibria involving gases**)

1) **Increasing** the pressure shifts the equilibrium to the side with the **fewest** gas molecules. This **reduces** the pressure.
2) **Decreasing** the pressure shifts the equilibrium to the side with **most** gas molecules. This **raises** the pressure again.

There's 3 moles on the left, but only 2 on the right.
So, an increase in pressure shifts the equilibrium to the right. ⟹ $2SO_{2(g)} + O_{2(g)} \rightleftharpoons 2SO_{3(g)}$

TEMPERATURE

1) If you **increase** the temperature, you **add heat**. The equilibrium shifts in the **endothermic (positive ΔH) direction** to absorb this heat.
2) **Decreasing** the temperature **removes heat**. The equilibrium shifts in the **exothermic (negative ΔH) direction** to try to replace the heat.
3) If the forward reaction's **endothermic**, the reverse reaction will be **exothermic**, and vice versa.

This reaction's exothermic in the forwards direction. If you increase the temperature, the equilibrium shifts to the left to absorb the extra heat.

Exothermic ⟹

$2SO_{2(g)} + O_{2(g)} \rightleftharpoons 2SO_{3(g)}$ $\Delta H = -197\ kJ\ mol^{-1}$

⟸ Endothermic

Catalysts have **NO EFFECT** on the **position of equilibrium**.
They **can't** increase **yield** — but they **do** mean equilibrium is reached **faster**.

Practice Questions

Q1 Using an example, explain the terms 'reversible' and 'dynamic equilibrium'.

Q2 What's the difference between homogeneous and heterogeneous equilibrium?

Q3 A reaction at equilibrium is endothermic in the forward direction.
What happens to the position of equilibrium as the temperature is increased?

Exam Question

Q1 Nitrogen and oxygen gases were reacted together in a closed flask and allowed to reach equilibrium with the nitrogen monoxide formed. The forward reaction is endothermic.

$$N_{2(g)} + O_{2(g)} \rightleftharpoons 2NO_{(g)}$$

a) State Le Chatelier's principle. [1 mark]

b) Explain how the following changes would affect the position of equilibrium of the above reaction:
(i) Pressure is **increased**. [2 marks]
(ii) Temperature **reduced**. [2 marks]
(iii) Nitrogen monoxide is removed. [1 mark]

c) What would be the effect of a catalyst on the composition of the equilibrium mixture? [1 mark]

Only going forward cos we can't find reverse...

Equilibria never do what you want them to do. They always **oppose** *you. Be sure you know what happens to an equilibrium if you change the conditions. A word about pressure — if there's the same number of gas moles on each side of the equation, then you can raise the pressure as high as you like and it won't make a blind bit of difference to the position of equilibrium.*

Equilibrium in Industrial Processes

Skip this page if you're doing Edexcel Nuffield or OCR Salters.

In industry, the big bosses want to make bags of money. So they need to pick the best conditions for their processes.

The **Haber Process** Combines **Nitrogen** and **Hydrogen** to make **Ammonia**

$N_{2(g)} + 3H_{2(g)} \rightleftharpoons 2NH_{3(g)} \quad \Delta H = -92 \text{ kJ mol}^{-1}$

This reaction is reversible and exothermic.

Industrial Conditions

Pressure: 200 atmospheres
Temperature: 450 °C
Catalyst: Iron

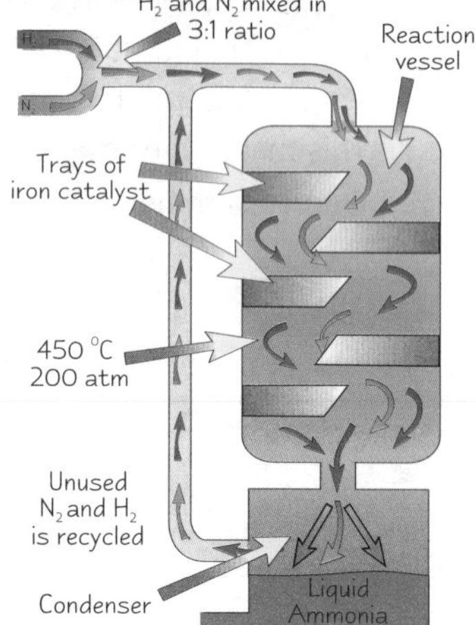

The **Temperature** Chosen is a **Compromise**

1) Because it's an **exothermic reaction**, **lower** temperatures favour the forward reaction. This means **more** hydrogen and nitrogen is converted to ammonia — you get a better **yield**.
2) The trouble is, **lower temperatures** mean a **slower rate of reaction**.
3) You'd be **daft** to try to get a **really high yield** of ammonia if it's going to take you 10 years. So the 450 °C is a **compromise** between **maximum yield** and **a faster reaction**.
4) As the gases **leave** the reactor, the **temperature** is **reduced** so that the **ammonia** can be **liquefied** and **removed**. The **hydrogen** and **nitrogen** which didn't react are **recycled**. Thanks to this recycling, a very respectable **98%** of these gases ends up being converted to ammonia.

High Pressure would give a **Big Yield** — but it'd be **Expensive**

1) **Higher pressures** favour the **forward reaction**, hence the **200 atmospheres** operating pressure.
2) This is because the equilibrium moves to the side with **fewer molecules**. There's **4 moles** of gas molecules on the **reactant side** ($N_{2(g)} + 3H_{2(g)}$) and only **2 moles** on the **product side** ($2NH_{3(g)}$).
3) **Increasing** the **pressure** also **increases** the **rate** of reaction.
4) Cranking up the pressure as high as you can sounds like a great idea so far. **But**, very **high pressures** are really **expensive** to produce. You also need **strong pipes** and **containers** to **withstand** the **high pressure**. So, **200 atmospheres** is a **compromise**. In the end, it all comes down to **minimising costs**.

A **Catalyst** Doesn't Affect the **Equilibrium Position** but will **Increase the Rate**

Without a **catalyst** the **reaction** is really, really **slow**.
The iron **catalyst** makes the **reaction** reach equilibrium much more quickly.

Ammonia's **Very Useful** Stuff

Ammonia's used to make **dyes**, **fibres**, **detergents**, **paint pigments** and **animal feed**.
It's also used to make **nitric acid** —

The **Ostwald process** is used to make **nitric acid** from **ammonia**. There's **two stages** to it:

Ammonia is **heated** in air with a **platinum and rhodium catalyst** to form **nitrogen monoxide**:

$$4NH_{3(g)} + 5O_{2(g)} \rightarrow 4NO_{(g)} + 6H_2O_{(g)}$$

Then the **nitrogen monoxide** reacts with **water** and **oxygen** to form **nitric acid**, HNO_3.

$$6NO_{(g)} + 3O_{2(g)} + 2H_2O_{(g)} \rightarrow 4HNO_{3(g)} + 2NO_{(g)}$$

The nitric acid can be used to make **nylon**, **plastics**, **rocket fuel**, **explosives** and **fertilisers**.

Equilibrium in Industrial Processes

The Contact Process is used to make Sulphuric Acid

Skip this bit if you're doing Edexcel Nuffield, OCR or OCR Salters.

Loads of modern industries use tonnes of **sulphuric acid**. It's used to make **dyes**, **soap**, **paint pigments** and **explosives**.

1) Sulphur dioxide is **oxidised** (with the help of a vanadium(V) oxide catalyst) to form **sulphur trioxide** (SO_3). It's an **exothermic, reversible** reaction:

$$2SO_{2(g)} + O_{2(g)} \xrightleftharpoons{V_2O_5} 2SO_{3(g)} \quad \Delta H = -196 \text{ kJ mol}^{-1}$$

2) Next, the sulphur trioxide is **dissolved** in concentrated sulphuric acid to form **fuming sulphuric acid**, or **oleum**.

$$SO_{3(g)} + H_2SO_{4(l)} \rightarrow H_2S_2O_{7(l)}$$

Dissolving SO_3 in water doesn't work — the reaction gives out a lot of heat and you end up with clouds of sulphuric acid which are hard to condense.

3) Finally, oleum is **diluted** with measured amounts of **water** to form **concentrated sulphuric acid**.

$$H_2S_2O_{7(l)} + H_2O_{(l)} \rightarrow 2H_2SO_{4(l)}$$

The conditions for the first reaction are chosen for **economic reasons** too.

1) **400-450 °C** is chosen because it produces a **fairly high** proportion of **sulphur trioxide** in a very **short time**.
2) The **reaction** is done at a relatively low pressure of about **10 atmospheres**. Even at this low pressure, you still convert **99.5%** of sulphur dioxide into sulphur trioxide. The very **small improvement** that you could get by increasing the pressure isn't worth the expense of producing the high pressures.
3) The **catalyst vanadium(V) oxide** (V_2O_5) helps the **reaction** reach equilibrium **really quickly**.

Practice Questions

Q1 What conditions are used in the Haber process?

Q2 Why isn't a higher temperature used?

Q3 How is nitric acid produced?

Q4 Why is sulphur trioxide dissolved in concentrated sulphuric acid before it is reacted with water?

Exam Question

Q1 The Haber synthesis of ammonia is represented by the reaction: $N_{2(g)} + 3H_{2(g)} \rightleftharpoons 2NH_{3(g)} \quad \Delta H = -92 \text{ kJ mol}^{-1}$
Typical conditions used industrially are 450 °C and 200 atmospheres.

a) Explain, in molecular terms, why a temperature lower than the one quoted is not used. [3 marks]

b) Explain why a pressure higher than the one quoted is not often used. [2 marks]

c) The gases are passed through a conversion chamber containing beds of granulated iron, which acts as a catalyst. Describe and explain the effect of the iron on:
i) the rate of the production of ammonia, [2 marks]
ii) the amount of ammonia in the equilibrium mixture. [1 mark]

d) The equilibrium mixture formed is passed into a refrigeration plant. Explain why this is done and what follows this process. [2 marks]

It's all about money — it's what makes the world go around...

Lots of lovely stuff here folks. It just goes to show you Le Chatelier's principle isn't just something they make you learn to fill up the AS Chemistry syllabus. It has uses in real life. Everyone in the manufacturing business wants to make as much stuff as they can, as quickly as they can and as cheaply as they can. It's just a fact of life.

Acids and Bases

AQA and Edexcel people — it's your lucky day. You can skip these two pages.
Acid's a word that's thrown around willy-nilly — but now for the truth...

Acids are all about Hydrated Protons

1) When mixed with **water**, all acids release **hydrogen ions** — H^+ (these are just **protons**, but you never get them by themselves in water — they're always combined with H_2O (hydrated) to form hydroxonium ions, $\mathbf{H_3O^+}$).

E.g.

$$HCl_{(g)} + \text{water} \rightarrow H^+_{(aq)} + Cl^-_{(aq)}$$
$$H_2SO_{4(l)} + \text{water} \rightarrow 2H^+_{(aq)} + SO_4^{2-}{}_{(aq)}$$

HCl doesn't release hydrogen ions until it meets water — so hydrogen chloride gas isn't an acid.

2) Bases do the opposite — they want to **grab H^+ ions**.

So,

Acids put $H^+_{(aq)}$ ions into a solution — i.e. they're **proton donors**.
Bases remove $H^+_{(aq)}$ ions from a solution — i.e. they're **proton acceptors**.

Acids can React with Metals and Carbonates

When acids react with **metals** and **carbonates**, **salts** are produced.
Different acids produce **different salts** — sulphuric acid (H_2SO_4) produces **sulphate salts** ...
...and hydrochloric acid (HCl) produces **chloride salts**.

Metal + Acid → Metal Salt + Hydrogen

E.g. $Mg_{(s)} + H_2SO_{4(aq)} \rightarrow MgSO_{4(aq)} + H_{2(g)}$

Or the ionic equation: $Mg_{(s)} + 2H^+_{(aq)} \rightarrow Mg^{2+}_{(aq)} + H_{2(g)}$

It's often easier to see what acids are doing in ionic equations. Have a look at pages 16 and 17 if you've forgotten what they are.

Metal Carbonate + Acid → Metal Salt + Carbon Dioxide + Water

E.g. $Na_2CO_{3(s)} + 2HCl_{(aq)} \rightarrow 2NaCl_{(aq)} + CO_{2(g)} + H_2O_{(l)}$

Ionic equation: $Na_2CO_{3(s)} + 2H^+_{(aq)} \rightarrow 2Na^+_{(aq)} + CO_{2(g)} + H_2O_{(l)}$

Professor Redmond's final classroom demonstration...

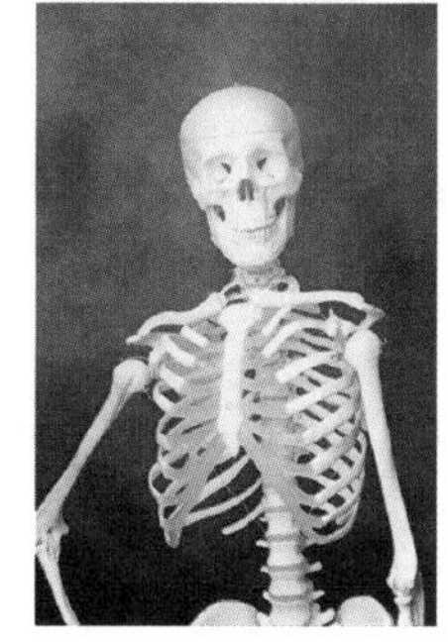

Effects of submersion in a bath of conc. H_2SO_4.

Acids React with Alkalis too

When **acids** react with **bases**, they **neutralise** each other. An **alkali** is just a base that dissolves in water. **Metal oxides** and **hydroxides** are generally alkalis.

Metal Oxide + Acid → Salt + Water

E.g. $MgO_{(s)} + 2HCl_{(aq)} \rightarrow MgCl_{2(aq)} + H_2O_{(l)}$

Ionic equation: $MgO_{(s)} + 2H^+_{(aq)} \rightarrow Mg^{2+}_{(aq)} + H_2O_{(l)}$

The O^{2-} ion accepts two H^+ ions which have been donated by the acid.

Metal Hydroxide + Acid → Salt + Water

E.g. $KOH_{(aq)} + HCl_{(aq)} \rightarrow KCl_{(aq)} + H_2O_{(l)}$

Ionic equation: $OH^-_{(aq)} + H^+_{(aq)} \rightarrow H_2O_{(l)}$

The ionic equation shows that a proton is transferred from the acid to the hydroxide ion. This ionic equation is the same for all reactions between metal hydroxides and acids.

Acids and Bases

Ammonia Reacts with Acids to Form Ammonium Salts

Edexcel Nuffield and OCR Salters people can skip this bit.

Ammonia, NH_3, is a **base**. It'll happily **accept a proton** from an acid to form an **ammonium salt**.
Some of these salts, like **ammonium sulphate**, make **good fertilisers** because they're great sources of nitrogen.

Here's how ammonia reacts with nitric acid and sulphuric acid ⟹

$$NH_{3(aq)} + HNO_{3(aq)} \rightarrow NH_4NO_{3(aq)}$$

$$2NH_{3(aq)} + H_2SO_{4(aq)} \rightarrow (NH_4)_2SO_{4(aq)}$$

And here's the ionic equation. It's dead useful because it applies to all reactions of ammonia with acids. ⟹

$$NH_{3(aq)} + H^+_{(aq)} \rightarrow NH_4^+{}_{(aq)}$$

Acids can be Strong or Weak

Not OCR Salters.

1) **Strong acids** (e.g. sulphuric) are **ionised almost completely** in water — they're almost **fully dissociated**. This means nearly **every** hydrogen atom is **released** to become a **hydrated proton** (so there are **loads** of $H^+_{(aq)}$ ions).
2) **Weak acids** (e.g. ethanoic, citric) ionise only very **slightly** — they only **partly dissociate**. So, only **some** of the hydrogen atoms in the compound are released — meaning relatively **small numbers** of $H^+_{(aq)}$ ions are formed.

Strong acid: $HCl + \text{water} \rightarrow H^+ + Cl^-$ **Weak acid:** $H_2CO_3 + \text{water} \rightleftharpoons H^+ + HCO_3^-$

Note the 'reversible reaction' symbol for a weak acid.
The equilibrium lies to the left so most of the acid won't be ionised.

3) Mind you don't confuse **strong** acids with **concentrated** acids or **weak** acids with **dilute** acids:
   - Strong and weak are about how much the acid has **ionised**.
   - Concentrated and dilute are about the number of **moles per dm³** of the acid.

Practice Questions

Q1 Sulphuric acid, H_2SO_4, reacts with both calcium and calcium carbonate, $CaCO_3$.
In each case, state the gas given off and the salt formed.

Q2 Write an ionic equation for the reaction between potassium hydroxide, KOH, and nitric acid, HNO_3.
Explain this reaction by considering the role of the proton.

Q3 Methanoic acid, HCOOH, is a weak acid. Define "weak acid" and illustrate this with an ionic equation.

Exam Question

Q1 Chloric(VII) acid, $HClO_4$, and sulphuric acid, H_2SO_4, are both strong acids.

a) Define the term 'strong acid'. Illustrate your answer by writing an equation involving chloric(VII) acid. [2 marks]

b) Write a balanced equation, including state symbols, for the reaction between chloric(VII) acid and calcium carbonate, $CaCO_3$. [3 marks]

c) Sulphuric acid reacts with lithium metal and potassium hydroxide, KOH.
i) Write an ionic equation for the reaction with lithium. [2 marks]
ii) Write an equation for the reaction with potassium hydroxide. [2 marks]

It's a stick-up — your protons or your life...

Remember — all acids have protons to give away and bases just love to take them. It's what makes them acids and bases. It's like how bus drivers drive buses...it's what makes them bus drivers. Ionic equations are super-important as far as acids and bases are concerned. They're not too awful, but you've gotta make sure those charges balance.

The Atmosphere

These two pages are just for those of you doing OCR Salters.

The atmosphere wasn't always like it is today. A few billion years ago it was full of carbon dioxide, with just a teeny-weeny bit of oxygen. Luckily, it evolved so we could breathe and stuff. We're starting to mess it up again with pollutants though.

Most of the Atmosphere is Nitrogen and Oxygen

Here's what the atmosphere's made of. The percentages are by **volume** of dry air (in the lower atmosphere).

Nitrogen	**78%**
Oxygen	**21%**
Argon	**1%**
Carbon dioxide	**0.035%**

Also:

1) Varying amounts of **water vapour**.
2) **Other gases** in tiny amounts.

It comes to over 100% because the first three are rounded off slightly.

So every **100 cm³** of air contains about **78 cm³** of nitrogen, **21 cm³** of oxygen and **1 cm³** of argon. And **tiny bits** of other stuff too.

We're also putting **pollutants** like **methane**, **sulphur dioxide** and **oxides of nitrogen** into the atmosphere (see pages 90-91). These are bad because they add to the **greenhouse effect** and **acid rain**.

Parts Per Million is used for Really Small Quantities

1) The **major gases** in the atmosphere are normally given as **percentages** of the **volume**. But some gases are present in such **tiny amounts** that it's **not very convenient** to write their quantities like this. For instance, **xenon** makes up only **0.000 009%** of the atmosphere. Numbers this small are a pain to work with.
2) So to get round this problem, another type of measurement is used. It is called **parts per million** or **ppm**.
3) So if there's **0.000 009 parts** of xenon in every **one hundred parts of air**, you can multiply both quantities by **10 000** to make the quantity **large enough** to work with, like this:

0.000 009% = 0.000 009 parts per 100 parts of air ⟹ **0.000 009 × 10 000 = 0.09**, **100 × 10 000 = 1 000 000** ⟹ **0.09 parts per million**

4) So there's 0.09 ppm xenon. The atmosphere also contains **0.1 ppm** carbon monoxide and **0.3 ppm** nitrous oxide.

Atmospheric Gases Absorb Radiation

1) Atmospheric gases **protect** us from the **Sun** by **absorbing ultraviolet radiation**.
2) The gas molecules have **certain fixed energy levels** (they're not continuous). These are called **quantised** levels. So, a molecule's energy can only **jump** from one level to another — like moving up a **staircase** in steps. (The energy can jump **more than one step** at a time though.)
3) The **electrons** in molecules also have **fixed energy levels** that they can **jump between**.
4) When **ultraviolet radiation** from the Sun hits a molecule of **gas** in the atmosphere, the molecule receives **an amount of energy**. This energy might **match** the **energy gap** in the levels for that molecule. If it does, the molecule will **absorb** the energy and **jump up** to the next energy level. It's like it's moved up a step in the energy staircase. The **electrons** can also **absorb** energy and **jump up** to their **next energy level**.

The **energy** depends on the **frequency** of the radiation. I reckon we're about due for an **equation**:

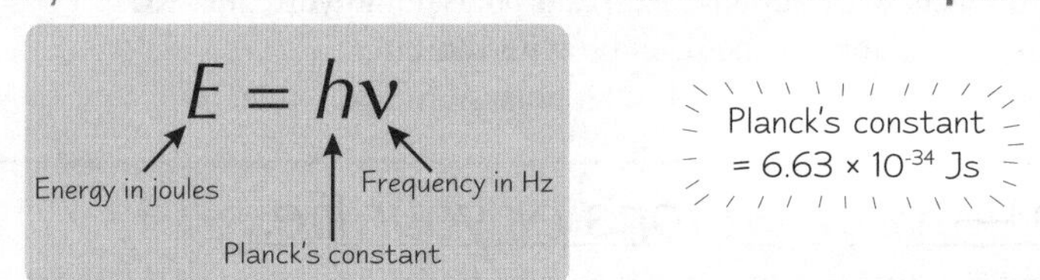

$$E = h\nu$$

Planck's constant $= 6.63 \times 10^{-34}$ Js

So, if you know **Planck's constant** and the **frequency**, you can calculate **how much energy** the molecule absorbed.

The Atmosphere

Radiation Makes Molecules Move Differently

When a molecule **absorbs energy**, it might **vibrate** or **rotate faster**.
Here's the **different ways** molecules can move.

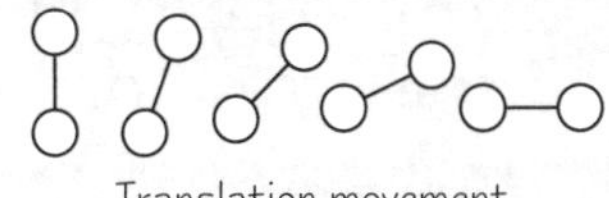

Translation movement

Gas molecules are always **zooming around**.
When the **whole molecule** moves, it's called **translation**.

Molecules also **rotate**.

Rotation movement

They **vibrate** too. This happens when the **bonds** of the molecule bend and stretch.

Vibration movement

The energy can also be used to move **electrons** to **higher energy levels**.
This can happen to the electrons making up the **covalent bonds** or to the electrons within the **atoms** themselves.

Different Energy Changes mean Different Types of Movement

1) If a molecule absorbs **one particular amount** of energy, it might make it **rotate faster**.
If it absorbs a **different amount**, it'll **vibrate faster** instead.
2) Different molecules have **different energy levels**. One molecule might need a bit **more energy** than another to make it vibrate faster.
3) So, there's a **range** of **energy changes** that can make molecules rotate or vibrate faster. There's also a **range** of **energy changes** that can make electrons move to higher energy levels.
This table shows these ranges. Now you can predict how certain energy changes will affect molecules.

Change happening	Size of energy change/J	Type of radiation absorbed
change of rotational energy level	1×10^{-22} to 1×10^{-20}	microwave and infra-red
change of vibrational energy level	1×10^{-20} to 1×10^{-19}	infra-red
change of electron energy level	1×10^{-19} to 1×10^{-16}	visible and ultraviolet

Infra-red radiation warms up gases. It makes them vibrate and rotate more, giving them extra kinetic energy.

Practice Questions

Q1 What is the difference between 'per cent' and 'parts per million'?

Q2 What does the word 'quantised' mean?

Q3 What changes does microwave radiation cause in a molecule?

Exam Questions

Q1 Molecules in the air absorb different types of radiation. Name the main type of radiation that makes the air warmer and explain how this happens. [2 marks]

Q2 Calculate the energy required to change one molecule of HCl from its ground vibrational level to the next level given that the frequency of radiation absorbed is 8.19×10^{13} Hz. [2 marks]

The atmosphere — it ain't made of custard...

If there were no atmospheric gases, bad sunburn would be the least of our worries. There'd be no oxygen, so we wouldn't be able to breathe. But at least there'd be no AS Chemistry either. I don't think this has been too bad a page — I hope you weren't too bored by the stuff on Planck's constant. Cor blimey, if ever there was a lame joke, that was it.

Basic Stuff

Here it is, the final section, but it's a biggie. Organic chemistry is all about carbon compounds. Read on...

There's Loads of Ways of Representing Organic Compounds

TYPE OF FORMULA	WHAT IT SHOWS YOU	FORMULA FOR BUTAN-1-OL
General formula	The **ratio** of carbon to hydrogen atoms and also any **functional groups**.	$C_nH_{2n+1}OH$
Empirical formula	The **simplest ratio** of atoms of each element in a compound (cancel the numbers down if possible).	$C_4H_{10}O$
Molecular formula	The **actual** number of atoms of each element in a molecule, with any **functional groups** indicated.	C_4H_9OH
Structural formula	Shows the atoms **carbon by carbon**, with the hydrogens and functional groups attached.	$CH_3CH_2CH_2CH_2OH$
Displayed formula	Shows how all the atoms are **arranged**, and all the bonds between them.	H–C(H)(H)–C(H)(H)–C(H)(H)–C(H)(H)–OH
Skeletal formula	Shows the **bonds** of the carbon skeleton **only**, with any functional groups. The hydrogen and carbon atoms aren't shown. This is handy for drawing large complicated structures, like cyclic hydrocarbons.	OH

A functional group is a reactive part of the molecule — it gives it many of its chemical properties.

Nomenclature is a Fancy Word for Naming Organic Compounds

You can name any organic compound using these **rules** of nomenclature.

1) Count the carbon atoms in the **longest continuous chain** — this gives you the stem:

No. of C	1	2	3	4	5	6
Stem	meth-	eth-	prop-	but-	pent-	hex-

2) The **main functional group** of the molecule usually gives you the end of the name (the **suffix**) — see the table.
3) Number the **longest** carbon chain so that the main functional group has the lowest possible number. If there's more than one longest chain, pick the one with the **most side-chains**.
4) Any side-chains or less important functional groups are added as prefixes at the start of the name. Put them in **alphabetical** order, with the **number** of the carbon atom each is attached to.
5) If there's more than one **identical** side-chain or functional group, use **di-** (2), **tri-** (3) or **tetra-** (4) before that part of the name — but ignore this when working out the alphabetical order.

A homologous series is a bunch of compounds which have the same general formula. Each member differs by $-CH_2-$.

Homologous series	Prefix or Suffix	Examples
alkanes	-ane	Propane $CH_3CH_2CH_3$
branched alkanes	alkyl- (-yl)	methylpropane $CH_3CH(CH_3)CH_3$
alkenes	-ene	propene $CH_3CH=CH_2$
haloalkanes/ halogenoalkanes	chloro- bromo- iodo-	chlorethane CH_3CH_2Cl
alcohols	-ol	ethanol CH_3CH_2OH
aldehydes	-al	ethanal CH_3CHO
ketones	-one	propanone CH_3COCH_3
cycloalkanes	cyclo- -ane	cyclohexane C_6H_{12}
arenes	benzene	ethylbenzene $C_6H_5C_2H_5$
esters	alkyl -oate	propyl ethanoate $CH_3COOCH_2CH_2CH_3$
carboxylic acids	-oic acid	ethanoic acid CH_3COOH
ethers	alkoxy-	methoxypropane $CH_3OCH_2CH_2CH_3$

Example:
$CH_3CH(CH_3)CH(CH_2CH_3)C(CH_3)_2OH$

1)	Longest chain is 5 carbons	**pent-**
2)	Main functional group is **-OH**	**pentanol**
3)	**Number** the longest carbon chain with most side-chains so that -OH has **lowest** possible number.	**pentan-2-ol**
4)	Add **prefixes** for side-chains.	**3-ethyl-2,4-dimethylpentan-2-ol**

Longest chain with most side-chains

Basic Stuff

The **Theoretical Yield** of a Product is the **Maximum** you could get

If you're doing AQA or OCR Salters, you can skip this bit.

When you make an organic compound:

1) The **theoretical yield** or **maximum yield** is the amount of product you'd get if **100%** of the reactants were converted and **no** product was lost.

Some potential product will always be lost, e.g. in side-reactions or purification.

2) The **percentage yield** is the **actual** amount of product you collect, written as a percentage of the theoretical yield.

Here's how to calculate **theoretical yield** and **percentage yield**:

Ethanol can be oxidised to form ethanal. $CH_3CH_2OH + [O] \rightarrow CH_3CHO + H_2O$
Say you start with **9.2 g** of ethanol and end up with an actual yield of **2.1 g**.
The oxidising agent is in **excess**.

'The oxidising agent is in excess' means there's more of it than you'll need. The amount of product will be limited by the amount of ethanol.

1) First work out the number of **moles** of reactant.

M_r of $C_2H_5OH = (2 \times 12) + (5 \times 1) + 16 + 1 = 46$ Moles of $C_2H_5OH = \frac{\text{mass}}{M_r} = \frac{9.2}{46} = 0.2$ moles

2) Now write down the **ratio** of moles of reactant to moles of product from the equation.

1 mole of C_2H_5OH produces 1 mole of CH_3CHO, so 0.2 moles of C_2H_5OH will produce 0.2 moles of CH_3CHO.

3) Calculate the maximum **mass** of product that could be produced — this is the **theoretical yield**.

M_r of $CH_3CHO = (2 \times 12) + (4 \times 1) + 16 = 44$

Theoretical yield (mass of CH_3CHO) = number of moles × M_r = 0.2 × 44 = 8.8 g

4) The **percentage yield** $= \frac{\text{mass of product}}{\text{theoretical yield}} \times 100$.

So, if the actual yield was 2.1 g, the percentage yield $= \frac{2.1}{8.8} \times 100 \approx$ **24%**

Practice Questions

Q1 Explain the difference between molecular formulas and structural formulas.

Q2 In what order should prefixes be listed in the name of an organic compound?

Q3 What is meant by the theoretical yield of a reaction?

Q4 How is percentage yield calculated?

Exam Question

Q1 1-bromobutane is prepared from butan-1-ol in this reaction: $C_4H_9OH + NaBr + H_2SO_4 \rightarrow C_4H_9Br + NaHSO_4 + H_2O$

a) Draw the displayed formulae for butan-1-ol and 1-bromobutane. [2 marks]

b) What is the functional group in butan-1-ol and why is it necessary to state its position on the carbon chain? [2 marks]

c) A student started the preparation with 8.0 g of butan-1-ol.
   i) Calculate the number of moles of butan-1-ol in 8.0 g. [2 marks]
   ii) How many moles of 1-bromobutane would be produced? [1 mark]
   iii) Calculate the maximum theoretical yield of 1-bromobutane. [2 marks]

d) The student's actual yield was 6.5 g.
   i) Calculate the percentage yield. [2 marks]
   ii) Give one reason why the percentage yield is so low. [1 mark]

It's as easy as 1, 2, 3 trimethylpentan-2-ol...

The best thing to do now is find some random organic compounds and work out their names using the rules. Then have a bash at it the other way around — read the name and draw the compound. It might seem a wee bit tedious now, but come the exam, you'll be thanking me. Doing the exam questions will give you practice at working out percentage yield too.

Isomerism

Isomers have the same molecular formula, but different arrangements of atoms.
There's two main types of isomerism — structural isomerism and stereoisomerism.

Structural Isomers *have different* ***Structural Arrangements*** *of Atoms*

In structural isomers the atoms are **connected** in different ways. But they still have the **same molecular formula**. There's **three types** of structural isomers — you need to know which is which:

CHAIN ISOMERS

Chain isomers have different arrangements of the **carbon skeleton**. Some are **straight chains** and others **branched** in different ways.

butane

methylpropane

POSITIONAL ISOMERS

Positional isomers have the **same skeleton** and the **same functional group**. The difference is that the group is attached to a **different carbon atom**.

butan-1-ol

butan-2-ol

FUNCTIONAL GROUP ISOMERS

Functional group isomers have the same atoms arranged into **different functional groups**.

butan-1-ol

ethoxyethane

Don't be Fooled *— What Looks Like an Isomer Might* ***Not*** *Be*

Atoms can rotate as much as they like around single **C–C bonds**. Remember this when you work out structural isomers — sometimes what looks like an isomer, isn't.

For example, there's only **two** chain or positional isomers of C_3H_7OH.

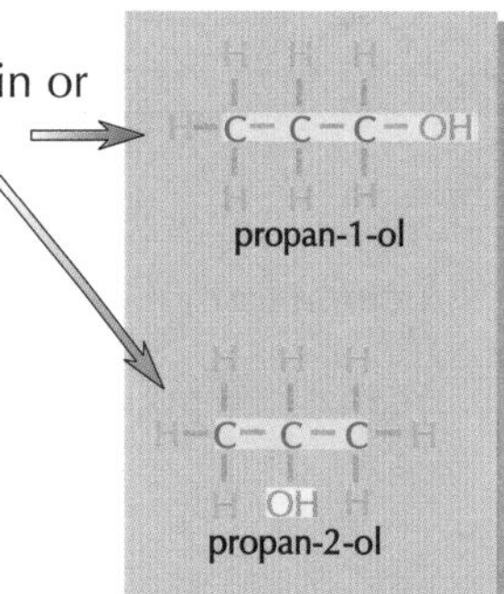

propan-1-ol again...

... and again propan-1-ol

... and again propan-1-ol

propan-2-ol again...

Structural Isomers have ***Different Properties***

The different arrangements of atoms can make isomers behave **very differently**.

1) **Chain isomers** have similar chemical properties — but their **physical properties**, like boiling point, will be different because of the change in shape of the molecule.
2) **Positional isomers** also have different **physical properties** and the **chemical properties** might be different too. A good example of this is the oxidation of alcohols (see pages 110-111).
3) **Functional group isomers** have **very** different **physical** and **chemical properties**.

Building ***Models*** *Makes it* ***Easier*** *to Understand Isomerism*

You can use a **molecular modelling** kit to get a better idea of molecular shape.

1) A **space-filling model** shows the shape of the atoms including the electron orbitals, but you can't easily see the bonding between atoms.
2) A **ball-and-stick model** shows the bonds between the atoms more clearly — you can see that atoms can **rotate freely** around **C–C** single bonds, but **C=C** double bonds have **restricted rotation**.

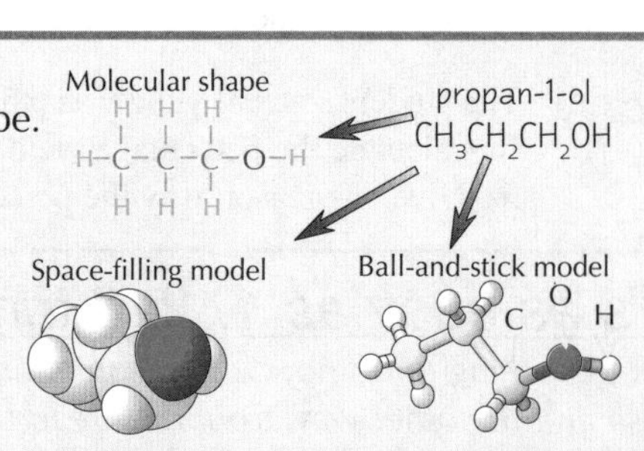

Isomerism

Geometric Isomers are a Form of Stereoisomerism

In stereoisomerism, all the atoms are connected to each other in the same way, but they're **arranged differently in space**. Stereoisomerism includes **geometric** isomers and **optical** isomers, but you only have to know about **geometric** (or **cis-trans**) isomers for AS Chemistry.

Geometric isomers **only** happen if —

- there's a C=C **double bond**, like in alkenes. C=C double bonds **can't rotate**.
- two **different** things are attached to **each** of the double bond carbon atoms.

Looking across the double bond...

Cis isomers are the ones with similar groups on the **same side** of the double bond.

Trans isomers have similar groups going diagonally across.

If there's two identical groups attached to a double bond carbon atom, then geometric isomerism won't happen.

But-2-ene shows geometric isomerism:

H_3C, CH_3, C=C, H, H — cis-but-2-ene

H_3C, H, C=C, H, CH_3 — trans-but-2-ene

But **but-1-ene** doesn't:

CH_3CH_2, H, C=C, H, H — identical groups — but-1-ene

Geometric Isomers have Different Physical Properties

The **physical properties** of geometric isomers are **different** — the different positions of the groups and chains affect shape, dipoles and intermolecular forces.

The **chemical properties** of geometric isomers are **usually pretty similar**. But, if the position of the two groups is important, the chemical properties will be different.

Practice Questions

Q1 What are isomers?

Q2 Name the three types of structural isomerism.

Q3 What is a positional isomer?

Q4 What is stereoisomerism?

Q5 Why doesn't but-1-ene have geometric isomers?

Exam Question

Q1 a) There are five chain isomers of the alkane C_6H_{14}.
(i) Draw and name all five isomers of C_6H_{14}. [10 marks]
(ii) Explain what is meant by the term 'chain isomerism'. [2 marks]

b) There are four isomers of the alkene C_3H_5Cl.
(i) Draw and name the pair of geometric isomers. [4 marks]
(ii) Draw and name the two isomers which do not show geometric isomerism. [4 marks]

c) Alkanes and alkenes are both examples of a homologous series. What is a homologous series? [2 marks]

Human structural isomers...

Alkanes

I'm an alkane and I'm OK — I sleep all night and I work all day...

Alkanes are **Saturated Hydrocarbons**

1) Alkanes have the **general formula C_nH_{2n+2}**. They've only got **carbon** and **hydrogen** atoms, so they're also **hydrocarbons**.
2) Every carbon atom in an alkane has **four single bonds** with other atoms. It's **impossible** for carbon to make more than four bonds, so alkanes are **saturated**.

Here's a few examples of alkanes —

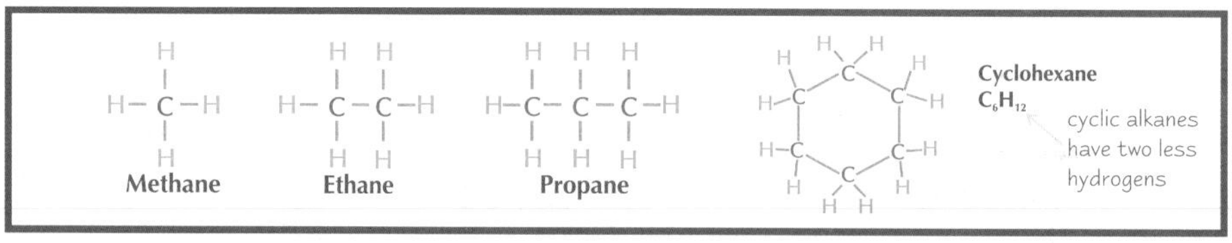

Methane
Ethane
Propane
Cyclohexane C_6H_{12}
cyclic alkanes have two less hydrogens

The **Boiling Point** of an Alkane Depends on its **Size** and **Shape**

The smallest alkanes, like methane, are **gases** at room temperature and pressure — they've got very low boiling points. Larger alkanes are **liquids** — they have higher boiling points.

1) Alkanes have **covalent bonds** inside the molecules. **Between** the molecules, there are **van der Waals** forces which hold them all together.
2) The **longer** the carbon chain, the **stronger** the van der Waals forces. This is because there's **more molecular surface area** and more electrons to interact.
3) So as the molecules get longer, it takes **more energy** to overcome the van der Waals forces and separate them, and the boiling point **rises**.
4) A **branched-chain** alkane has a **lower** boiling point than its straight-chain isomer. Branched-chain alkanes can't **pack closely** together and they have smaller **molecular surface areas** — so the van der Waals forces are reduced.

Example: Isomers of C_4H_{10}

Butane, boiling point = 272.5 K

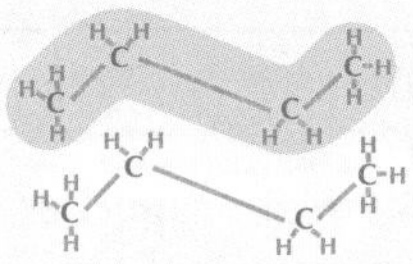

Molecules can pack closely.

Methylpropane, boiling point = 261.4 K

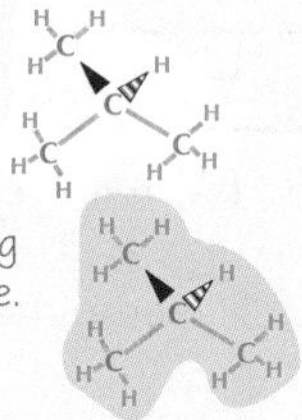

Close packing isn't possible.

Alkanes **don't React** with Most Chemicals

1) The C–C bonds and C–H bonds in alkanes are pretty **non-polar**. But most chemicals are **polar** — like water, haloalkanes, acids and alkalis.
2) Polar chemicals are attracted to the **polar groups** on molecules they attack. Alkanes don't have any polar groups, so they **don't** react with polar chemicals.
3) Alkanes **don't dissolve** in polar solvents, like water, either. They'll just sit there and look at you.
4) Alkanes **will** react with some **non-polar** things though — such as oxygen or the halogens. But they'll **only** bother if you give them enough **energy**.

If all this polar talk means nothing to you, flick back to p28. It's all explained there.

Alkanes Burn **Completely** in Oxygen

1) If you burn (**oxidise**) alkanes with **oxygen**, you'll get **carbon dioxide** and water — this is a **combustion reaction**.

Here's the equation for the combustion of propane — $C_3H_{8(g)} + 5O_{2(g)} \rightarrow 3CO_{2(g)} + 4H_2O_{(g)}$

2) Combustion reactions happen between **gases**, so liquid alkanes have to be **vaporised** first. Smaller alkanes turn into **gases** more easily (they're more **volatile**), so they'll **burn** more easily too.
3) Larger alkanes release heaps more **energy** per mole because they have more bonds to react. For every extra **$-CH_2-$** unit, the **enthalpy change of combustion**, ΔH_c, increases on average by a whopping **654 kJ mol^{-1}**.

Alkanes

Halogens React with Alkanes, Forming Haloalkanes

A hydrogen atom is **substituted** (replaced) by chlorine or bromine in a **photochemical** reaction. This is a **free-radical substitution reaction**.

Free radicals are particles with an unpaired electron, written like this — Cl· or CH_3·
You get them when bonds split equally — see the example below... (and also page 72).

Photochemical reactions are started by ultraviolet light.

Chlorine and **methane** react with a bit of a bang to form **chloromethane**: $CH_4 + Cl_2 \xrightarrow{u.v.} CH_3Cl + HCl$

The **reaction mechanism** has three stages:

Initiation reactions — free radicals are produced.

1) Sunlight provides enough energy to break the Cl-Cl bond — this is **photodissociation**. $Cl_2 \xrightarrow{u.v.} 2Cl\cdot$
2) The bond splits **equally** and each atom gets to keep one electron — **homolytic fission**. The atom becomes a highly reactive **free radical**, Cl·, because of its **unpaired electron**.

If a bond's broken unequally and both electrons are kept by one atom, it's called heterolytic fission.

Propagation reactions — free radicals are used up and created in a chain reaction.

1) Cl· attacks a **methane** molecule: $Cl\cdot + CH_4 \rightarrow CH_3\cdot + HCl$
2) The new **methyl free radical**, $CH_3\cdot$, can attack another Cl_2 molecule: $CH_3\cdot + Cl_2 \rightarrow CH_3Cl + Cl\cdot$
3) The new Cl· can attack **another** CH_4 molecule, and so on, until all the Cl_2 or CH_4 molecules are wiped out.

Termination reactions — free radicals are mopped up.

1) If two free radicals join together, they make a **stable molecule**.
2) There are **heaps** of possible termination reactions. Here's a few of them to give you the idea:
   $Cl\cdot + CH_3\cdot \rightarrow CH_3Cl$
   $CH_3\cdot + CH_3\cdot \rightarrow C_2H_6$

Some products formed will be trace impurities in the final sample.

More substitutions

What happens now **depends** on whether there's too much **chlorine** or too much **methane**:

1) If the **chlorine's** in excess, Cl· free radicals will start attacking chloromethane, producing **dichloromethane** CH_2Cl_2, **trichloromethane** $CHCl_3$, and **tetrachloromethane** CCl_4.
2) **But** if the **methane's** in excess, then the product will mostly be **chloromethane**.

Practice Questions

Q1 What's the general formula for alkanes?

Q2 What kind of intermolecular forces are there between alkane molecules?

Q3 Why do straight-chain alkanes have higher boiling points than branched-chain alkanes?

Q4 What's photodissociation?

Q5 What's a free radical?

Q6 What's homolytic fission?

Exam Question

Q1 The alkane ethane is a saturated hydrocarbon. It is mostly unreactive, but will react with oxygen in a combustion reaction and bromine in a photochemical reaction.

(a) What is a saturated hydrocarbon? [2 marks]
(b) Why is ethane unreactive with most reagents? [2 marks]
(c) Write a balanced equation for the complete combustion of ethane. [2 marks]
(d) Write an equation and outline the mechanism for the photochemical reaction of bromine with ethane. Assume ethane is in excess. What type of mechanism is it? [8 marks]

This page is like...totally radical, man...

Mechanisms are an absolute pain in the bum to learn, but unfortunately reactions are what Chemistry's all about. If you don't like it, you should have taken art — no mechanisms in that, just pretty pictures. Ah well, there's no going back now. You've just got to sit down and learn the stuff. Keep hacking away at it, till you know it all off by heart.

Petroleum

Edexcel people can skip these two pages.
Petroleum is just a poncy word for crude oil — the black, yukky stuff they get out the ground with huge oil wells.

Crude Oil is a Mixture of Hydrocarbons

1) Petroleum or crude oil is mostly **alkanes**. They range from **smallish alkanes**, like pentane, to **massive alkanes** with more than 50 carbons.
2) Crude oil isn't very useful as it is, but you can **separate** it into more useful bits (or **fractions**) by **fractional distillation**.

Here's how fractional distillation works — don't try this at home.

1) First, the crude oil is **vaporised** at about 350 °C.
2) The vaporised crude oil goes into the **fractionating column** and rises up through the trays. The largest hydrocarbons don't **vaporise** at all, because their boiling points are too high — they just run to the bottom and form a gooey **residue**.
3) As the crude oil vapour goes up the fractionating column, it gets **cooler**. Because of the different chain lengths, each fraction **condenses** at a different temperature. The fractions are **drawn off** at different levels in the column.
4) The hydrocarbons with the **lowest boiling points** don't condense. They're drawn off as **gases** at the top of the column.

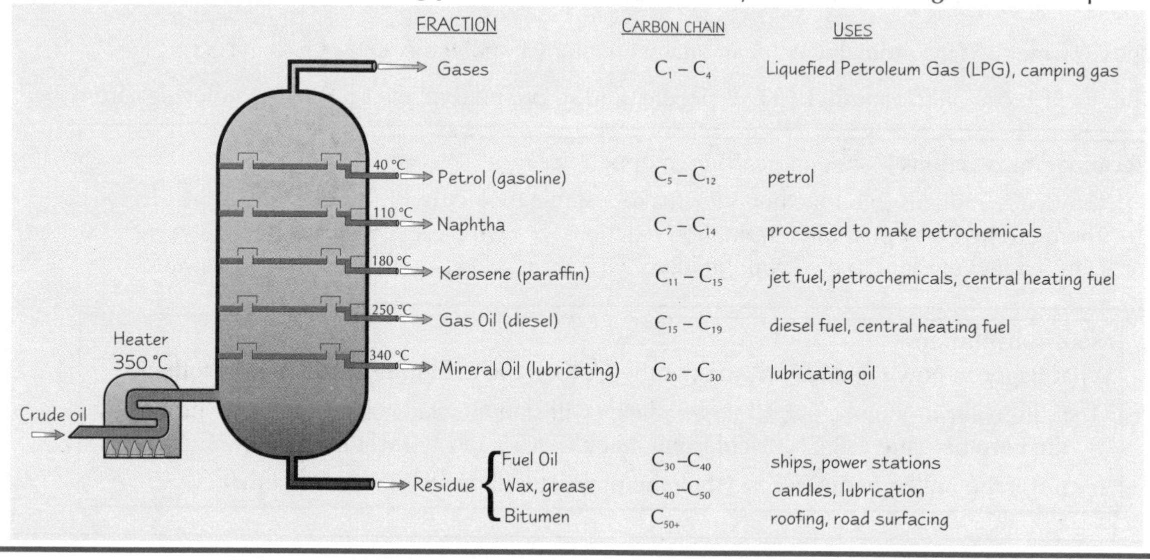

Heavy Fractions can be 'Cracked' to Make Smaller Molecules

1) People want loads of the **light** fractions, like petrol and naphtha. They don't want so much of the **heavier** stuff like bitumen though.
2) To meet this demand, the less popular heavier fractions are **cracked**. Cracking is **breaking** long-chain alkanes into **smaller** hydrocarbons (which can include alkenes). It involves breaking the **C–C bonds**.

   You could crack **decane** like this —

$$\underset{\text{decane}}{C_{10}H_{22}} \rightarrow \underset{\text{ethene}}{C_2H_4} + \underset{\text{octane}}{C_8H_{18}}$$

There are **two types** of **cracking** you need to know about:

THERMAL CRACKING

- It's a **free radical** reaction and takes place at **high temperature** (up to 1000 °C) and **high pressure** (up to 70 atm).
- It produces a lot of **alkenes**.
- These **alkenes** are used to make heaps of valuable products, like **polymers**. A good example is **poly(ethene)**, which is made from ethene (have a squiz at page 96 for more on polymers).

CATALYTIC CRACKING

- This makes mostly **motor fuels** and **aromatic** hydrocarbons (see page 92).
- It works by a **carbocation mechanism**, using something called a **zeolite catalyst**, at a **slight pressure** and **high temperature** (about 450 °C).
- Using a catalyst **cuts costs**, because the reaction can be done at a **lower** temperature and pressure. The catalyst also **speeds** up the reaction, and time is money and all that.

Petroleum

AQA people can skip this page (except for the questions).

Hydrocarbons with a **High Octane Rating** Burn More **Smoothly**

1) Here's a super-quick whizz through how a **petrol engine** works:
   The **fuel/air** mixture is squashed by a **piston** and **ignited** with a spark, creating an **explosion**. This drives the piston up again, turning the **crankshaft**. Four pistons work **one after the other**, so that the engine runs smoothly.
2) The problem is, **straight-chain alkanes** in petrol tend to **auto-ignite** — when the fuel/air mixture is compressed they explode without being ignited. They then explode **again** with the spark, causing '**knocking**' in the engine.
3) To get rid of knocking and make combustion more efficient, **shorter branched-chain alkanes**, **cycloalkanes** and **arenes** are included in petrols, creating a **high octane rating**.

The octane rating of a petrol tells you how likely it is to auto-ignite. The higher the number, the less likely it is to auto-ignite. It's based on a scale where 100% heptane has a rating of 0, and 100% 2,2,4-trimethylpentane has a rating of 100.

Heptane C_7H_{16}
(a straight-chain alkane)

2,2,4–trimethylpentane
$C(CH_3)_3CH_2CH(CH_3)_2$
(a branched-chain alkane)

Isomerisation creates **Branched-Chain Isomers**

Isomerisation happens when a **straight-chain** alkane is heated with a **platinum catalyst**, stuck on inert aluminium oxide. The molecule is broken up and put back together as a **branched-chain isomer**.

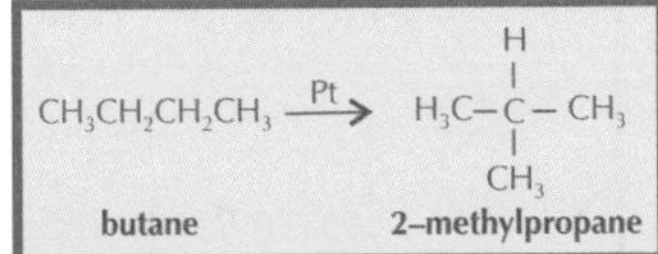

A form of **zeolite** (a mineral with minute tunnels and cavities) is used as a **molecular sieve** to separate the isomers. The molecules which still have **straight chains** go through the zeolite 'sieve' and are **recycled**.

Alkanes can be **Reformed** into **Cycloalkanes** and **Arenes**

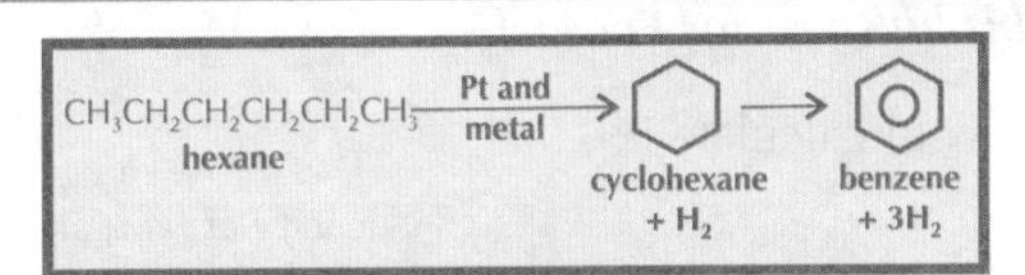

Reforming converts **alkanes** into **arenes** (aromatic hydrocarbons — see page 92).

It uses a **bimetallic** catalyst made of **platinum** and another metal. Again, you need to stick the catalyst on inert aluminium oxide.

Practice Questions

Q1 What is the naphtha fraction used for?

Q2 What is cracking?

Q3 In isomerisation, what is zeolite used for?

Exam Question

Q1 Crude oil is a source of fuels and petrochemicals. It's vaporised and separated into fractions using fractional distillation.

a) Some heavier fractions are processed using cracking.
   i) Give one reason why cracking is carried out. [2 marks]
   ii) Name the reaction mechanism involved in catalytic cracking. [1 mark]
   iii) Write a possible equation for the cracking of dodecane, $C_{12}H_{26}$. [1 mark]

b) Some hydrocarbons are processed using isomerisation or reforming, producing a petrol with a high octane rating.
   i) What is meant by a petrol's octane rating? [3 marks]
   ii) What kinds of compounds are found in a petrol with a high octane rating?
   What effect do they have on the petrol's performance? [4 marks]
   iii) Draw and name two isomers formed from pentane by isomerisation.
   Which isomer would increase the octane rating of a petrol the most? [5 marks]

Crude oil — not the kind of oil you could take home to meet your mother...

This ain't the most exciting page in the history of the known universe. Although in a galaxy far, far away there may be lots of pages on even more boring topics. But, that's neither here nor there, cos you've got to learn the stuff anyway. Get fractional distillation and cracking straight in your brain and make sure you know why people bother to do it.

Fuels

If we didn't burn fuels to keep warm and power vehicles, we'd all wear lots of jumpers and use pogo sticks. Maybe.

Alkanes are Useful Fuels

When you **burn** an alkane in plenty of air, you end up with **carbon dioxide** and **water**. It's an **exothermic** combustion reaction. Alkanes make great fuels — burning just **one mole** of **methane** releases a humungous **890 kJ of energy**.

Here's a few uses of alkane fuels:

1) Methane's used for **central heating** and **cooking** in homes.
2) Alkanes with 5-12 carbon atoms are used in **petrol**.
3) Kerosene is used as **jet fuel**. Its alkanes have 11-15 carbon atoms.
4) **Diesel** is made of a mixture of alkanes with 15-19 carbon atoms.

Fuels Need Certain Properties

A good fuel gives out loads of energy when it's burned. So, it needs a highly **exothermic** enthalpy change of combustion. Also, an ideal fuel:

- is **cheap**
- is **safe** — it needs a **high activation energy** for its combustion reaction, or it'll catch fire too easily.
- is **easy to transport**. Liquid fuels like ethanol and octane are carried in **tankers**. Gases like methane travel through **pipes** to homes and factories.
- is **easy to store**. Gaseous fuels like hydrogen, methane and butane are hard to store — you'd need an enormous container to store enough hydrogen to get the same car mileage as from a tank of petrol. It is better to store these fuels as **liquids** in **high pressure tanks**.
- has a **high energy density** — the more energy you get per kilogram of fuel, the better.
- causes as **little pollution** as possible.

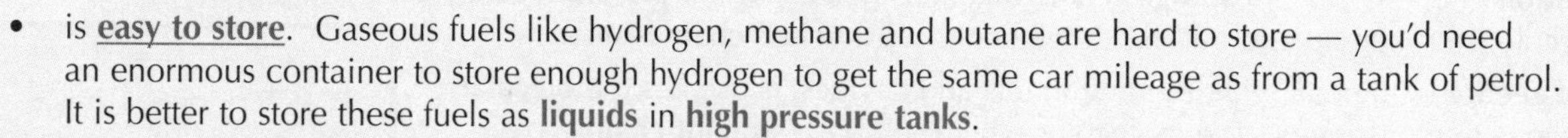

You can Calculate a Fuel's Energy Density

This bit's just for Edexcel.

Energy density is the amount of energy you get **per kg** of fuel. Here's how to calculate it:

For methane, $\Delta H_c^\circ = -890 \text{ kJ mol}^{-1}$ ← see page 63

Mass of 1 mole of methane (CH_4) = 12 + (1 × 4) = 16 g

so, 1g of methane releases $\frac{890}{16} \approx 55.6$ kJ when it burns and **1 kg** of methane releases 55.6 × 1000 = **55 600 kJ kg^{-1}**

This is the energy density of methane.

You can also calculate the amount of energy given out **per unit volume**:

1 mole of methane gas occupies **24 dm^3** at room temperature and pressure, ← see page 13

So, 1 dm^3 of methane gas releases $\frac{890}{24} \approx 37.1$ kJ when it burns.

So, the energy released per unit volume = **37.1 kJ dm^{-3}**

Burning Fuels Makes Greenhouse Gases

1) The **greenhouse effect** is causing the Earth to **warm up** slowly and is a **huge** problem. It's causing **climate changes** and melting the polar ice caps — this could lead to **flooding**. It's due to increasing amounts of greenhouse gases, such as **carbon dioxide**, **water vapour** and **methane**, in the atmosphere. Burning fuels is a major cause of this increase.
2) Greenhouse gases absorb **infra-red radiation**, but not visible or ultraviolet radiation from the Sun. They let the Sun's radiation **in**, but stop some of the Earth's infra-red radiation getting **out**.
3) Controlling global warming isn't easy. One way of trying to do this is to encourage people to **use cars less** by providing better public transport. Another way is to replace fossil fuels with **other sources of energy**. For example, electricity can be generated from wind, water (hydroelectric) or wave power, instead of by burning fossil fuels.

Layer of greenhouse gases
Visible and ultraviolet radiation from the Sun
Some infra-red radiation emitted by the Earth gets absorbed by greenhouse gases
Some infra-red radiation emitted by the Earth escapes

Fuels

Burning Fuels Causes **Acid Rain**

Power stations add loads of sulphur oxides, including sulphur dioxide, to the air. **Scrubbers** are used to reduce the sulphur dioxide emissions, but they don't get rid of them all. Sulphur oxides are **really nasty**:

1) They're **poisonous** and cause problems for people with asthma.
2) They cause **acid rain**. Acid rain makes **lakes** and **rivers** acidic, which kills fish and other aquatic life. It also kills trees and damages buildings.

And if that's Not Bad Enough...**Burning Fuels** Produces Other **Pollutants** Too

1) Sometimes there isn't enough **oxygen** in an engine for the fuel to burn completely. This is **incomplete combustion**. When this happens, carbon dioxide and water aren't the only things produced. **Carbon monoxide**, a poisonous gas, is also produced.
2) Vehicle engines also make **oxides of nitrogen** (NO_x). These add to the **acid rain** problem.
3) Sometimes, some of the fuel in an engine comes out of the exhaust pipe without burning at all. These **unburned hydrocarbons** escape into the air as pollutants.

Luckily, all these pollutants can be removed from car and lorry exhausts by **catalytic converters** (see page 73).

Fossil Fuels are **Non-Renewable**

Crude oil, **coal** and **natural gas** are all **fossil fuels**. They're **non-renewable** — we're using them much more quickly than they can be replaced. With this in mind, scientists are trying to develop **renewable biofuels** from things like plants. These produce **carbon dioxide** when they burn, but the plants they come from **take in** carbon dioxide. So using biofuels **won't** add to the carbon dioxide in the atmosphere if the plants are being replaced. Here's a few examples that might come in handy in the exam:

1) **Biodiesel** is made from **rapeseed oil**, and is used in vehicles.
2) **Ethanol** can be made by **fermenting sugar cane**. It is mixed with petrol and used as a fuel in vehicles.

Practice Questions

Q1 Are the combustion reactions of alkanes endothermic or exothermic?

Q2 Which fuel consists of a mixture of alkanes that have between 11 and 15 carbon atoms?

Q3 List 5 desirable properties of fuels.

Q4 Define a fuel's energy density.

Q5 Name two gases which contribute to the greenhouse effect.

Q6 Name two types of radiation that greenhouse gases do not absorb.

Exam Question

Q1 a) Calculate the amount of energy that is released by burning 30 dm^3 of hexane.
The standard enthalpy change of combustion of hexane is -4163 kJ mol^{-1}. Its density is 0.7 g cm^{-3}. [4 marks]

b) Calculate the volume (at r.t.p.) and mass of hydrogen that would be needed to produce the same amount of energy as 30 dm^3 of hexane. The enthalpy of combustion of hydrogen is -286 kJ mol^{-1}. 1 mole of gas at 25 °C and atmospheric pressure occupies 24 dm^3. [2 marks]

Cars that eat hay — so that's what they mean by horsepower...

We rely on fuels to provide the energy for our 21st century lifestyles — cars-a-plenty, power on tap, and so on. It's certainly convenient, but there are problems too — such as the greenhouse effect, plus the fact that we're going to run out of fossil fuels fairly soon-ish. Learn all the stuff and all the biz on these pages — even those fiddly technical details.

Alkenes

I'll warn you now — some of this stuff gets a bit heavy — but stick with it, as it's pretty important.

Alkenes are Unsaturated Hydrocarbons

1) Alkenes have the **general formula C_nH_{2n}**. They're just made of carbon and hydrogen atoms, so they're **hydrocarbons**.
2) Alkene molecules **all** have at least one **C=C double covalent bond**. Molecules with C=C double bonds are **unsaturated** because they can make more bonds with extra atoms in **addition** reactions.
3) The **physical properties** of alkenes and alkanes are pretty similar. The C=C double bonds **lower** the **melting** and **boiling points** of alkenes though. (There's **less** hydrogen atoms sticking out, so there's **lower van der Waals forces**.)

Here's a few pretty diagrams of **alkenes**:

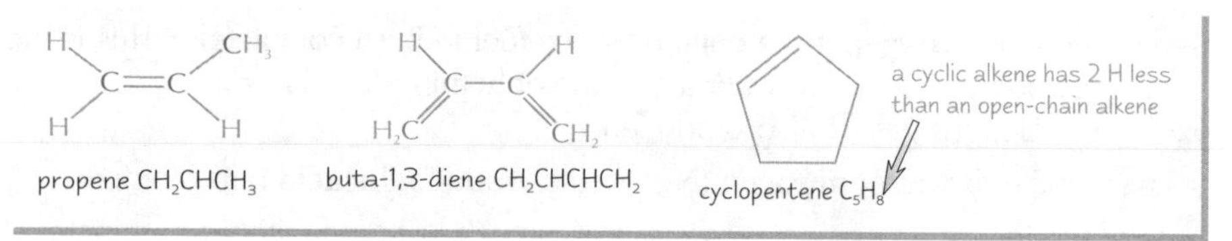

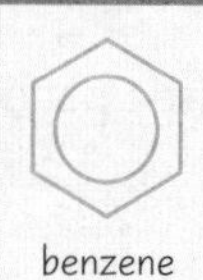

Benzene (C_6H_6) is like a **cyclic alkene** with 6 carbons and 3 double bonds. It's more **stable** (less reactive) than you'd expect though, because the double bond electrons are **delocalised** around the carbon ring. That's why its symbol has a **circle** in it.

Compounds with **ring structures** like benzene are called **arenes**, or **aromatic compounds**.
All other organic compounds (e.g. alkanes and alkenes) are called **aliphatic compounds**.

Alkenes are Much More Reactive than Alkanes

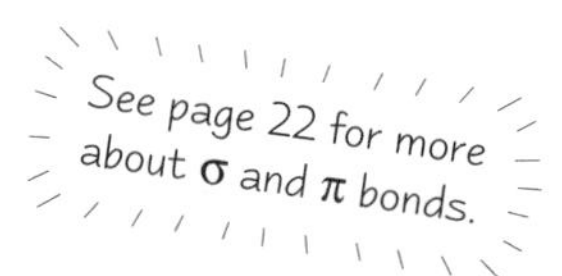

See page 22 for more about σ and π bonds.

1) Each **double bond** in an alkene is made up of a **σ bond and a π bond**. It's a bit like a hot dog. The **π bond** is the bun and the **σ bond** is sandwiched in the middle like the sausage.
2) Because there's two pairs of electrons in the bond, the C=C double bond has a really **high electron density**. This makes alkenes pretty reactive.
3) Another reason for the high reactivity is that the **π bond** sticks out above and below the rest of the molecule. So, the **π bond** is likely to be attacked by **electrophiles** (see p94).
4) Because the double bond's so **reactive**, alkenes are handy **starting points** for making other organic compounds and for making **petrochemicals**.

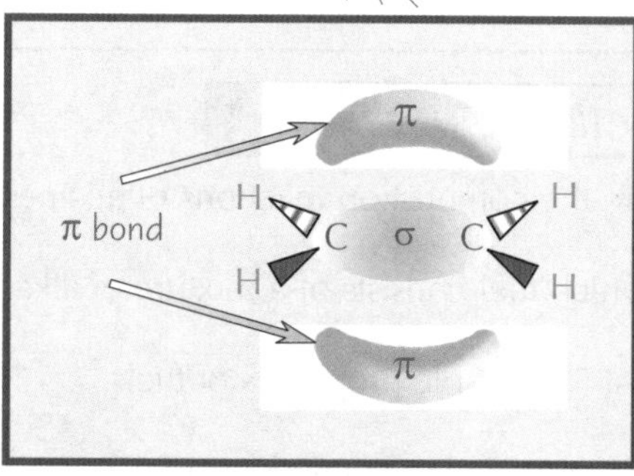

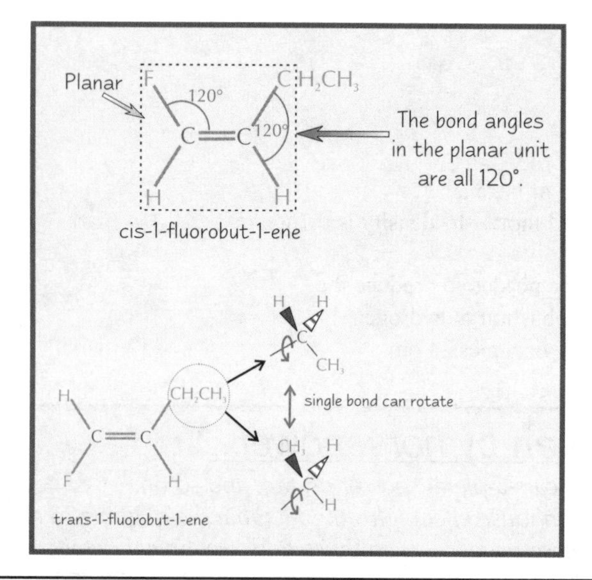

Double Bonds Can't Rotate

1) The carbon atoms in the C=C double bond can't **rotate**. This is because the p orbitals have to **overlap** to form a **π bond**. The C=C double bond and the atoms bonded to these carbons are **planar** (flat) and **rigid** (they can't bend or twist much).
2) Ethene, C_2H_2, is completely planar, but in larger alkenes, only the >C=C< unit is planar — atoms can still rotate around other **single bonds** within the molecule.
3) The **restricted rotation** around the C=C double bond is what causes **cis-trans** or **geometric isomerism**.

Alkenes

Limonene is Extracted from Oranges by Steam Distillation

If you're not doing Edexcel Nuffield you can skip this top bit.

Limonene is an alkene. It's an oil found in the rind of **citrus fruits**.
You have to extract it by **steam distillation**, as heating it to its boiling point will destroy it.

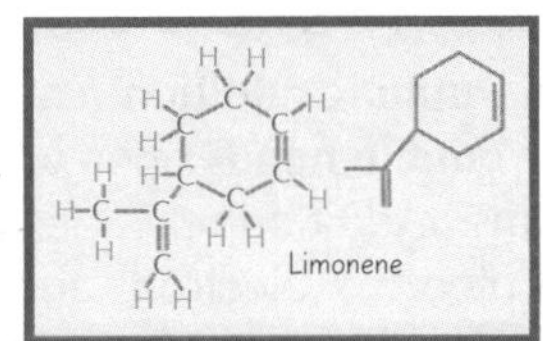

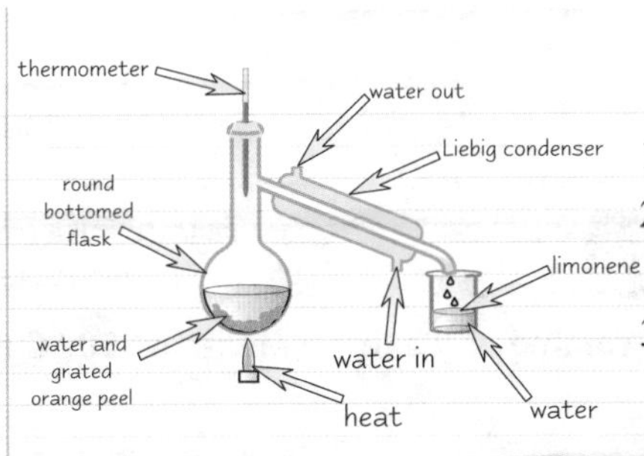

Extracting Limonene

1) Mix finely grated orange rind with water.
2) **Boil** the mixture in **distillation apparatus**.
   The limonene combines with the steam and distils at just below **373 K** (100 °C).
3) Collect the **distillate**. The limonene forms an **oily layer** on the surface of the water. You can suck this off with a **pipette**.

And this bit's just for Edexcel and Edexcel Nuffield.

Distillation is an Important Technique in Organic Chemistry

You use distillation to **separate** a mixture of liquids. It's useful if you've made an organic liquid, but it's ended up with some other stuff mixed in — it's a way to **purify** it. You **vaporise** the substance and then **condense** it into a different container. The stuff collected is the **distillate**.

Miscible liquids are soluble in each other, so they mix together well, e.g. organic liquids.
Immiscible liquids won't dissolve in each other. They separate into two layers if you mix them, e.g. water and limonene.

Simple distillation is used to separate **miscible** mixtures.

Fractional distillation uses a fractionating column to separate miscible mixtures where the boiling points of the liquids are really close.

Steam distillation is when you distill two **immiscible** liquids — the mixture boils at a **lower** temperature than the boiling point of either liquid by itself.

Practice Questions

Q1 How do the melting and boiling points of alkenes and alkanes differ? Why?

Q2 Why are alkenes more reactive than alkanes?

Q3 Where is limonene found?

Q4 What is distillation used for?

Exam Questions

Q1 Ethene has the molecular formula C_2H_4. Explain why it is described as being unsaturated. [2 marks]

Q2 The alkene myrcene can be isolated from bay leaves.
  a) What is the general formula for alkenes? [1 mark]
  b) The structural formula for myrcene is $(CH_3)_2CCHCH_2CH_2C(CH_2)CHCH_2$.
    i) What is its molecular formula? [1 mark]
    ii) How many double bonds does myrcene contain, assuming that there are no cyclic groups in its structure? [1 mark]
    iii) Draw the displayed (full structural) formula for myrcene. [2 marks]
  c) Myrcene can be extracted from bay leaves by steam distillation. Why would this be a good choice of technique to use? [1 mark]

Double bond hot dog — Brosnan's the bun, Dalton's the dog...

What ON EARTH are you talking about, man? Search me — I'm just here to tell you about Organic Chemistry. Alkenes are really important. Make sure you understand why they're so much more reactive than alkanes. It's all to do with the double bond. So get that Double Bond Hot Dog thingy learned. And remember — Connery's the ketchup, Moore's the mustard...

Reactions of Alkenes

Alkenes do loads of weird and wacky stuff — but I've squished all that you need to know on this double-page spread.

***Electrophilic Addition Reactions** Happen to Alkenes*

Electrophilic addition reactions aren't too complicated. The **double bonds** open up and atoms are **added** to the carbon atoms. Addition reactions happen because the double bond has got plenty of electrons and is easily attacked by electrophiles. The double bond is also **nucleophilic** — it's attracted to places that don't have enough **electrons**.

> Electrophiles are electron-pair acceptors — they're usually a bit short of electrons, so they're attracted to areas where there's lots of them about. Here's a few examples:
> - Positively charged ions, like H^+, NO_2^+.
> - Polar molecules — the δ+ atom is attracted to places with lots of electrons

See page 28 for a reminder about polar molecules.

*Adding **Hydrogen** to C=C Bonds Produces **Alkanes***

1) Ethene will react with **hydrogen** gas to produce ethane. It needs a **nickel catalyst** and a temperature of **150 °C** though.

$$H_2C{=}CH_2 + H_2 \xrightarrow[150\ °C]{Ni} CH_3CH_3$$

2) **Margarine's** made by **'hydrogenating' unsaturated vegetable oils**. By removing some **double bonds**, you raise the **melting point** of the oil so that it becomes **solid** at room temperature.

*Use **Bromine Water** to Test for C=C Double Bonds*

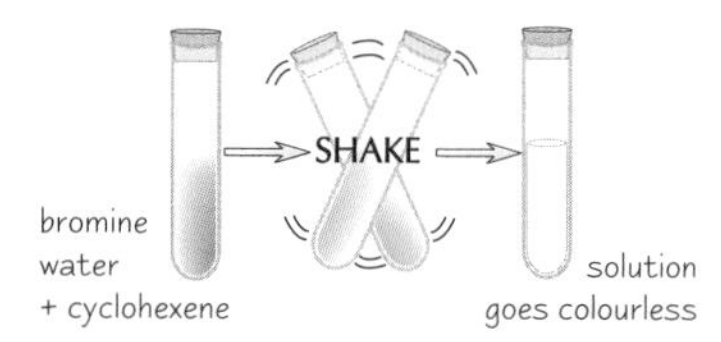

When you shake an alkene with **orange bromine water**, the solution quickly **decolourises**. Bromine is added across the double bond to form a **dibromoalkane** — this happens by **electrophilic addition**. Here's the mechanism...

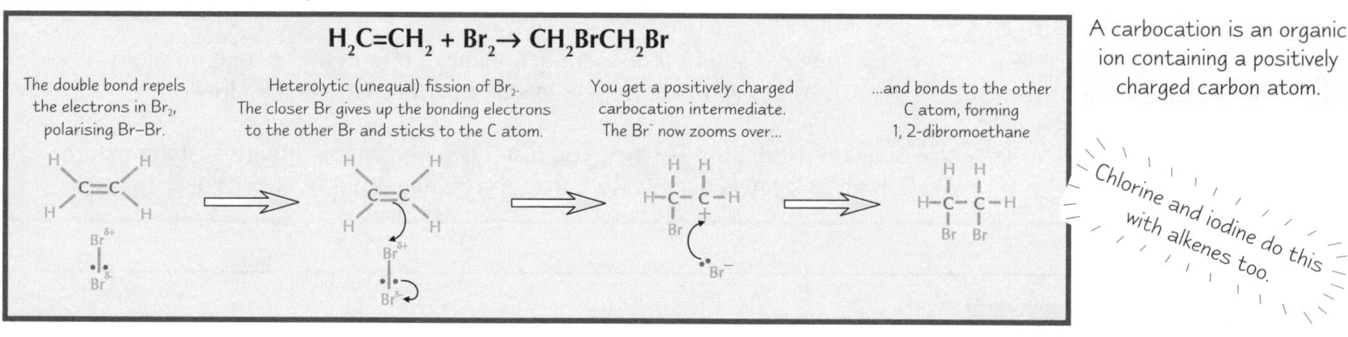

$H_2C{=}CH_2 + Br_2 \rightarrow CH_2BrCH_2Br$
The double bond repels the electrons in Br_2, polarising Br–Br.
Heterolytic (unequal) fission of Br_2. The closer Br gives up the bonding electrons to the other Br and sticks to the C atom.
You get a positively charged carbocation intermediate. The Br^- now zooms over...
...and bonds to the other C atom, forming 1, 2-dibromoethane
A carbocation is an organic ion containing a positively charged carbon atom.
Chlorine and iodine do this with alkenes too.

*Adding **Hydrogen Halides** to **Unsymmetrical Alkenes** Forms **Two Products***

1) Alkenes also undergo **electrophilic addition** reactions with HBr, to form **bromoalkanes**.
2) If the HBr adds to an **unsymmetrical** alkene, there are two possible products. The amount of each product formed depends on how **stable** the **carbocation** formed in the middle of the reaction is. Carbocations with more **alkyl groups** are more stable because the alkyl groups feed **electrons** towards the positive charge. The **more stable carbocation** is much more likely to form.

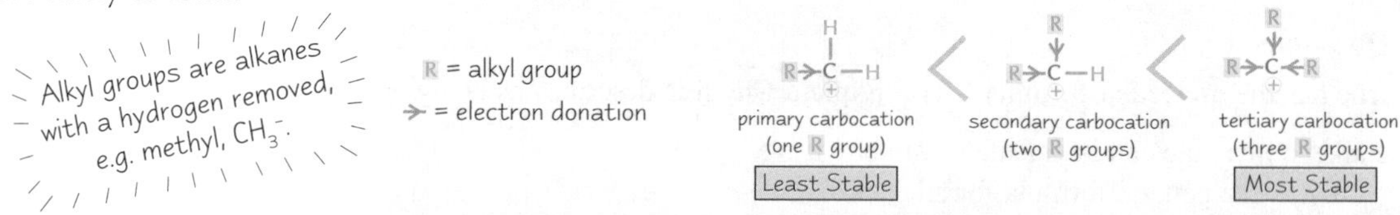

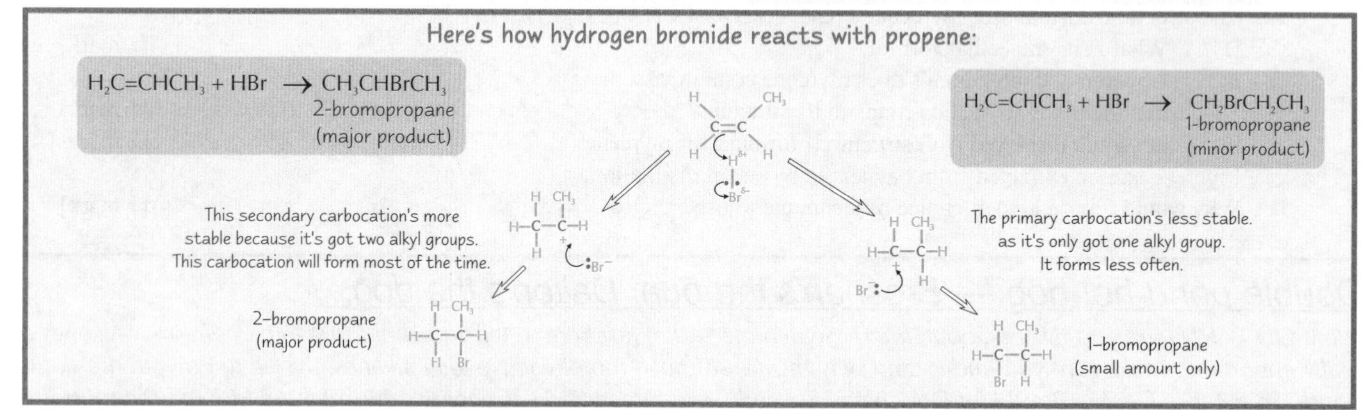

Alkyl groups are alkanes with a hydrogen removed, e.g. methyl, CH_3^-.

→ = electron donation

Least Stable

Here's how hydrogen bromide reacts with propene:
$H_2C{=}CHCH_3 + HBr \rightarrow CH_3CHBrCH_3$
2-bromopropane (major product)
$H_2C{=}CHCH_3 + HBr \rightarrow CH_2BrCH_2CH_3$
1-bromopropane (minor product)
This secondary carbocation's more stable because it's got two alkyl groups. This carbocation will form most of the time.
The primary carbocation's less stable, as it's only got one alkyl group. It forms less often.
2-bromopropane (major product)
1-bromopropane (small amount only)

Reactions of Alkenes

Reacting **Sulphuric Acid** *with* **Alkenes** *Produces* **Alcohols**

1) Cold concentrated **sulphuric acid** reacts with an alkene in an **electrophilic addition** reaction.

$$H_2C=CH_2 + H_2SO_4 \longrightarrow CH_3CH_2OSO_2OH$$
ethene + sulphuric acid → ethyl hydrogen sulphate

2) If you then add cold **water** and warm the product, it's **hydrolysed** to form an alcohol.

$$CH_3CH_2OSO_2OH + H_2O \longrightarrow CH_3CH_2OH + H_2SO_4$$
ethyl hydrogen sulphate + water → ethanol + sulphuric acid

3) The **sulphuric acid** isn't used up — it acts as a **catalyst**.

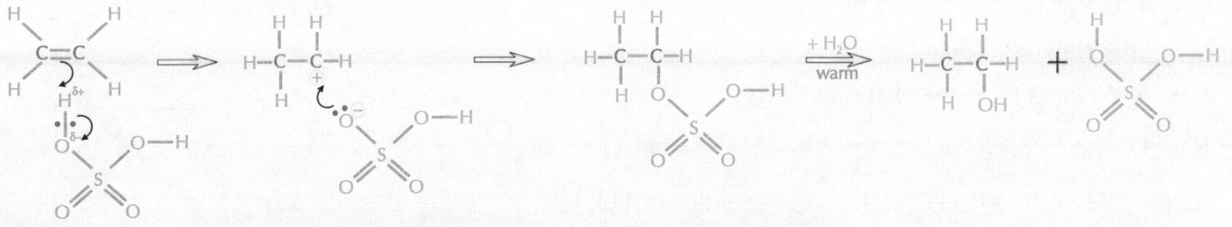

Hydrolysis is the breaking of covalent bonds by reaction with water.

Ethanol *is Manufactured by* **Steam Hydration**

1) Ethene can be **hydrated** by **steam** at 300 °C and a pressure of 60 atm. It needs a solid **phosphoric(V) acid catalyst**.
2) The reaction's **reversible** and the reaction yield is low — only about 5%. This sounds rubbish, but you can **recycle** the unreacted ethene gas, making the overall yield a much more profitable **95%**.

$$H_2C=CH_{2(g)} + H_2O_{(g)} \underset{300\ °C,\ 60\ atm}{\overset{H_3PO_4}{\rightleftharpoons}} CH_3CH_2OH_{(g)}$$

Alkenes are **Oxidised** *by* **Acidified Potassium Manganate(VII)**

If you shake an alkene with **acidified potassium manganate(VII)**, the purple solution is decolourised. You've **oxidised** the alkene and made a diol (an alcohol with two -OH groups).

This is another useful **test** for a double C=C bond.

Here's how **ethene** reacts with acidified potassium manganate(VII)

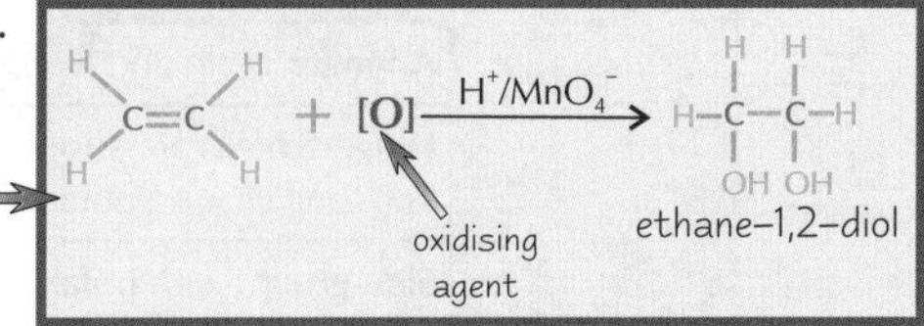

[O] is often used to show an oxidising agent in an organic equation.

Practice Questions

Q1 What is an electrophile?

Q2 Why do alkenes react with electrophiles?

Q3 Write an equation for the hydrogenation of ethene.

Q4 What is a carbocation?

Exam Question

Q1 But-1-ene is an alkene. Alkenes contain at least one C=C double bond.

a) Describe how bromine water can be used to test for C=C double bonds. [2 marks]

b) Name the reaction mechanism involved in the above test. [2 marks]

c) Hydrogen bromide will react with but-1-ene by this mechanism, producing two isomeric products.

i) Write a mechanism for the reaction of HBr with $CH_2=CHCH_2CH_3$, showing the formation of the major product only. Name the product. [3 marks]

ii) Explain why it is the major product for this reaction. [2 marks]

This section is free from all GM ingredients...

Wow...this page really is jam-packed. There's not one, not two, but three mechanisms to learn. And learn you must. Get the book shut and scribble them out. Make sure you know the two tests for double bonds too. They mightn't be as handy in real life as, say, a tin opener, but you won't need a tin opener in the exam.

Polymers

Polymers are long stringy molecules made by joining lots of little molecules together.

*Alkenes **Join up** to form **Addition Polymers***

1) The **double bonds** in alkenes can open up and join together to make long chains called **polymers**. It's kind of like they're holding hands in a big line. The individual, small alkenes are called **monomers**.
2) This is called **addition polymerisation** — it's a **free radical addition** reaction. You need a **catalyst** (e.g. oxygen) to start it.

Poly(ethene) is made by the **addition polymerisation** of **ethene**.
It's one of those complicated reactions I'm afraid:

(Ra• = Free radical)

Initiation $Ra\bullet + CH_2{=}CH_2 \longrightarrow RaCH_2CH_2\bullet$

Propagation $RaCH_2CH_2\bullet + CH_2{=}CH_2 \longrightarrow RaCH_2CH_2CH_2CH_2\bullet$ etc.

Termination $Ra(CH_2CH_2)_n\bullet + \bullet(CH_2CH_2)_nRa \longrightarrow Ra(CH_2CH_2)_{2n}Ra$

Overall $nCH_2{=}CH_2 \xrightarrow[\text{2000 atm, oxygen}]{\text{500 K}} -\!(CH_2{-}CH_2)\!-_n$

Here's an easier way to look at it:

monomer ⟶ polymer

$n\ H_2C{=}CH_2 \longrightarrow -\!(CH_2{-}CH_2)\!-_n$

'side-links' show that both sides are attached to other units

n represents the number of repeated units

3) **Copolymers** are made from more than one type of monomer. They join together in a random order.

nA + mB ⟶ –A–A–B–B–B–A–B–A–A–B–A–A–B–A–A–B–B–

*The Structure and Bonding of Polymers Affect Their **Properties***

Not AQA or Edexcel Nuffield.

Polymers are usually **flexibile** and **strong**. But the properties of individual polymers depend on a few different things.

Property	Factors affecting the property
Melting point	**A longer chain** and a **higher molecular mass** increases melting point.
Tensile strength and flexibility	**Longer chains** are stronger, because there's greater **van der Waals forces** between molecules. The long chains get tangled though, making the polymer **less flexible**.
	Side-groups with **polar bonds** attract polar side groups on other chains. This makes the polymer **stronger.**
	Chain-branching stops chains from **packing closely** together. This reduces the intermolecular forces, so the polymer's **weaker** and **more flexible**.
	Chain flexibility is a feature of hydrocarbon chains. If the chain can be made less flexible, the polymer will be **stronger.**
	Cross-linking is when covalent bonds are formed between polymer chains — this makes the polymer less flexible but **stronger.**
	A **stereoregular** polymer has a regular pattern of side groups along its chains — the chains can pack closely together. This means more intermolecular forces, so it's **stronger.**
	Crystalline polymers have **regularly packed polymer chains.** This is because they have stereoregular chain structures, no chain-branching and no large side-groups. Highly crystalline polymers are **stronger** and more **rigid**.
	Amorphous regions of a polymer have **irregularly packed polymer chains.** This is due to chain-branching and big side-groups. Polymers with lots of amorphous areas are **weaker** and more **flexible**.

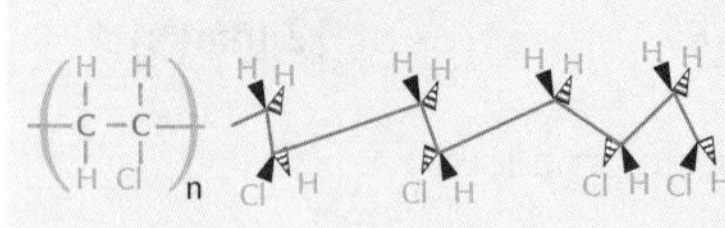

Poly(chloroethene), otherwise known as PVC (polyvinyl chloride)

Large **chlorines** stick out randomly from the chains, so they **don't pack closely** — so PVC is mainly **amorphous**. **BUT**, the C–Cl bonds are **polarised**, so there are **dipole-dipole** interactions between the chains. This makes poly(chloroethene) **hard** and **rigid**. To make PVC **more flexible**, manufacturers add things called **plasticisers**.

Poly(tetrafluoroethene) or PTFE

PTFE is **strong** and has a **high melting point**. This is because fluorine atoms have loads of **electrons** (compared to hydrogen), making the **van der Waals forces** pretty strong. Also, the chains **pack closely** together. PTFE is **very unreactive** and **'non-stick'** because the C–F bond is strong and the relatively big fluorine atoms **protect** the carbon chain from chemical attack.

$-\!(CF_2{-}CF_2)\!-_n$

Polymers

This page is just for OCR Salters (except the questions).

Hydrogen Bonding Means Some Polymers **Dissolve in Water**

Some polymers form **hydrogen bonds**, so they **dissolve in water**.

- **Liquid washing detergent** is sold sealed in **sachets** made from **soluble polyvinyl alcohol** (PVA — poly(ethanol)). The sachets just **dissolve** in the wash. This saves people from the terrible hassle of unscrewing the lid of a bottle. Hmmm...
- PVA is also put to good use as **soluble laundry bags** in **hospitals**. This reduces the **infection risks** from dirty laundry.

OH OH OH OH OH

poly(ethanol)

Cross-Linking Affects how Polymers Behave when they're **Heated**

Thermoplastic polymers, like poly(ethene), don't have cross-linking between chains.
It's only **weak intermolecular forces** that hold the chains together.
These forces are really easy to overcome, so it's dead easy to **melt** the plastic.
When it **cools**, the thermoplastic hardens into a new shape.
You can melt these plastics and **remould** them as many times as you like.

Thermosetting polymers, like bakelite, have **covalent cross-links**.
These hold the chains together in a **3D giant covalent structure**.
The polymer doesn't soften when it's heated — but too much heat makes it **burn**.
Thermosetting polymers are the **tough guys** of the plastic world.
They're **strong**, **hard**, **rigid** and **insoluble**.

Practice Questions

Q1 What kind of reaction is addition polymerisation?

Q2 What is a copolymer?

Q3 What is stereoregularity?

Q4 What is the difference between thermoplastic and thermosetting polymers?

Exam Question

Q1 Alkenes can form addition polymers and the properties of the polymers can be explained by looking at their molecular structures.

a) Chloroethene CH_2=CHCl forms the polymer poly(chloroethene), commonly known as PVC.

i) Write an equation for the polymerisation of chloroethene, including a full structural formula showing the repeating unit in poly(chloroethene). [2 marks]

ii) Poly(chloroethene) is hard and rigid. This is surprising considering the random orientation of the chlorine atoms on the chain. Explain these observations. [4 marks]

b) Tetrafluoroethene CF_2=CF_2 forms a polymer which is fairly crystalline and inert.

i) What is meant by the term 'crystalline'? [1 mark]

ii) How does increased crystallinity affect polymer properties? [2 marks]

iii) Why is PTFE so unreactive? [1 mark]

iv) Suggest a possible use for PTFE. [1 mark]

Barbie plastic surgery — gas mark 4, 20 minutes...

You can have hours of fun melting stuff — chocolate, cheese, CDs, candles, crayons, laundry baskets, snails. You're only limited by your imagination. The potential for setting stuff on fire is a bit of a problem and some things'll give off nasty fumes. So maybe you'd better find yourself a different pastime instead. Like learning AS Chemistry. That'll keep you busy.

Polymers

Miss these two pages out if you're doing Edexcel Nuffield or AQA.
You might spend years trying to discover something exciting — or you might get lucky and it'll bite you on the bum.

Poly(ethene) was Discovered Accidently

Poly(ethene) was discovered by **accident**.
Two chaps were trying to make a ketone from benzaldehyde and ethene, as you do. Their apparatus **leaked**, so they had to add **extra ethene**. **Oxygen** got in through the leak, too. They were amazed to find a **white waxy solid — poly(ethene)**.

There are Two Different Kinds of Poly(ethene)

The two types of poly(ethene) are **low-density poly(ethene) (LDPE)** and **high-density poly(ethene) (HDPE)**.

1) The polymer chains in **LDPE** have **lots of branches**, so they **can't pack together closely**.
2) In **HDPE**, the polymer chains have hardly any branching, so the chains **line up** and **pack together closely**. And surprise, surprise... they're more dense.

LDPE and HDPE are **manufactured differently**. They've got **different properties** and **uses**, too.

Substance	How it's made	Properties	Used to Make
Low Density Poly(ethene)	Heat ethene to 170 °C at 1400 atm. Add organic peroxide to start off this free-radical reaction	• Flexible • Strong • Deformed by heat	• Bags • Squeezy bottles
High Density Poly(ethene)	Heat ethene to 70 °C at 2 atm. Use a Ziegler-Natta catalyst (based on titanium(IV) chloride and triethyl aluminium)	• Rigid • Strong • Easy to mould • Not deformed by heat	• Car petrol tanks • Water pipes • Hospital equipment that needs sterilising (like bedpans)

Ziegler-Natta Catalysts produce Stereoregular Isomers

Ziegler-Natta catalysts are based on **titanium(IV) chloride** and **triethyl aluminium** (don't lose sleep over what this means). They're used to make polymers with **regular structures**.

There are two forms of **poly(propene)**:
Isotactic poly(propene) — the methyl groups are all pointing the **same way** along the polymer chain.

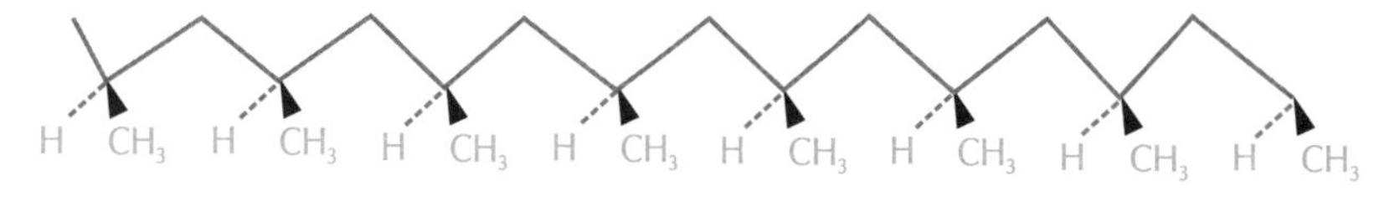

Isotactic poly(propene) has a crystalline structure. It's strong and rigid and is used to make **fibres for carpets and ropes**.

Atactic — the methyl groups are **randomly** oriented along the chain.

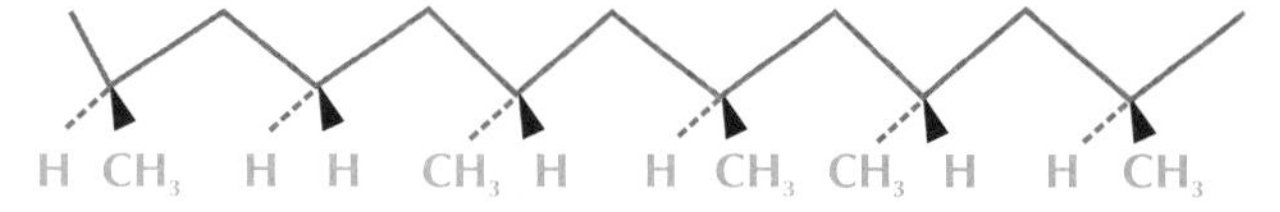

Atactic poly(propene) has an amorphous structure.
It's soft and flexible and used in **roofing materials**.

If you use **different conditions** and **catalysts**, you can control **how much** of each type of poly(propene) is made.

Polymers have Pretty Amazing Properties

This bit's just for OCR Salters — but it's very cool.

1) **Trans-poly(ethyne)** conducts electricity if it's 'doped' with iodine. Conducting polymers are handy as antistatics in **loudspeakers**.

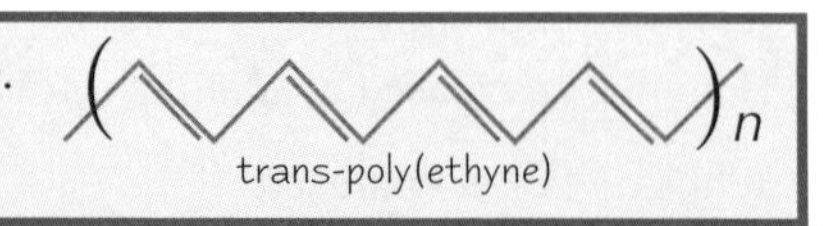

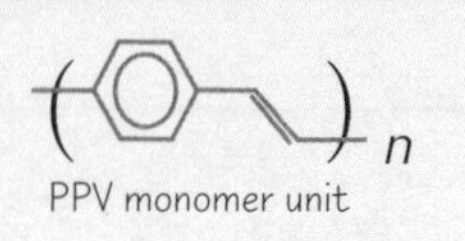

2) If you apply a **voltage** to a thin film of a PPV-based polymer, believe it or not, **coloured light** is emitted. A scientist discovered this accidentally. I bet he thought he'd had one whisky too many. In the future, PPV polymers might be made into cool **2 mm thick computer screens**.

Polymers

Skip this page if you're doing Edexcel Nuffield, AQA or OCR Salters (except for the questions).

It's Hard to **Dispose** of Polymers **Safely**

1) The problem with a lot of polymers is they're **non-biodegradable**, which means bacteria and fungi can't break them down. So these polymers all end up in landfill sites, which are a big eyesore.
2) Most polymers give off **toxic fumes** when they burn, which isn't exactly ideal. It also takes a lot of **energy** to burn waste polymers.

There are **Safer Ways** of to Get Rid of Them

1) Some polymers get **recycled**. This works best for **thermoplastics** — they can be heated and moulded into new products. The main problem with recycling is that the plastics need sorting out before they can be used. It's really expensive to do this.
2) Some **toxic waste products** can be **removed** as the polymers are burned. E.g. when PVC burns it makes hydrogen chloride gas, amongst other things. But the gas can be neutralised before it escapes to the atmosphere.
3) Polymers can be **burned for energy production**. Specially designed incinerators are used which trap toxic gases and smoke.
4) Another thing you can do is break waste polymers into smaller molecules by **cracking**. Then you can use the small molecules as raw materials for making new polymers or other chemicals.

Halogen Compounds are Also Pretty hard to Dispose of Safely

Some polymers and pesticides contain **halogen atoms**. Carbon-halogen bonds are **very strong**, so compounds that contain them don't easily decompose — they'll sit around for years.

This is can cause problems — e.g. organohalogen pesticides and herbicides accumulate on **crops** or in the **soil**. They dissolve in the fat of insects that accidentally eat them. Birds eat the insects, and the organohalogens get **concentrated** in their fatty tissues. This is **bioaccumulation** — the pesticides build up in the food chain.

Practice Questions

Q1 Name two types of polymer that scientists discovered accidentally.

Q2 What is the difference between isotactic and atactic poly(propene)?

Q3 Why is it a bad idea to dispose of polymers by burning them?

Q4 Write down four relatively safe ways of disposing of waste polymers.

Q5 Describe two problems caused by organic halogen compounds.

Exam Question

Q1 There are two types of poly(ethene), low-density poly(ethene) (LDPE) and high-density poly(ethene) (HDPE).

a) Low-density poly(ethene) and high-density poly(ethene) have different physical properties. Describe some of these differences and give reasons for them in terms of their structure and bonding. [4 marks]

b) Suggest two uses for low-density poly(ethene) and two uses for high-density poly(ethene). [4 marks]

c) Describe the differences in the conditions required for the manufacture of low-density poly(ethene) and high-density poly(ethene). [6 marks]

Ziegler-Natta...This is Zion control...you have permission to land...

There's some funny names in this Organic Chemistry, in't there? No offence to Mr Ziegler or Mr Natta, but Ziegler-Natta does sound like a ship from The Matrix. I reckon most Chemists only got into it so they could invent stupid names for things... and they've all read too much sci-fi. Or maybe sci-fi writers just know a lot of Chemistry... actually, maybe I'm just talking complete rubbish...

Epoxyethane

These two pages are just for AQA.
This stuff'll do more than get your nail varnish off.

Epoxyethane is an Important Intermediate

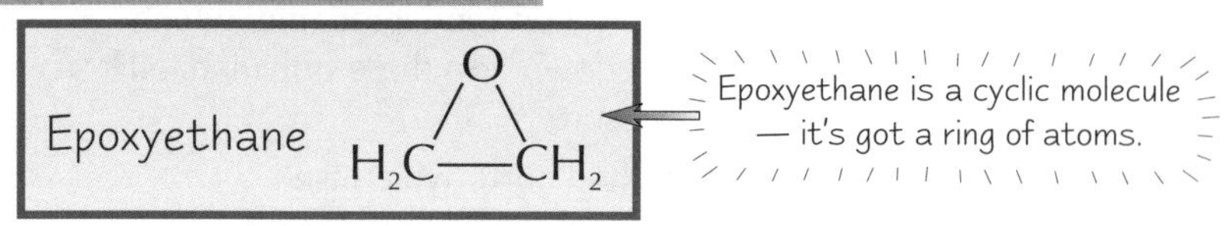

1) About **25%** of the **ethene** made by **cracking crude oil** is used to make **epoxyethane**. So, it's really **important stuff**.
2) Epoxyethane's called an **intermediate** because it can be changed in loads of **different ways** to make lots of **useful products**. It's used to make **antifreeze**, **polyesters**, **solvents**, **plasticisers** and **detergents**.

Epoxyethane is made from Ethene and Oxygen

You make **epoxyethane** by reacting **ethene** with **oxygen** (or air). You need a **silver catalyst** too.

$$2\ H_2C{=}CH_2 + O_2 \xrightarrow[\text{250-400 °C, 10-30 atm}]{Ag} 2\ H_2C{-}CH_2\ (\text{with O bridging, ring})$$

1) The **silver** catalyst is a **heterogeneous catalyst**. It's **finely divided** to make the surface area bigger. (See pages 72-73.)
2) You have to **purify** the epoxyethane by **fractional distillation**.

Epoxyethane is an Unstable Molecule

The **ring** in epoxyethane is **very strained**. This is because the **bond angles** are so **tight** — the structure is just **bursting** to open up — this makes it **very reactive**.
Because it's so reactive, you have to be **really careful** with it.

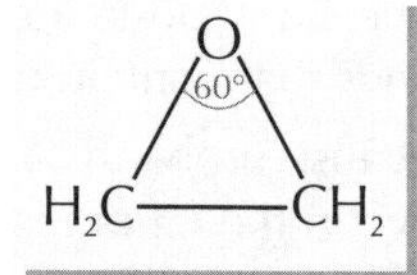

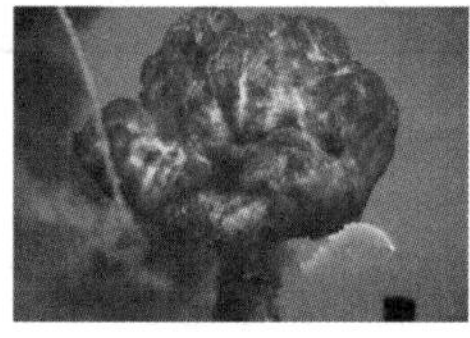
Epoxyethane by night

1) Epoxyethane has a low **boiling point** of **13 °C**. It's **flammable and explosive** too. You have to be careful **heat** doesn't build up and cause an **explosion**.
2) Epoxyethane **polymerises easily** and this reaction is **exothermic**. This gives out **enough heat** to cause an explosion.
3) Epoxyethane is **toxic**. It irritates your **lungs** and damages your **nervous system**. It also causes **skin blisters** and burns. It's basically **nasty stuff**.

Epoxyethane is Used to Make Antifreeze

The **oxygen atom** in epoxyethane is pretty **electronegative**, so the molecule's **polarised**.
The **δ+** end of the molecule is attacked by **nucleophiles**, like water.
Nucleophiles have **too many electrons** — so they're attracted to places which are **short of electrons**.

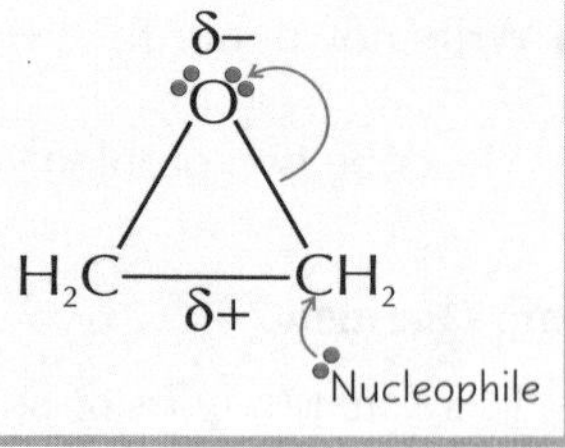

Hydrolysis of epoxyethane gives **ethane-1,2-diol** as the product.

$$H_2C{-}CH_2\ (\text{O ring}) + H_2O \xrightarrow[\text{60 °C, } H_2SO_4]{\text{excess } H_2O} H_2C(OH){-}CH_2(OH)$$

The solution has to be concentrated and then purified by fractional distillation.

Ethane-1,2-diol has **two important uses**.

- It's **antifreeze**. It's got a nice **low melting point** of -12 °C. It also **mixes** really well with water because the two **-OH** groups form **hydrogen bonds** with the water molecules (see page 31). So, it **lowers the freezing point** of water loads.
- Ethane-1,2-diol is used to make **polyesters**.

Epoxyethane

Epoxyethane Reacts with *Alcohols* too

1) You can react epoxyethane with **alcohols**. The reaction mechanism's almost the same as the **hydrolysis** reaction.
2) The main products are **ethers of ethane-1,2-diol**. These are used as **solvents** to make paints and printing inks. Here's the reaction of **epoxyethane** with **ethanol** —

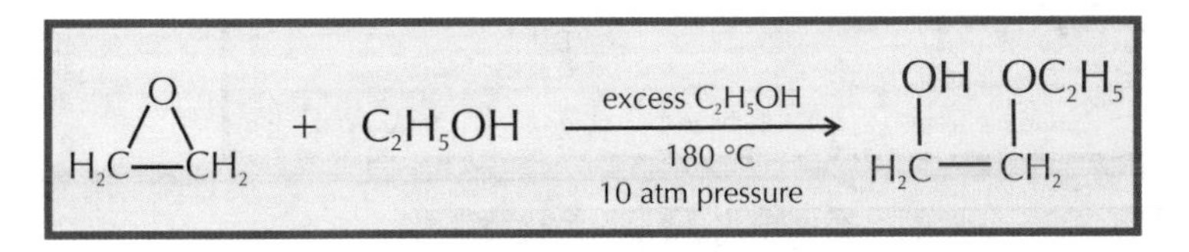

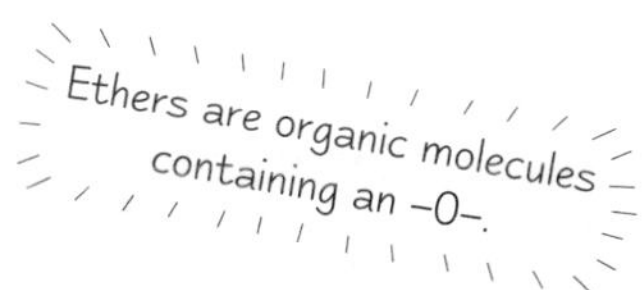

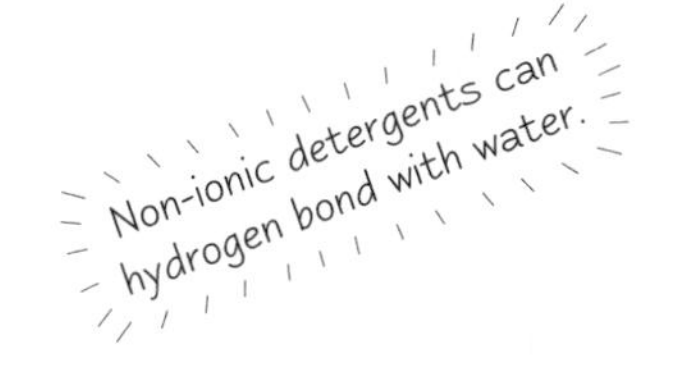

Non-ionic detergents can hydrogen bond with water.

3) If you use **different proportions** of epoxyethane in the reaction mixture, you can make more complex molecules.
4) These products are used in **brake fluids**, as **plasticisers** and as **non-ionic detergents**.

Practice Questions

Q1 What is epoxyethane made from?

Q2 Name four things made from epoxyethane.

Q3 How is the epoxyethane purified?

Q4 Why does epoxyethane react with nucleophiles?

Q5 What is formed when epoxyethane reacts with an alcohol?

Q6 What are ethers?

Exam Question

Q1 Epoxyethane is a useful intermediate in organic synthesis.

a) i) Write an equation for the formation of epoxyethane from ethene, showing clearly the structure of the product. [2 marks]

ii) State the catalyst for the reaction. [1 mark]

iii) Give two different hazards associated with the manufacture of epoxyethane. [2 marks]

iv) Why is epoxyethane such a reactive molecule? [1 mark]

b) Epoxyethane will react with water in the presence of an acid catalyst.

i) Draw and name the product formed by a 1:1 reaction of epoxyethane and water. [2 marks]

ii) Give one major use for this product. [1 mark]

Epoxyethane — it sounds a bit like a spot removal cream to me...

Pretty scary stuff this epoxyethane. A little bit of heat and BOOM, your eyebrows are gone. Or even worse, your head. You might be asked about ANY of this stuff, so make sure you know all the details, including the equations and conditions. Test yourself by doing the questions. If you make a total hash of them, have another go. Keep at them till you're spot on.

Haloalkanes

Don't worry if you see haloalkanes called halogenoalkanes. It's a government conspiracy to confuse you.

Haloalkanes are Alkanes with Halogen Atoms

A **haloalkane** is an alkane with at least one **halogen atom** in place of a hydrogen atom.

E.g.

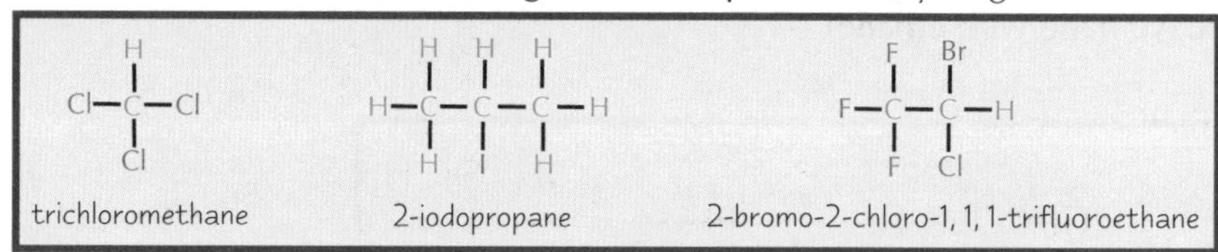

Haloalkanes are special amongst alkanes...

Haloalkanes can be Primary, Secondary or Tertiary

Haloalkanes with just **one halogen atom** can be **primary**, **secondary** or **tertiary** haloalkanes.

On the **carbon** with the **halogen** attached:

1) A **primary** haloalkane has **two hydrogen atoms** and just **one alkyl group**.
2) A **secondary** haloalkane has **just one hydrogen atom** and **two alkyl groups**.
3) A **tertiary** haloalkane has **no hydrogen atoms** and **three alkyl groups**.

X = halogen
R = alkyl group

primary	secondary	tertiary
$X-CH_2-R_1$	$X-CH(R_1)(R_2)$	$X-C(R_1)(R_2)(R_3)$
1 alkyl group	2 alkyl groups	3 alkyl groups

This is just the same as for alcohols.

Haloalkanes can be Made from Alcohols

1) It's dead easy to replace the hydroxyl (–OH) group in a **tertiary alcohol** with a **halogen**. It's harder with **secondary** and **primary** alcohols though.

To make **2-chloro-2-methylpropane** (a tertiary haloalkane) you just need to shake **2-methylpropan-2-ol** (a tertiary alcohol) with **concentrated hydrochloric acid** at room temperature.

$$CH_3-C(OH)(CH_3)-CH_3 + HCl \longrightarrow CH_3-C(Cl)(CH_3)-CH_3 + H_2O$$

2-methylpropan-2-ol → 2-chloro-2-methylpropane

2) Making **bromoethane** (a primary haloalkane) isn't quite so easy. You need to use **ethanol** and a mixture of **sodium bromide** and **concentrated sulphuric acid**. You heat the mixture gently in distillation apparatus. (See page 108 for the details.)
3) Haloalkanes are also made by **electrophilic addition reactions** between **alkenes** and **halogens** or **hydrogen halides** (see page 94).

Bigger Haloalkanes have Higher Boiling Points

1) Haloalkanes are **polarised molecules** — so their melting and boiling points are **higher** than alkanes of the same length. This is because the δ+ and δ– charges on nearby molecules attract each other.
2) Most shortish haloalkanes are **liquids** or **gases** at room temperature. Their **boiling points** depend on **how strong** the **intermolecular forces** are.

1) **Longer chain** haloalkanes have **higher boiling points** than shorter chain molecules. This is because there's greater **van der Waals forces** between longer chains. So, 1-chlorobutane has a higher boiling point than chloroethane.
2) Haloalkanes with **larger halogen atoms** have higher boiling points. So, chloromethane has a higher boiling point than fluoromethane. This is due to increased **van der Waals forces** again.
3) Haloalkanes with **more halogen atoms** have higher boiling points too. So, dibromomethane has a higher boiling point than bromomethane. This is also because of greater **van der Waals forces**.

Haloalkanes

AQA people — you can skip this page (except for the questions).

CFCs are Haloalkanes

1) **Chlorofluorocarbons** (**CFCs**) are well-known haloalkanes. They used to be used lots in **fridges**, **aerosol cans** and **dry cleaning**. They're very **stable**, **non-flammable** and **non-toxic** — wow. They sound great.

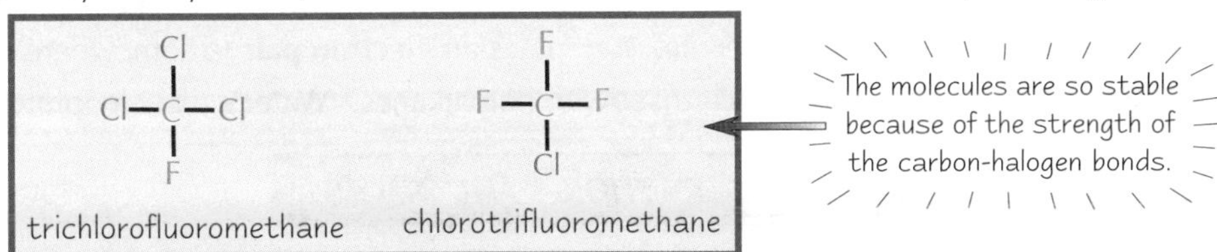

2) The problem is, CFCs destroy the **ozone layer** (see page 72). **Ultraviolet radiation** from the Sun has enough energy to break **C–Cl** (and **C–Br**) bonds. This makes **free radicals** which attack **ozone** molecules.
3) CFCs have now been **banned**. Scientists are still searching for stuff to use **instead**. They've made a bit of progress —
   - **Hydrochlorofluorocarbons** (HCFCs) are **less damaging** to ozone. They're **less stable** and decompose **lower** in the atmosphere. But they're not great — they still contain **chlorine**.
   - **Hydrofluorocarbons** (HFCs) are the best thing so far. HFCs are broken down **lower** in the atmosphere.
   - **Alkanes** are being used in aerosol sprays. They're **cheap**, but the problem is, they're **flammable**.

   None of these are the ideal solution. They all add to the **greenhouse effect** (see page 90).

Haloalkanes have Other Uses too

1) Haloalkanes are important **intermediates** for making other chemicals. The **halogen atom** can be **replaced** with other things to give useful compounds.
2) If the haloalkane contains **bromine** as well as **fluorine** and **chlorine**, it's called a **halon**. Halons are very **unreactive** and **heavier** than air. This makes them good in **fire extinguishers**. They form an **inert** blanket over the fire, cutting off the **oxygen**.

Practice Questions

Q1 What is a haloalkane?

Q2 What is a tertiary haloalkane?

Q3 What factors influence the boiling points of haloalkanes?

Q4 What are halons and what are they used for?

Exam Question

Q1 Up until very recently, CFCs were used for a wide variety of purposes.
However, now chemists are involved in developing alternative chemicals to use.

a) What does CFC stand for? [1 mark]

b) Give two important properties of CFCs. [2 marks]

c) Give one use for CFCs. [1 mark]

d) Explain briefly what environmental problem the use of CFCs has caused. [4 marks]

e) Give an example of an alternative chemical to CFCs and state an advantage and a disadvantage for its use. [3 marks]

Hydrochlorofluorocarbon — yeah, like that's a real word...

I don't reckon there's anything too complicated about this stuff. Just learn the facts and you'll be fine. The stuff about CFCs and the ozone layer is important. The Examiners think they'll save the world if they set you questions on the environment. There's bags of details about how the ozone layer's being destroyed on page 72. So read it.

Haloalkanes

*If you haven't had enough of haloakanes yet, there's more. If you **have** had enough — there's still more.*

The **Carbon–Halogen Bond** in Haloalkanes is **Polar**

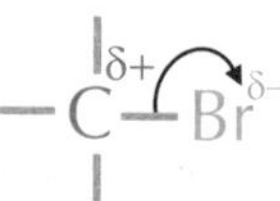

1) Halogens are much more **electronegative** than carbon. So, the **carbon–halogen bond** is **polar**.
2) The **δ+ carbon** doesn't have enough electrons. This means it can be attacked by a **nucleophile**. A nucleophile's an **electron-rich** ion or molecule. It donates an **electron pair** to somewhere without enough electrons.
3) **OH^-**, **CN^-** and **NH_3** are all **nucleophiles** which react with haloalkanes. **Water's** a nucleophile too, but it reacts slowly.

Haloalkanes can be **Hydrolysed** to make **Alcohols**

Hydrolysis is when water breaks bonds.

Bromoethane can be **hydrolysed** to **ethanol**. You have to use **warm aqueous sodium** or **potassium hydroxide** or it won't work.

$$CH_3CH_2Br + OH \xrightarrow[\text{reflux}]{OH^- / H_2O} C_2H_5OH + Br^-$$

If you don't know what 'reflux' is check out the bottom of page 110.

Here's what happens. It's a nice simple **one-step mechanism**.

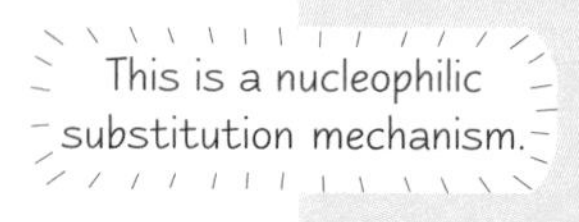

$$H{-}\overset{H}{\underset{H}{C}}{-}\overset{H}{\underset{H}{C^{\delta+}}}{-}Br^{\delta-} \;\; :OH^- \longrightarrow H{-}\overset{H}{\underset{H}{C}}{-}\overset{H}{\underset{H}{C}}{-}OH + :Br^-$$

1) OH- is the **nucleophile** which provides a **pair of electrons** for the **$C^{\delta+}$**.
2) The C-Br bond breaks **heterolytically** — **both** electrons from the bond are taken by **Br^-**.
3) **Br^-** falls off as **OH^-** bonds to the carbon.

If you don't know what halogen was in your haloalkane, now's a good time to find out.
Just add **acidified silver nitrate** and you'll get a **silver halide precipitate**.
If it's **white**, it's silver chloride, if it's **cream** it's silver bromide and if it's **yellow** it's silver iodide (see p57).

Iodoalkanes are **Hydrolysed** the **Fastest**

1) **Weaker** carbon-halogen bonds **break** more easily — so, they react **faster**.
2) **Iodoalkanes** have the **weakest bonds**, so they hydrolyse the **fastest**.
3) **Fluoroalkanes** have the **strongest bonds**, so they're the **slowest** at hydrolysing.

bond	bond enthalpy kJ mol⁻¹
C–F	467
C–Cl	346
C–Br	290
C–I	228

Faster hydrolysis as bond enthalpy decreases (the bonds are getting weaker).

Haloalkanes React With **Ammonia** to Form **Amines**

Ethanolic ammonia is just ammonia dissolved in ethanol.

If you **warm** a haloalkane with excess **ethanolic** ammonia, the **ammonia** swaps places with the **halogen** — yes, it's another one of those **nucleophilic substitution reactions**.

$$CH_3{-}\overset{H}{\underset{H}{C}}{-}Br + NH_3 \xrightarrow[\text{ethanol}]{\text{reflux}} CH_3{-}\overset{H}{\underset{H}{C}}{-}NH_2 + HBr$$

Hydrogen bromide then reacts with excess ammonia to give ammonium bromide.

$$NH_3 + HBr \rightarrow NH_4Br$$

You can use **Haloalkanes** to form **Nitriles**

This bit's just for Edexcel and AQA.

Nitriles have –C≡N groups.

If you **warm** a haloalkane with **ethanolic potassium cyanide** you get a **nitrile**.
It's yet another **nucleophilic substitution reaction** — the **cyanide ion**, CN^-, is the **nucleophile**.

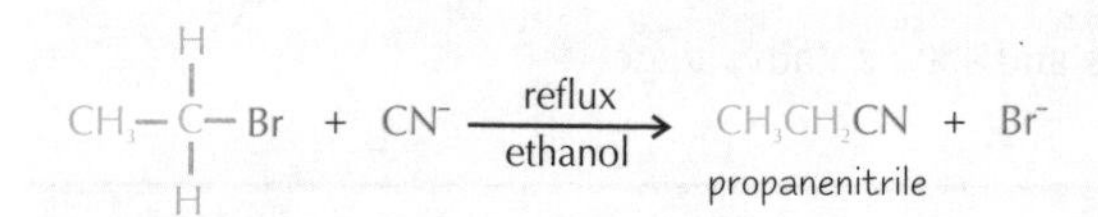

The propanenitrile's got one extra carbon atom. This is a good way to make the carbon chain longer.

You can **hydrolyse** the **nitrile** with hot acid to form a **carboxylic acid**.

Carboxylic acids have –COOH groups.

$$CH_3CH_2CN + 2H_2O \xrightarrow{\text{acid hydrolysis}} CH_3CH_2COOH + NH_3$$

Haloalkanes

Haloalkanes also Undergo Elimination Reactions

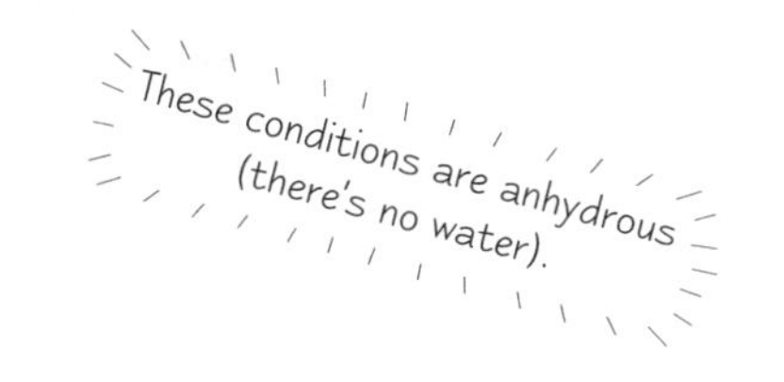

1) If you use warm alkali **dissolved in ethanol** instead, you get an **alkene**. The mixture must be **heated under reflux** or volatile stuff will be lost.

$$CH_3CH_2Br + KOH \xrightarrow[\text{reflux}]{OH^- / \text{ethanol}} CH_2{=}CH_2 + H_2O + KBr$$

2) This is an **elimination reaction**. Here's how it works.

OH^- acts as a base and takes a proton, H^+, from the carbon on the left. This makes water. The left carbon now has a spare electron, so it forms a double bond with the other carbon. To form the double bond, the right carbon has to let go of the Br, which drops off as a Br^- ion.

The Type of Reaction Depends on the Conditions

Not OCR Salters.

You can control what **type of reaction** happens by **changing the conditions**.

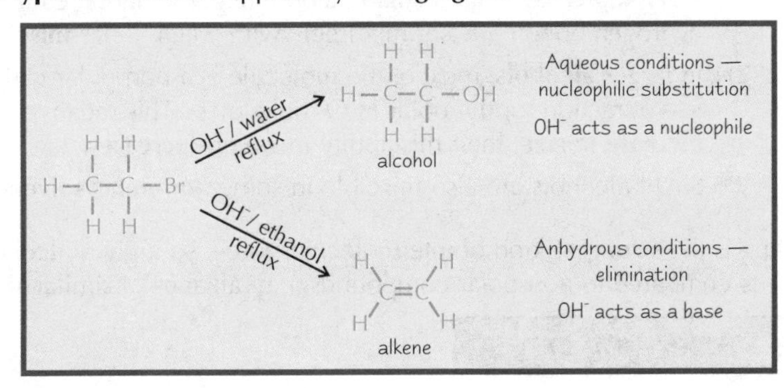

Practice Questions

Q1 What is a nucleophile?

Q2 Why is the carbon-halogen bond polar?

Q3 Why does iodoethane react faster than chloro- or bromoethane with warm, aqueous sodium hydroxide?

Exam Question

Q1 Some reactions of 2-bromopropane, $CH_3CHBrCH_3$, are shown below.

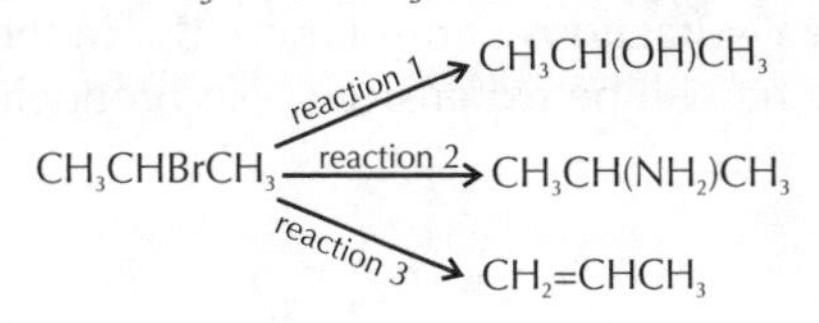

a) For each reaction, name the reagent and solvent used. [6 marks]

b) Under the same conditions, 2-iodopropane was used in reaction 1 in place of 2-bromopropane. What difference (if any) would you expect in the rate of the reaction? Explain your answer. [2 marks]

If you don't learn this — you will be eliminated. Resistance is nitrile...

Polar bonds get in just about every area of Chemistry. If you still think they're something to do with either bears or mints, you need to flick back to Section 3 and have a good read of pages 28 and 29. Make sure you learn the stuff about elimination and substitution reactions. It's always coming up in exams. Ruin the examiner's day and get it right.

Alcohols

Alcohol — evil stuff, it is. I could start preaching, but I won't, because this page is enough to put you off alcohol for life...

Alcohols are **Primary**, **Secondary** or **Tertiary**

1) The alcohol homologous series has the **general formula $C_nH_{2n+1}OH$**.
2) An alcohol is **primary**, **secondary** or **tertiary**, depending on which carbon atom the hydroxyl group **–OH** is bonded to...

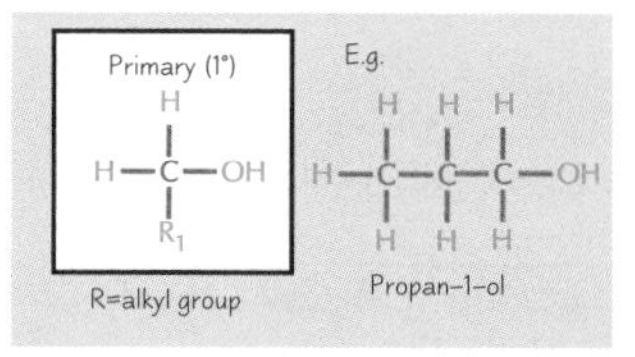

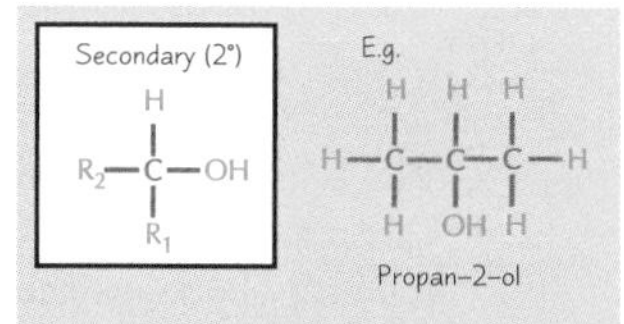

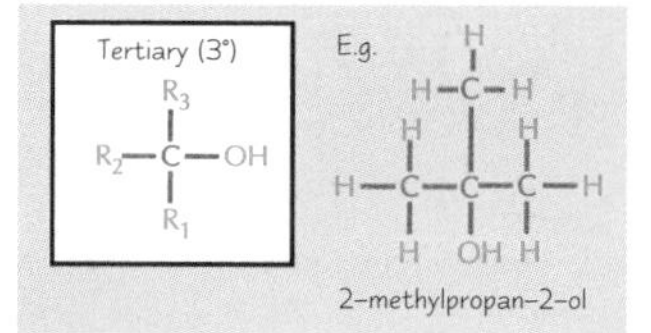

The Hydroxyl Group –OH can form **Hydrogen Bonds**

The **polar** –OH group on alcohols helps them to form **hydrogen bonds** (see p31), which gives them certain properties...

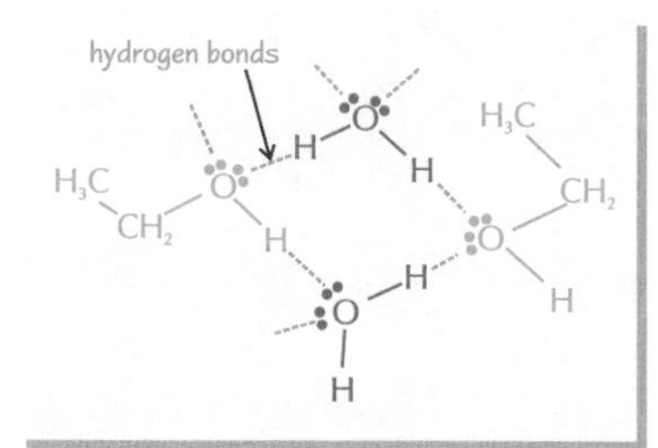

1) When you mix an alcohol with water, hydrogen bonds form between the **–OH** and **H_2O**. If it's a **small** alcohol (e.g. methanol, ethanol or propan-1-ol), hydrogen bonding lets it mix freely with water — it's **miscible** with water.
2) In **larger alcohols**, most of the molecule is a non-polar carbon chain, so there's less attraction for the polar H_2O molecules. This means that as alcohols **increase in size**, their miscibility in water **decreases.**
3) Small alcohols are also miscible in some **non-polar solvents** like cyclohexane.
4) Hydrogen bonding is the **strongest** kind of intermolecular force, so it gives alcohols **high boiling points** compared to non-polar compounds, e.g. alkanes of similar sizes.

Alcohols Have a **Wide Variety** of Uses

1) **Ethanol** is the basic alcohol found in **alcoholic drinks**. (But don't ever try drinking it – it'll leave you deader than a really dead thing.)
2) **Methylated spirits** is an important **solvent**. It's basically ethanol, with some toxic methanol and purple dye added to make it **undrinkable** and tax-exempt (sneaky). Ethanol will dissolve **polar**, **non-polar** and some **ionic compounds**.
3) Ethanol is also being used increasingly as a **fuel**, particularly in countries with few oil reserves. E.g. in Brazil, **sugars** from sugar cane are **fermented** to produce alcohol, which is used instead of petrol.
4) **Unleaded petrol** contains 5% methanol and 15% MTBE (an ether made using methanol) to improve combustion.
5) Methanol is important as a **feedstock** (starting point) for manufacturing organic chemicals, e.g. plastics and dyes.

Ethanol can be Produced Industrially by **Fermentation**

Not OCR Salters, Edexcel or Edexcel Nuffield.

At the moment most industrial ethanol is produced by **steam hydration of ethene** with a **phosphoric acid catalyst** (see page 95). The ethene comes from cracking heavy fractions of crude oil. But in the future, when crude oil supplies start **running out**, petrochemicals like ethene will be expensive — so producing ethanol by **fermentation** will become much more important...

Industrial Production of Ethanol by Fermentation

$$\underset{\text{glucose}}{C_6H_{12}O_{6(aq)}} \xrightarrow[\text{yeast}]{\text{warm}} 2C_2H_5OH_{(aq)} + 2CO_{2(g)}$$

1) Fermentation is an **exothermic** process, carried out by **yeast** in **anaerobic conditions** (without oxygen).
2) Yeast produces an **enzyme** which converts sugars, such as glucose, into **ethanol** and **carbon dioxide**.
3) The enzyme works at an **optimum** (ideal) temperature of **30-40 °C**. If it's too cold, the reaction is **slow** — if it's too hot, the enzyme is **denatured** (damaged).
4) When the solution reaches about **15% ethanol**, the yeast dies. **Fractional distillation** is used to increase the concentration of ethanol.
5) Fermentation is **low-tech** — it uses cheap equipment and **renewable resources**. The ethanol produced by this method has to be **purified** though.

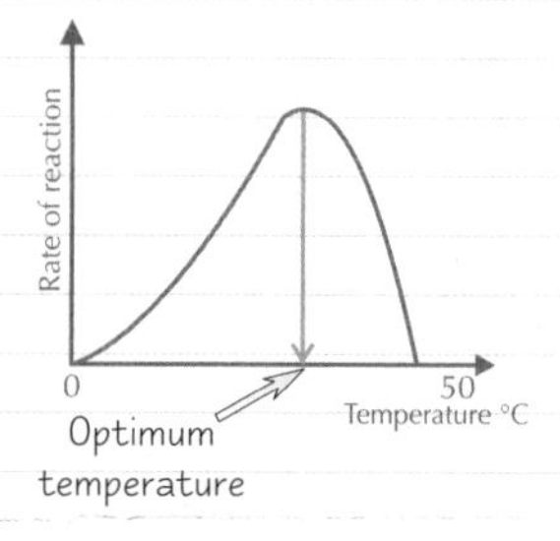

Alcohols

Phenols are Benzene Rings with –OH Groups Attached

This page is just for OCR Salters (except for the questions).

Here's a few examples of **phenols** —

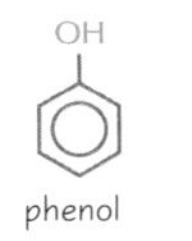

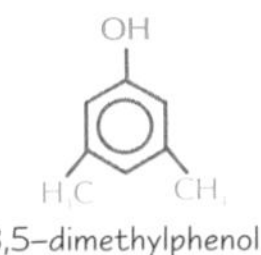

See page 92 for more on benzene.

Testing for Phenols:
Mix the unknown liquid with neutral iron(III) chloride solution.
Phenols will produce a **purple** colour.

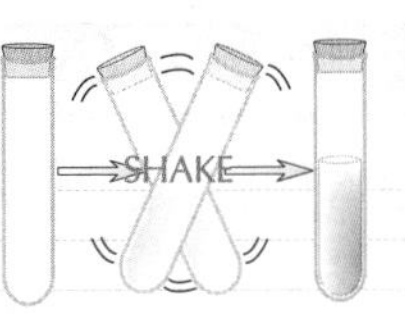

Alcohols and Phenols are Weakly Acidic

1) The polarised O-H bond in alcohols and phenols **dissociates** in water, releasing a **proton H^+**.
2) Just to get some kind of scale on things... alcohols are **weaker** acids than phenols, which are **weaker** acids than **carboxylic acids**:

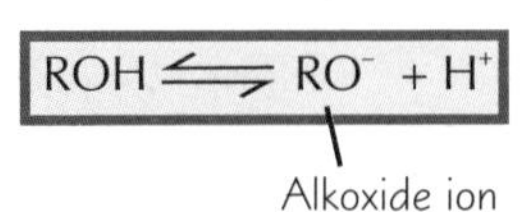

The more **stable** the ion formed, the **stronger** the acid...

Greater stability and stronger acids

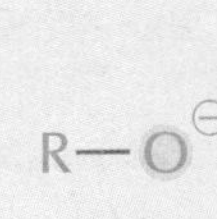

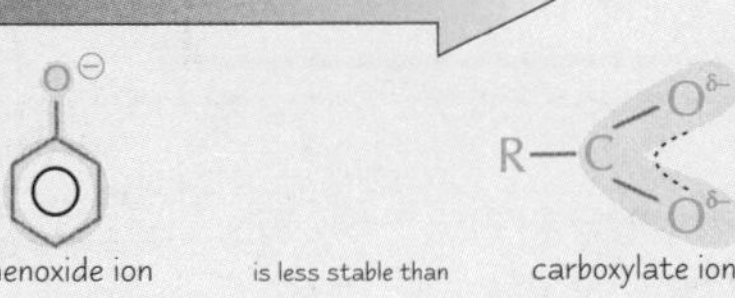

alkoxide ion — is less stable than — phenoxide ion — is less stable than — carboxylate ion

Alkoxide ions don't have double bonds, so there's no delocalisation. The negative charge is concentrated on oxygen, making it very attractive to H^+ and very unstable.

Phenoxide ions have a delocalised electron ring, overlapped by the oxygen's π orbital. The negative charge is spread over the ring, but mostly it's centered on the single oxygen, so the ion is fairly attractive to H^+ and only moderately stable.

Carboxylate ions have a -COO- functional group. The π bond electron density in the 'double bond' is delocalised over both C–O bonds, mostly near the electronegative oxygens. Because the negative charge is shared between the oxygens, it's less attractive to H^+ ions and is more stable.

Practice Questions

Q1 What is the general formula for an alcohol?

Q2 How do the boiling points of alcohols compare with the boiling points of similarly sized alkanes?

Q3 Which is a stronger acid, an alcohol or a phenol?

Exam Questions

Q1 Butanol C_4H_9OH has three chain and positional isomers.
Name each isomer and class it as primary, secondary or tertiary.

a)
```
   H  H  H  H
   |  |  |  |
H–C–C–C–C–OH
   |  |  |  |
   H  H  H  H
```

b)
```
      H
    H-C-H
  H   |   H
  |   |   |
H-C - C - C - H
  |   |   |
  H  OH   H
```

c)
```
   H  H  H  H
   |  |  |  |
H–C–C–C–C–H
   |  |  |  |
   H  H OH  H
```

[6 marks]

Q2 Ethanol is a useful alcohol.

a) State whether ethanol is a primary, secondary or tertiary alcohol, and explain why. [2 marks]

b) Industrially, ethanol can be produced by fermentation of glucose, $C_6H_{12}O_6$.

i) Write a balanced equation for this reaction. [1 mark]

ii) State the optimum conditions for fermentation. [3 marks]

c) At present most ethanol is produced by the acid-catalysed hydration of ethene.
Why is this? Why might this change in the future? [3 marks]

d) Ethanol is an important solvent. Explain why this is, with reference to the structure and intermolecular forces in ethanol. [4 marks]

Euuurghh, what a page... I think I need a drink...

Not much to learn here —a few basic definitions, some fiddly explanations of properties in terms of bonding, 4 or 5 uses, an industrial process, a couple more definitions, a lab test, another bonding explanation... Like I said, not much here at all. Think I'm going to faint. *[THWACK]*

Reactions of Alcohols

Another page about alcohols — jam-packed tighter than 25 fully grown elephants in a tube of Smarties. You wouldn't have it any other way...

–OH can be Swapped for a Halogen to make a Haloalkane

Not AQA.

Ethanol reacts with HBr in a **nucleophilic substitution** reaction.
The **–OH** group is replaced with **–Br** and you end up with bromoethane...

$$NaBr_{(s)} + H_2SO_{4(l)} \rightarrow NaHSO_{4(s)} + HBr_{(g)}$$
$$HBr_{(g)} + C_2H_5OH_{(l)} \rightarrow C_2H_5Br_{(l)} + H_2O_{(l)}$$

The HBr gas is made on the spot by heating conc. H_2SO_4 with solid NaBr.

Br^- is the electron-heavy nucleophile. It's attracted towards the polarised carbon atom in the $C^{\delta+}$–$O^{\delta-}$ bond, and the –OH snaps off.

Here's a couple of other ways of making haloalkanes:

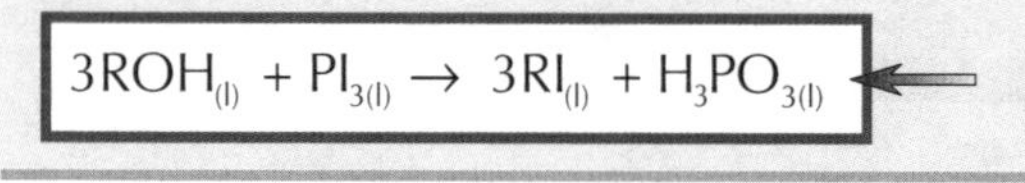

$$3ROH_{(l)} + PI_{3(l)} \rightarrow 3RI_{(l)} + H_3PO_{3(l)}$$

Iodoalkanes can be made using red phosphorus and iodine to generate phosphorus(III) iodide (PI_3).

Chloroalkanes can be made by using phosphorus(V) chloride.

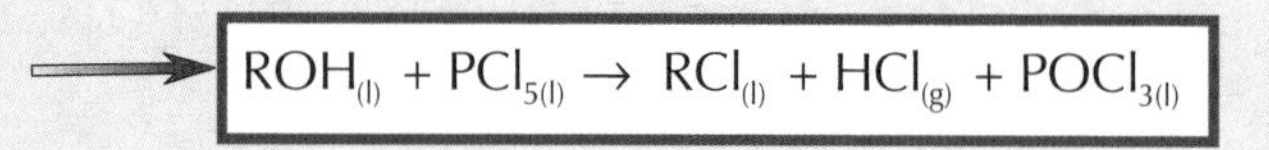

$$ROH_{(l)} + PCl_{5(l)} \rightarrow RCl_{(l)} + HCl_{(g)} + POCl_{3(l)}$$

This reaction's used to test for alcohols...

Test for the Hydroxyl Group (–OH)

Add **phosphorus(V) chloride** to the unknown liquid.
If -OH is present, you'll get **steamy fumes** which turn **blue litmus red**.

Alcohols can be Dehydrated to Form Alkenes

You can make ethene by **eliminating** water from **ethanol** in a **dehydration reaction**.
The experiment isn't too tricky, but there's two ways of doing it...

$$C_2H_5OH \longrightarrow CH_2{=}CH_2 + H_2O$$

Dehydrating Alcohols to form Alkenes

1) Ethanol vapour is passed over a hot **catalyst** of pumice stone or aluminium oxide, Al_2O_3 — the catalyst provides a **large surface area** for the reaction.
2) **OR**, you can heat ethanol with **excess** concentrated sulphuric acid at 170 °C. The ethene produced is then collected over water.

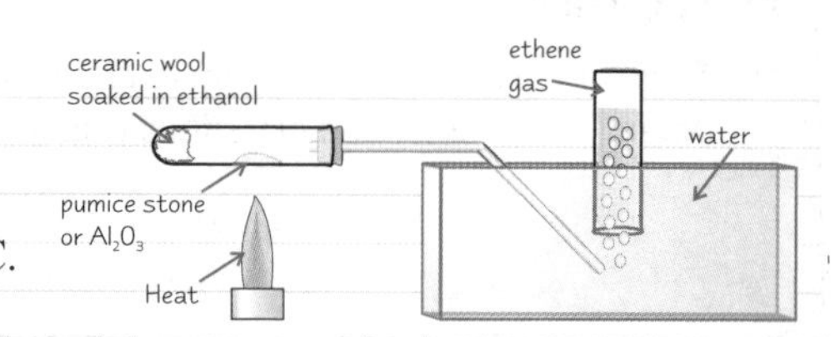

Here's what's going on in the second method (the one with the sulphuric acid)...

The **concentrated sulphuric acid** acts as a **dehydrating agent** in the **elimination** reaction.

$$CH_3CH_2OH + H^{\oplus} \Longrightarrow CH_3CH_2O^{\oplus}H_2 \Longrightarrow [CH_3CH_2^{\oplus}] + H_2O \Longrightarrow CH_2{=}CH_2 + H_2O + H^+$$

The **hydroxyl group** will bond to **H⁺ ions** from the strong acid. The alcohol is then **protonated**, giving the oxygen atom a **positive charge**.

The positively charged oxygen will **pull** electrons away from the neighbouring carbon, and water will 'fall off', creating an **unstable carbocation intermediate**.

The carbocation loses H⁺ and the **alkene** is formed.

Reactions of Alcohols

Cyclohexanol can be Used to Prepare *Cyclohexene*

Edexcel Nuffield only.

Making Cyclohexene from Cyclohexanol

1) Add concentrated phosphoric acid to cyclohexanol — the phosphoric acid is the **dehydrating agent**.
2) Heat gently, collecting the **distillate** at 70–90 °C.

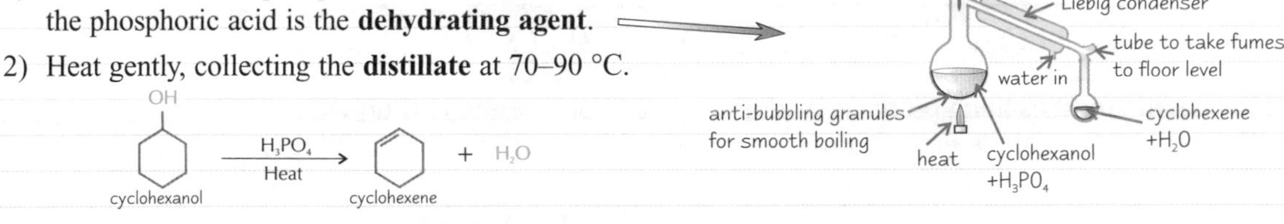

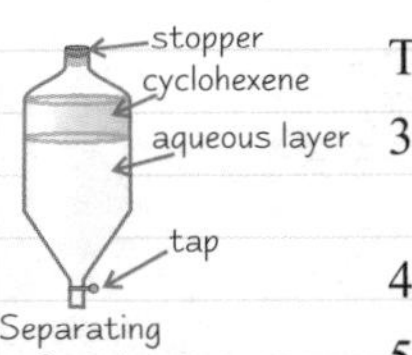

The distillate is impure cyclohexene, so it needs to be **purified**.

3) **Separate** the cyclohexene out using a **separating funnel** — shake the mixture with saturated sodium chloride solution, let the layers separate, then **drain off** the lower aqueous layer.
4) **Dry** the cyclohexene by shaking it with **anhydrous calcium chloride**.
5) **Re-distil** the cyclohexene, collecting the distillate which comes over at 81-85 °C.

Anhydrous means 'without water'.

You can also do this with smaller amounts using microscale apparatus — it's better for the environment this way.

Here's a Few More *Alcohol Reactions* to Learn

Not AQA or Edexcel Nuffield.

Sodium Reacts with Alcohols to Produce Alkoxides

$$2CH_3CH_2OH_{(l)} + 2Na_{(s)} \rightarrow 2CH_3CH_2O^-Na^+_{(alcohol)} + H_{2(g)}$$

1) **Sodium metal** reacts gently with **ethanol**, breaking the **O–H** bonds to produce ionic sodium ethoxide and hydrogen.
2) The longer the **hydrocarbon chain** of the alcohol gets, the **less** reactive it is with sodium.

Reacting a Carboxylic Acid with Ethanol Produces an Ester

1) If you warm **ethanol** with a **carboxylic acid** (like ethanoic acid) and a **strong acid catalyst** (concentrated sulphuric acid will do), it forms an ester (**ethyl ethanoate** in this case).
2) The **O–H** bond in ethanol is broken in the **esterification** reaction.

$$C_2H_5OH + CH_3COOH \rightleftharpoons CH_3C(=O)O{-}CH_2CH_3 + H_2O$$

This stuff smells of pear drops — aliphatic esters generally smell fruity.

Practice Questions

Q1 What reagents are used to generate phosphorus(III) iodide?

Q2 What is a protonated alcohol?

Q3 Describe how to make cyclohexene from cyclohexanol.

Exam Question

Q1 The alcohol ethanol undergoes various chemical reactions.

a) Fill in the missing reagents and products in the diagram to the right:

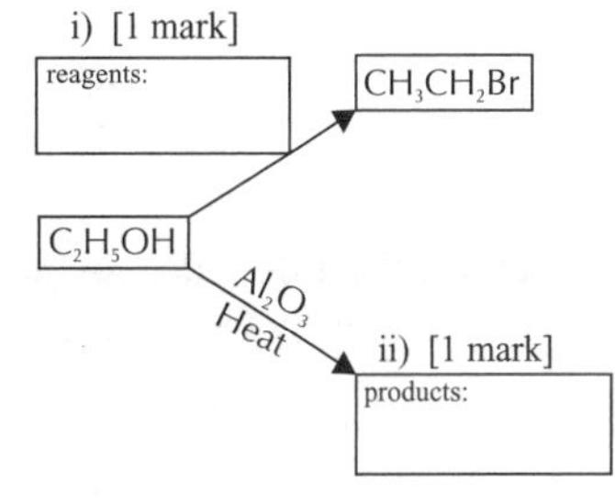

b) i) What type of mechanism is involved in the formation of bromoethane, CH_3CH_2Br? [2 marks]

ii) Phosphorus(V) chloride is used to test for the presence of hydroxyl groups. What would you observe happening if hydroxyl groups were present? [2 marks]

Carboxylic acid + ethanol produces Ester — well, that's life...

Oh, my goodness me... those reaction mechanism blighters are a bit of a pain, aren't they... but don't get stressed about them. Just read them real carefully, and do your best to get your head round them. Then, whether or not you fully understand the blessed things, just learn them. Flicking back to page 28 will help you out with polarisation...

Oxidation of Alcohols

Another page of alcohol reactions. Probably not what you wanted for Christmas... But at least you are almost at the end of the section... and the book for that matter... and your wits, probably.

The Simple way to Oxidise Alcohols is to **Burn Them**

It doesn't take much to set ethanol alight and it burns with a **pale blue flame**. The C–C and C–H bonds are broken as the ethanol is **completely oxidised** to make carbon dioxide and water. This is a **combustion** reaction.

$$C_2H_5OH_{(l)} + 3O_{2(g)} \rightarrow 2CO_{2(g)} + 3H_2O_{(g)}$$

But you don't get the most exciting products by doing this. If you want to end up with something more interesting at the end, you need a more sophisticated way of oxidising...

How Much an Alcohol can be **Oxidised** Depends on its **Structure**

You can use the **oxidising agent acidified potassium dichromate(VI)** to **mildly** oxidise alcohols.

- **Primary** alcohols are oxidised to **aldehydes** and then to **carboxylic acids.**
- **Secondary** alcohols are oxidised to **ketones** only.
- **Tertiary** alcohols won't be oxidised.

The orange dichromate(VI) ion is reduced to the green chromium(III) ion, Cr^{3+}.

Aldehydes and **ketones** are **carbonyl** compounds — they have the functional group C=O. Their general formula is $\mathbf{C_nH_{2n}O}$.

1) **Aldehydes** have a **hydrogen** and **one alkyl group** attached to the carbonyl carbon atom. E.g.
2) **Ketones** have **two alkyl groups** attached to the carbonyl carbon atom.

propanone CH_3COCH_3

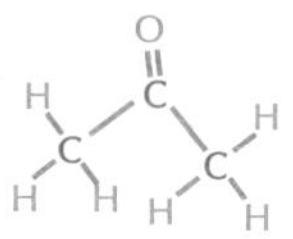

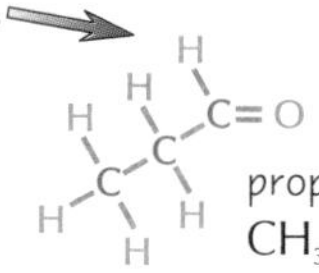

propanal CH_3CH_2CHO

Primary Alcohols will Oxidise to **Aldehydes** and **Carboxylic Acids**

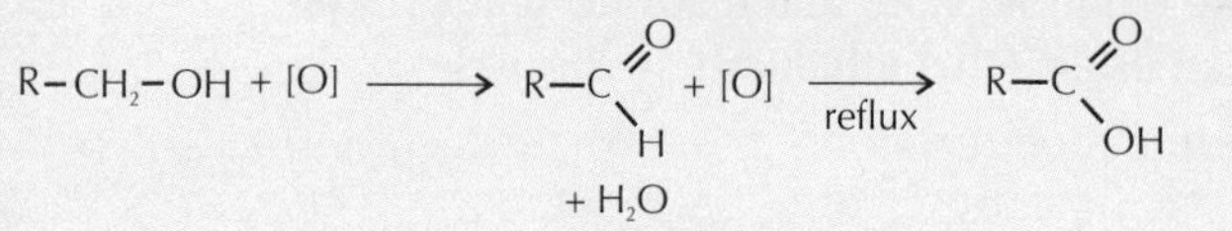

$$R{-}CH_2{-}OH + [O] \longrightarrow R{-}CHO + H_2O \; + [O] \xrightarrow{\text{reflux}} R{-}COOH$$

primary alcohol → aldehyde → carboxylic acid

[O] = oxidising agent

You can control how **far** the alcohol is oxidised by controlling the **reaction conditions**:

Oxidising Primary Alcohols

1) Gently heating ethanol with potassium dichromate(VI) solution and sulphuric acid in a test tube should produce "apple" smelling **ethanal** (an aldehyde). However, it's **really tricky** to control the amount of heat and the aldehyde is usually oxidised to form "vinegar" smelling **ethanoic acid**.
2) To get just the **aldehyde**, you need to get it out of the oxidising solution **as soon** as it's formed. You can do this by gently heating excess alcohol with a **controlled** amount of oxidising agent in **distillation apparatus**, so the aldehyde (which boils at a lower temperature than the alcohol) is distilled off **immediately**.
3) To produce the **carboxylic acid**, the alcohol has to be **vigorously oxidised**. The alcohol is mixed with excess oxidising agent and heated under **reflux**. Heating under reflux means you can increase the **temperature** of an organic reaction to boiling without losing **volatile** solvents, reactants or products. Any vaporised compounds are cooled, condense and drip back into the reaction mixture. Handy, hey.

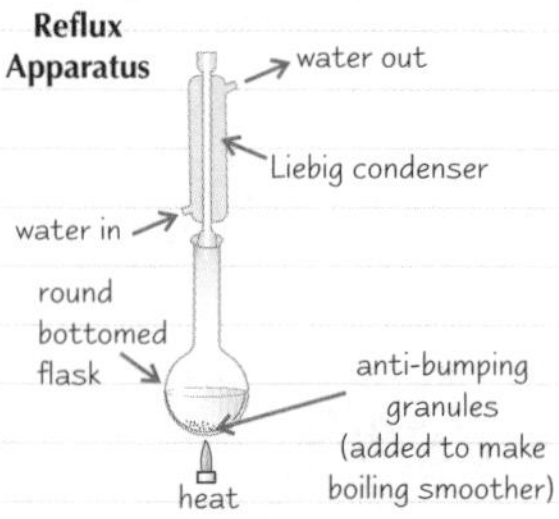

Reflux Apparatus
water out
Liebig condenser
water in
round bottomed flask
anti-bumping granules (added to make boiling smoother)
heat

Oxidation of Alcohols

Secondary Alcohols will Oxidise to Ketones

$$R_1-\underset{R_2}{\overset{H}{C}}-OH + [O] \xrightarrow{\text{reflux}} R_1R_2C=O + H_2O$$

1) Refluxing a secondary alcohol, e.g. propan-2-ol, with acidified dichromate(VI) will produce a **ketone**.
2) Ketones can't be oxidised easily, so even prolonged refluxing won't produce anything more.

Tertiary Alcohols can't be Oxidised Easily

Tertiary alcohols don't react with potassium dichromate(VI) at all — the solution stays orange. The only way to oxidise tertiary alcohols is by **burning** them.

Use Oxidising Agents to Distinguish Between Aldehydes and Ketones

Aldehydes and ketones can be distinguished using **oxidising agents** — aldehydes are easily oxidised but ketones aren't.

1) **Fehling's solution** and **Benedict's solution** are both deep blue Cu^{2+} complexes, which reduce to brick-red Cu_2O when warmed with an aldehyde, but stay blue with a ketone.
2) **Tollen's reagent** is $[Ag(NH_3)_2]^+$ — it's reduced to **silver** when warmed with an aldehyde, but not with a ketone. The silver will coat the inside of the apparatus to form a **mirror**.

Practice Questions

Q1 What's the difference between an aldehyde and a ketone?

Q2 What will acidified potassium dichromate(VI) oxidise secondary alcohols to?

Q3 What is the colour change when potassium dichromate(VI) is reduced?

Q4 Why are anti-bumping granules used in distillation and reflux?

Exam Question

Q1 A student wanted to produce the aldehyde propanal from propanol, and set up a reflux apparatus using acidified potassium dichromate(VI) as the oxidising agent.

a) Draw a labelled diagram of a reflux apparatus. Explain why reflux apparatus is arranged in this way. [3 marks]

b) The student tested his product and found that he had not produced propanal.
i) Describe a test for an aldehyde. [2 marks]
ii) What is the student's product? [1 mark]
iii) Write equations to show the two-stage reaction. You may use [O] to represent the oxidising agent. [2 marks]
iv) What technique should the student have used and why? [2 marks]

c) The student also tried to oxidise 2-methylpropan-2-ol, unsuccessfully.
i) Draw the full structural formula for 2-methylpropan-2-ol. [1 mark]
ii) Why is it not possible to oxidise 2-methylpropan-2-ol with an oxidising agent? [1 mark]

I.... I .... just can't do it, R2...

Don't give up now. You're so close to the end... Only as a fully-trained Chemistry Jedi, with the force as your ally, can you take on the Examiner. If you quit now, if you choose the easy path as Wader did, all the marks you've fought for will be lost. Be strong. Don't give in to hate — that leads to the dark side... *(Only one more double page to go now...)*

Analytical Techniques

Only worry about these two pages if you're doing OCR or OCR Salters.
If you've got some stuff and don't know what it is, don't taste it.

Chromatography is Useful for Checking things are Pure

OCR Salters only.

Chromatography is used to **separate** a mixture. **Thin-layer chromatography** (**TLC**) is handy for checking if stuff is pure.

1) A spot of the **sample** is put on a **plate**. Spots of **known solutions** are dotted alongside to make **identifying** stuff easier.
2) Next the plate is dipped in a **solvent**. The solvent moves **up the plate**, moving different substances at **different rates**.

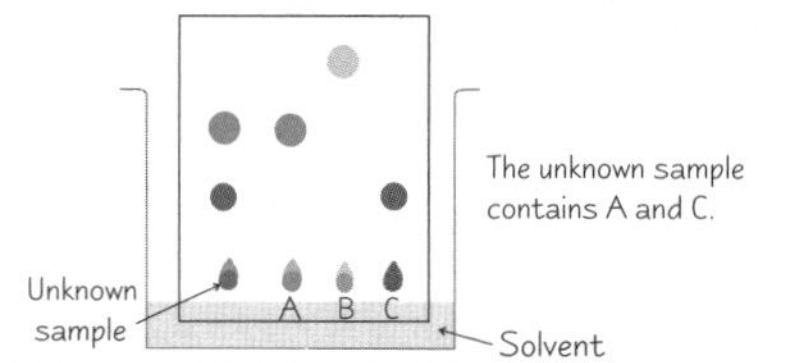

3) The stuff in coloured solutions is **easy** to identify. If the solution's **colourless**, you might need to use **UV light** or **iodine** to be able to **see** the spots.

Infra-red Spectroscopy Lets You Identify Organic Molecules

Infra-red spectroscopy produces **scary** looking graphs. Just learn the basics and you'll be fine.

1) In infra-red spectroscopy, a beam of **infra-red radiation** goes through the sample.
2) **Different bond types** absorb **different wavelengths**. Bonds in different **places** in the molecule absorb different wavelengths too. So, the O-H group in an **alcohol** and the O-H in a **carboxylic acid** absorb different wavelengths.
3) This table shows what **frequencies** different groups absorb —

Functional group	Where it's found	Frequency/ Wavenumber	Type of absorption
O-H	alcohols	3200 - 3600	strong, broad
O-H	carboxylic acids	2500 - 3500	medium, very broad
C=O	aldehydes, ketones, acids and esters	1680 - 1750	strong, sharp

This tells you what the trough on the graph will look like.

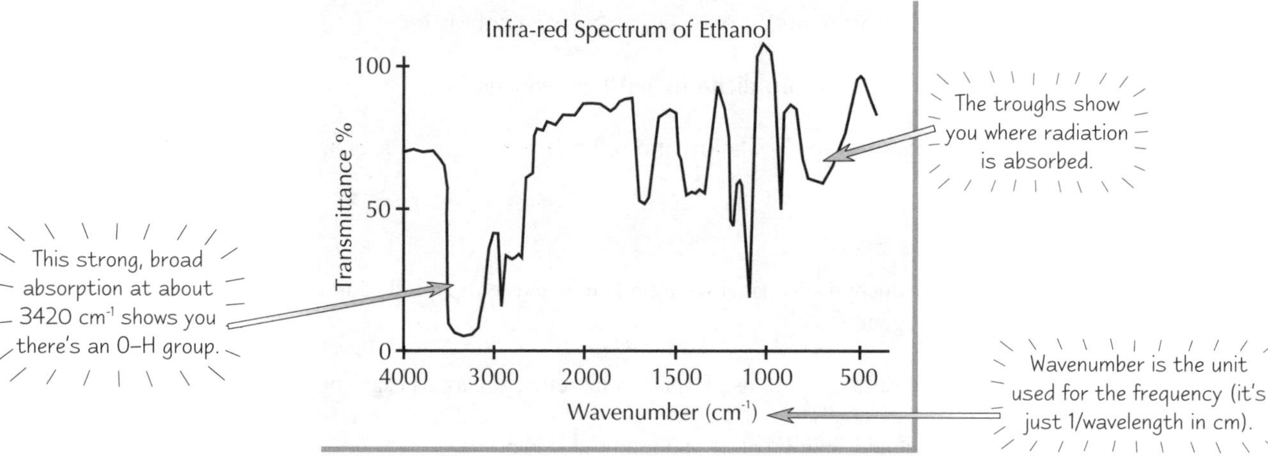

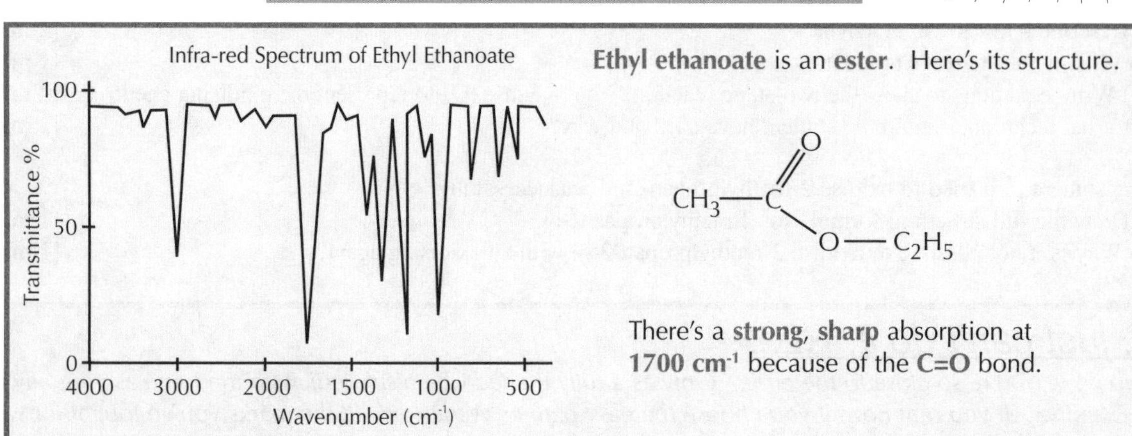

Ethyl ethanoate is an **ester**. Here's its structure.

There's a **strong, sharp** absorption at **1700 cm^{-1}** because of the **C=O** bond.

Analytical Techniques

Aspirin is made from Salicylic Acid

OCR Salters only.

Nowadays, drugs have to go through rigorous testing to make sure they're safe.

1) The Ancient Greeks used **white willow bark** to reduce pain — the problem was it also caused **vomiting**. The painkilling ingredient was **salicylic acid**.
2) In 1893 a German scientist used salicylic acid to make a similar chemical with **fewer side effects**. This drug is known as **aspirin** — it's now the **largest selling** drug in the world.

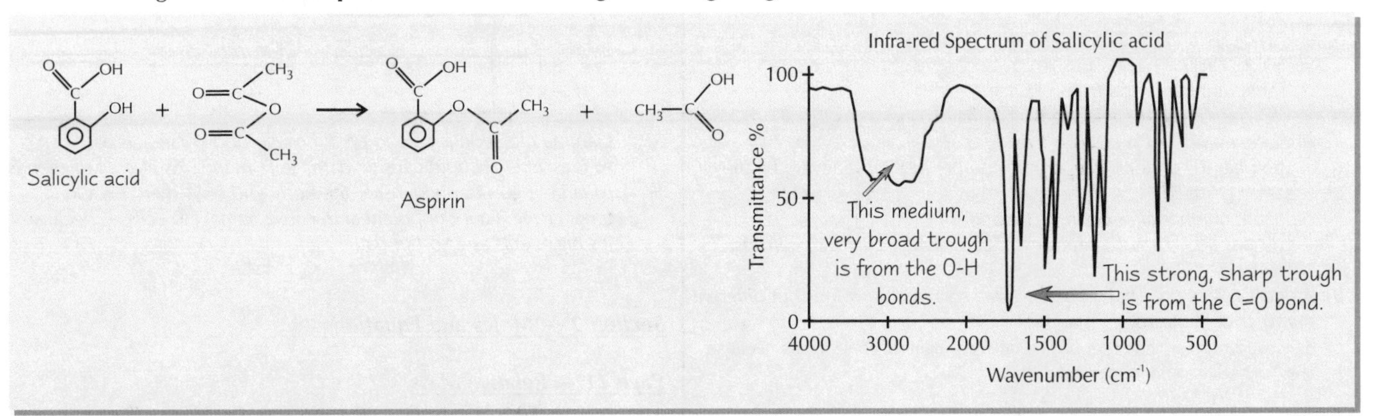

Practice Questions

Q1 What is thin-layer chromatography used for?

Q2 What might you need to use to identify the components of a colourless solution in thin-layer chromatography?

Q3 What unit is used to measure the frequency of the absorbed radiation in infra-red spectroscopy?

Q4 What do the troughs of infra-red spectra tell you?

Q5 What chemical is aspirin made from?

Exam Question

Q1 A student produced samples of ethanoic acid and ethanal by oxidising ethanol, and decided produce infra-red spectra for the samples.

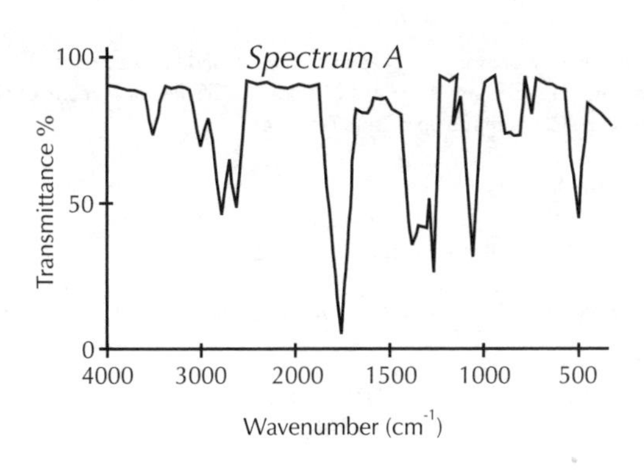

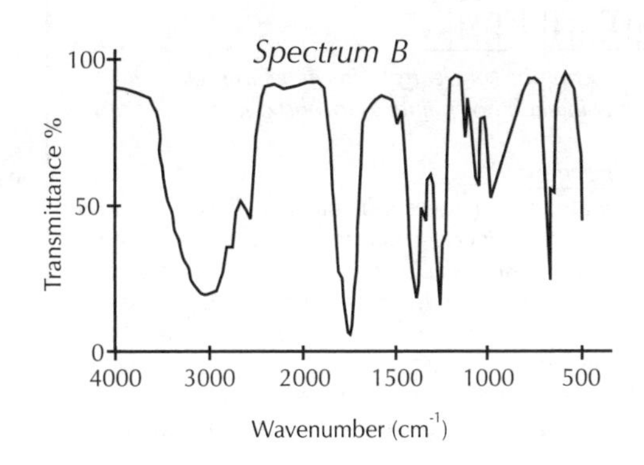

a) By using the data on page 112, identify the most important absorptions in each spectrum and state the functional groups which caused them. [6 marks]
b) Identify which spectrum is which. [1 mark]
c) If the student had produced a spectrum for ethanol as well, which absorption would be missing from it that is present in the spectra above? [2 marks]

You can't play Jet Set Willy on an infra-red spectrum...

These graphs are enough to make your eyes go fuzzy. Lucky it's the end of the book, hey. You don't have to memorise the exact wiggles and squiggles, but you do have to be able to interpret the major bumps. The practice exam question's great for checking you can do this. Now you've got all this info in your brain, put custard in your ears to keep it there.

Answers

Section 1 — Atomic Structure

Page 3 — The Atom

1) a) *Similarity — They've all got the same number of protons/electrons. [1 mark]*
Difference — They all have different numbers of neutrons. [1 mark]
b) *1 proton [1 mark], 1 neutron (2 – 1) [1 mark], 1 electron [1 mark].*
c) *^{3}H. [1 mark]*
Since tritium has 2 neutrons in the nucleus and also 1 proton, it has a mass number of 3. You could also write $^3_1$H but you don't really need the atomic number.

2) a) *(i) Same number of electrons. [1 mark]*
$^{32}S^{2-}$ has 16 + 2 = 18electrons. ^{40}Ar has 18 electrons too. [1 mark]
(ii)Same number of protons. [1 mark].
Each has 16 protons (the atomic number of S must always be the same) [1 mark].
(iii)Same number of neutrons. [1 mark]
^{40}Ar has 40 – 18 = 22 neutrons. ^{42}Ca has 42 – 20 = 22 neutrons. [1 mark]
b) ***A** and **C**. [1 mark] They have the same number of protons but different numbers of neutrons. [1 mark].*
It doesn't matter that they have a different number of electrons because they are still the same element.

Page 5 — Electronic Structure

1) a) *K atom: $1s^2\ 2s^2\ 2p^6\ 3s^2\ 3p^6\ 4s^1$ [1 mark]*
K^+ ion: $1s^2\ 2s^2\ 2p^6\ 3s^2\ 3p^6$ [1 mark]
b)
Oxygen electron Configuration — 1s: ↑↓ 2s: ↑↓ 2p: ↑↓ ↑ ↑
1 mark for the correct number of electrons in each sub-shell.
1 mark for having spin-pairing in one of the p orbitals and parallel spins in the other two p orbitals. A box filled with 2 arrows is spin pairing — 1 up and 1 down. If you've put the four p electrons into just 2 orbitals, it's wrong.
c) *The outer shell electrons in potassium and oxygen can get close to the outer shells of other atoms so they can be transferred or shared [1 mark]. The inner shell electrons are tightly held and shielded from the electrons in other atoms/molecules [1 mark].*

2) a) *$1s^2\ 2s^2\ 2p^6\ 3s^2\ 3p^6\ 3d^5\ 4s^2$. [1 mark]*
b) *Germanium ($1s^2\ 2s^2\ 2p^6\ 3s^2\ 3p^6\ 3d^{10}\ 4s^2\ 4p^2$). [1 mark].*
(The 4p sub-shell is partly filled so it must be a p block element.)
c) *Ar (atom) [1 mark], K^+ (positive ion) [1 mark], Cl^- (negative ion) [1 mark]. You also could have suggested Ca^{2+}, S^{2-} or P^{3-}.*
d)
Al^{3+} electron Configuration — 1s: ↑↓ 2s: ↑↓ 2p: ↑↓ ↑↓ ↑↓
1 mark for the correct number of electrons in each sub-shell.
1 mark for one arrow in each box pointing up, and one pointing down.

Page 7 — Ionisation Energies

1) a) *There's an increasing attraction between the outer shell electrons and the nucleus. This is due to an increase in nuclear charge since there are more protons [1 mark]. Also, shielding is roughly constant since each additional electron is added to the same shell. [1 mark]*
b) *For Li and Be, the 2s sub-shell is filling [1 mark]. For B to N, the 2p sub-shell is half filling. This sub-shell is further out so it's easier to remove electrons [1 mark]. For O to Ne, the electrons begin spin-pairing in the 2p sub-shell. There's extra repulsion between the electrons, so they're easier to remove [1 mark]. This 2, 3, 3 pattern of first ionisation energies shows the sub-shell structure.*

Page 9 — Nuclear Chemistry

1)
$$^{216}_{84}Po \rightarrow {}^{212}_{82}Pb + {}^{4}_{2}He$$
(216 – 212 = 4; 84 – 82 = 2)

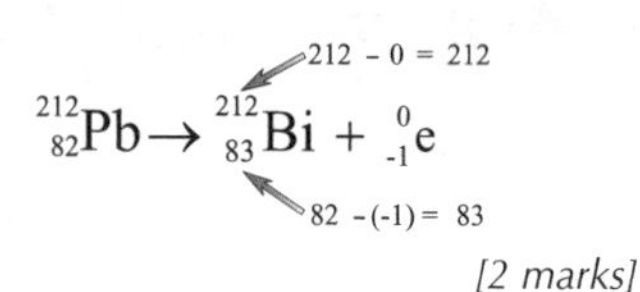

[2 marks]

2)
a) Electron excited *[1 mark]*
Step 1
Step 2
b) Energy emitted *[1 mark]*

3) *Gamma radiation is able to pass through body materials easily, so it escapes without causing damage [1 mark]. As alpha radiation is so large it gets trapped inside the body and stays there for a long time, giving it a lot of potential to cause damageto cells — because it's big, it acts as a sort of battering ram [1 mark].*

Section 2 — Moles and Equations

Page 11 — Relative Mass

1) a) *First multiply each relative abundance by the relative mass —*
120.8 × 63 = 7610.4, 54.0 × 65 = 3510.0
Next add up the products —
7610.4 + 3510.0 = 11 120.4 *[1 mark]*
Now divide by the total abundance (120.8 + 54.0 = 174.8)

$$A_r(Cu) = \frac{11120.4}{174.8} \approx \mathbf{63.6}$$ *[1 mark]*

You can check you answer by seeing if A_r(Cu) is in between 63 and 65 (the lowest and highest relative isotopic masses).
b) *A sample of copper is a mixture of 2 isotopes in different abundances [1 mark]. The weighted average mass of these isotopes isn't a whole number [1 mark].*

2) a) *Mass spectroscopy. [1 mark]*
b) *You use pretty much the same method here as for question 1)a).*
93.11 × 39 = 3631.29, (0.12 × 40) = 4.8, (6.77 × 41) = 277.57
3631.29 + 4.8 + 277.57 = 3913.66 *[1 mark]*
This time you divide by 100 because they're percentages.

$$A_r(K) = \frac{3913.66}{100} \approx \mathbf{39.14}$$ *[1 mark]*

Again check your answer's between the lowest and highest relative isotopic masses, 39 and 41. A_r(K) is closer to 39 because most of the sample (93.11 %) is made up of this isotope.

Page 13 — The Mole

1) *M of CH_3COOH = (12 x 2) + (4 × 1) + (2 × 16) = 60 g* *[1 mark]*
*so mass of 0.36 moles = 60 × 0.36 = **21.6 g*** *[1 mark]*

2) *No. of moles = $\frac{0.25 \times 60}{1000}$ = 0.015 moles H_2SO_4* *[1 mark]*
M of H_2SO_4 = (2 × 1) + (1 × 32) + (4 × 16) = 98 g
*Mass of 0.015 H_2SO_4 = 98 x 0.015 = **1.47 g*** *[1 mark]*

3) *M of C_3H_8 = (3 × 12) + (8 × 1) = 44 g*
No. of moles of C_3H_8 = $\frac{88}{44}$ = 2 moles *[1 mark]*
At r.t.p. 1 mole of gas occupies 24 dm^3
*so 2 moles of gas occupies 2 x 24 = **48 dm^3*** *[1 mark].*

Page 15 — Empirical and Molecular Formulae

1) *Assume you've got 100 g of the compound so you can turn the % straight into mass.*

No. of moles of C = $\frac{92.3}{12}$ = 7.69 moles

No. of moles of H = $\frac{7.7}{1}$ = 7.7 moles *[1 mark]*

Answers

Divide both by the smallest number, in this case 7.69.
So ratio C : H = 1 : 1
So, the empirical formula = CH [1 mark]

The empirical mass = 12 + 1 = 13

No. of empirical units in molecule = $\frac{78}{13} = 6$

So the molecular formula = C_6H_6 [1 mark]

2) *The magnesium is burning, so it's reacting with oxygen and the product is magnesium oxide.*
First work out the number of moles of each element.

No. of moles Mg = $\frac{1.2}{24} = 0.05$ *moles*

Mass of O is everything that isn't Mg: 2 – 1.2 = 0.8 g

No. of moles O = $\frac{0.8}{16} = 0.05$ *moles* [1 mark]

Ratio Mg : O = 0.05 : 0.05
Divide both by the smallest number, in this case 0.05.
So ratio Mg : O = 1 : 1
So the empirical formula is MgO [1 mark]

3) *First calculate the no. of moles of each product and then the mass of C and H:*

No. of moles of $CO_2 = \frac{33}{44} = 0.75$ *moles*

Mass of C = 0.75 × 12 = 9 g

No. of moles of $H_2O = \frac{10.8}{18} = 0.6$ *moles*

0.6 moles H_2O *= 1.2 moles H*
Mass of H = 1.2 × 1 = 1.2 g [1 mark]

Organic acids contain C, H and O, so the rest of the mass must be O.
Mass of O = 19.8 – (9 + 1.2) = 9.6 g

No. of moles of O = $\frac{9.6}{16} = 0.6$ *moles* [1 mark]

Mole ratio = C : H : O = 0.75 : 1.2 : 0.6
Divide by smallest 1.25 : 2 : 1
The carbon ratio isn't a whole number, so you have to multiply them all up until it is. As its fraction is ¼, multiply them all by 4.
So, mole ratio = C : H : O = 5 : 8 : 4
Empirical formula = $\mathbf{C_5H_8O_4}$ [1 mark]
Empirical mass = (12 × 5) + (1 × 8) + (16 × 4) = 132 g
This is the same as what we're told the molecular mass is, so the molecular formula is also $\mathbf{C_5H_8O_4}$. [1 mark]

Page 17 — Equations and Calculations

1) *M of* C_2H_5Cl *= (2 × 12) + (5 × 1) + (1 × 35.5) = 64.5 g* [1 mark]

Number of moles of $C_2H_5Cl = \frac{258}{64.5} = 4$ *moles* [1 mark]

From the equation, 1 mole C_2H_5Cl *is made from 1 mole* C_2H_4
so, 4 moles C_2H_5Cl *is made from 4 moles* C_2H_4. [1 mark]
M of C_2H_4 *= (2 × 12) + (4 × 1) = 28 g*
so, the mass of 4 moles C_2H_4 *= 4 × 28 =* ***112 g*** [1 mark]

2) *M of* $CaCO_3$ *= 40 + 12 + (3 × 16) = 100 g*

Number of moles of $CaCO_3 = \frac{15}{100} = 0.15$ *moles*

a) *From the equation, 1 mole* $CaCO_3$ *produces 1 mole CaO*
so, 0.15 moles of $CaCO_3$ *produces 0.15 moles of CaO.* [1 mark]
M of CaO = 40 + 16 = 56 g [1 mark]
so, mass of 0.15 moles of CaO = 56 × 0.15 = ***8.4 g*** [1 mark]

b) *From the equation, 1 mole* $CaCO_3$ *produces 1 mole* CO_2
so, 0.15 moles of $CaCO_3$ *produces 0.15 moles of* CO_2. [1 mark]
1 mole gas occupies 24 dm^3, [1 mark]
so, 0.15 moles occupies = 24 × 0.15 = 3.6 dm^3 [1 mark]

3) *First count the atoms on both sides of the equation —*

$KI + Pb(NO_3)_2 \rightarrow PbI_2 + 2KNO_3$

LHS	RHS
K = 1	K = 2
I = 1	I = 2
Pb = 1	Pb = 1
NO_3 = 2	NO_3 = 2

[1 mark]

On the LHS, you need 2 each of K and I, so use 2KI
This makes the final equation: $\mathbf{2KI + Pb(NO_3)_2 \rightarrow PbI_2 + 2KNO_3}$ [1 mark]

In this equation, the NO_3 particle remains unchanged, so it makes balancing much easier if you treat it as one indivisible lump.

Page 19 — Titrations

1) *First write down what you know —*

$CH_3COOH + NaOH \rightarrow CH_3COONa + H_2O$
25.4 cm^3 *14.6* cm^3
? 0.5 M

Number of moles of NaOH = $\frac{0.5 \times 14.6}{1000} = 0.0073$ *moles* [1 mark]

From the equation, you know 1 mole NaOH neutralises 1 mole of CH_3COOH, *so if you've used 0.0073 moles NaOH you must have neutralised 0.0073 moles* CH_3COOH. [1 mark]

Concentration of $CH_3COOH = \frac{0.0073 \times 1000}{25.4} =$ ***0.287 M*** [1 mark]

2) *First write down what you know again —*

$CaCO_3 + H_2SO_4 \rightarrow CaSO_4 + H_2O + CO_2$
0.75 g 0.25 M

M of $CaCO_3$ *= 40 + 12 + (3 × 16) = 100 g* [1 mark]

Number of moles of $CaCO_3 = \frac{0.75}{100} = 7.5 \times 10^{-3}$ *moles* [1 mark]

From the equation, 1 mole $CaCO_3$ *reacts with 1 mole* H_2SO_4
so, 7.5×10^{-3} *moles* $CaCO_3$ *reacts with* 7.5×10^{-3} *moles* H_2SO_4. [1 mark]

The volume needed is = $\frac{(7.5 \times 10^{-3}) \times 1000}{0.25} = 30\ cm^3$ [1 mark]

If the question mentions concentration or molarities, you can bet your last clean pair of underwear that you'll need to use the formula

$$\text{number of moles} = \frac{\text{concentration} \times \text{volume}}{1000}$$

Just make sure the volume's in cm^3 though.

Section 3 — Bonding and Structure

Page 21 — Ionic Bonding

1) a)

Your diagram should show the following —
- *cubic structure with ions at corners [1 mark]*
- *sodium ions and chloride ions labelled [1 mark]*
- *alternating sodium ions and chloride ions [1 mark]*

b) *giant ionic/crystal (lattice) [1 mark]*

c) *You'd expect it to have a high melting point [1 mark]. Because there are strong bonds between the ions [1 mark] due to the electrostatic forces [1 mark]. A lot of energy is required to overcome these bonds [1 mark].*

Answers

2) a) Electrons move from one atom to another [1 mark].
Any correct examples of ions, one positive, one negative.
E.g. Na^+, Cl^-. [2 x 1 mark]

b) In a solid, ions are held in place by strong ionic bonds [1 mark]. When the solid is heated to melting point, the ions gain enough energy [1 mark] to overcome the forces of attraction [1 mark] enough to become mobile [1 mark] and so carry charge (and hence electricity) through the substance [1 mark].

Page 23 — Covalent Bonding

1) a) Covalent [1 mark]

b)

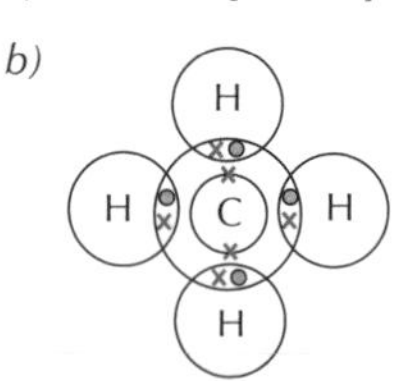

Your diagram should show the following —
- a completely correct electron arrangement [1 mark]
- all 4 overlaps correct (one dot + one cross in each) [1 mark]

2) a) Ethene has a (C=C) double bond, made up of a σ and a π bond [1 mark]. Ethane only has a σ bond [1 mark]. The π bond is less tightly bound to the two nuclei than the σ bond (the π electron density is lower) [1 mark].

b) (i) Dative covalent/coordinate bond [1 mark]
(ii) One atom [1 mark] donates a pair of electrons to the bond [1 mark].

Page 25 — Giant Molecular Structures and Metallic Bonding

1) a) Giant molecular/macromolecular/giant covalent [1 mark]

b) 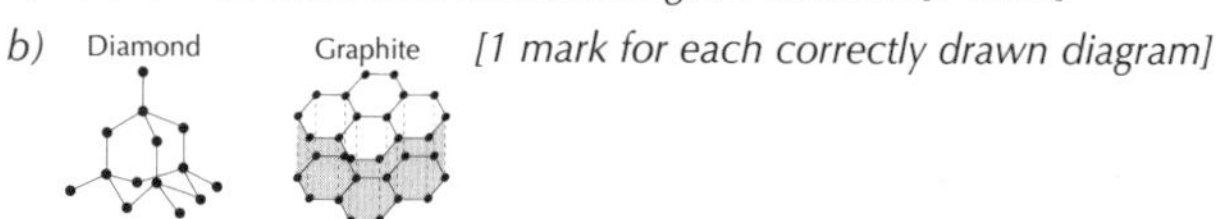

[1 mark for each correctly drawn diagram]

Diamond's a bit awkward to draw without it looking like a bunch of ballet dancing spiders — just make sure each central carbon is connected to four others.

c) Diamond has electrons in localised covalent bonds [1 mark], so is a poor electrical conductor [1 mark]. Graphite has delocalised electrons between the sheets [1 mark] which can flow, so is a good electrical conductor [1 mark].

2)

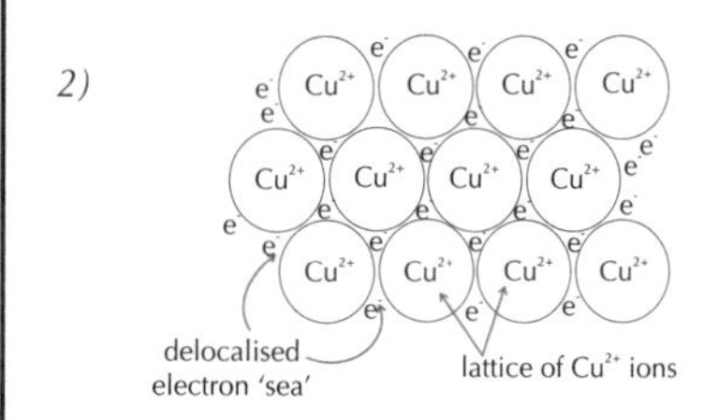

[2 marks for reasonable diagram showing closely packed Cu^{2+} ions and a sea of delocalised electrons]
Metallic bonding results from the attraction between positive metal ions [1 mark] and a sea of delocalised electrons [1 mark].

Page 27 — Shapes of Molecules

1) a) NCl_3 BCl_3 [2 marks]

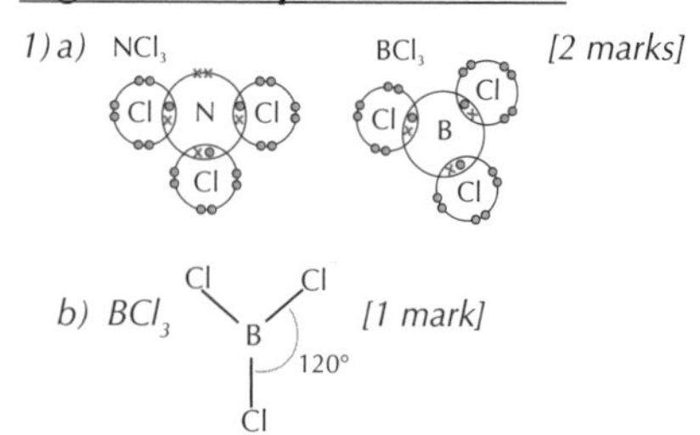

b) BCl_3 [1 mark]

(It must be a reasonable "Y" shaped molecule.)
shape: trigonal planar [1 mark],
bond angle: 120° exactly [1 mark]

NCl_3 [1 mark]

shape: trigonal pyramidal [1 mark],
bond angle: 107° [1 mark]

c) BCl_3 has three electron pairs only around B. [1 mark]
NCl_3 has four electron pairs around N [1 mark], including one lone pair. [1 mark]

Page 29 — Polarisation of Molecules and Ions

1) a) The power of an atom to withdraw electron density [1 mark] from a covalent bond [1 mark] OR the ability of an atom to attract the bonding electrons [1 mark] in a covalent bond [1 mark].

b) (i) Br — Br
non-polar
(or no dipole)

(ii) polar
(or dipole)

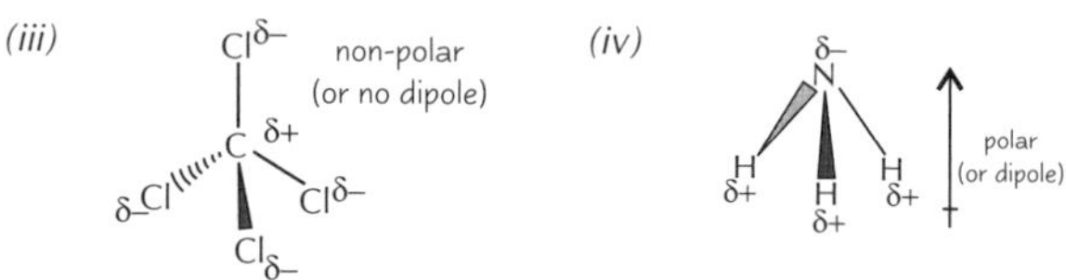

[1 mark each for correct shape and bond polarities, 1 mark each for correct overall polarity].
To help you decide if the molecule's polar or not, imagine the atoms are having a tug of war with the electrons. If they're all pulling the same amount in different directions, the electrons aren't going to go anywhere.

c) The lone pair of electrons on nitrogen [1 mark] cancels out the dipole or polarity [1 mark].
This can't happen with NH_3 because the dipole's in the opposite direction.

2) Al^{3+} has a high charge/volume ratio (or a small radius AND a large positive charge) [1 mark], so it has a high polarising ability [1 mark] and can pull electron density away from Cl^- [1 mark] to create a mostly covalent bond [1 mark].

Page 31 — Intermolecular forces

1) a) Van der Waals OR instantaneous/temporary dipole-induced dipole OR dispersion forces.
Permanent dipole-dipole interactions/forces.
Hydrogen bonding.
Permanent dipole-induced dipole interactions.
[1 mark each for any three]

b)

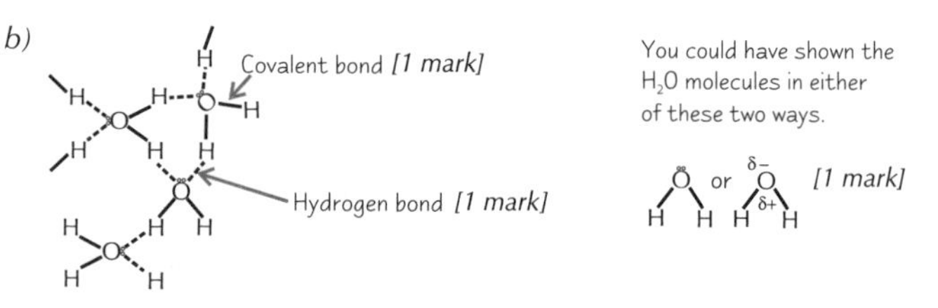

Van der Waals OR instantaneous/temporary dipole-induced dipole OR dispersion forces of attraction between water molecules. [1 mark]

c) Except for water, there's an increase in boiling point going down the group [1 mark]. The increase in the size/M_r and the number of electrons [1 mark] leads to an increase in van der Waals OR instantaneous/temporary dipole-induced dipole OR dispersion forces [1 mark].
More energy [1 mark] is needed to break the hydrogen bonds between water molecules [1 mark].

Page 33 — Properties of Structures

1) a) A — Ionic
B — (Simple) molecular
C — Metallic
D — Giant molecular (macromolecular) [1 mark for each]

b) i) Diamond — D ii) Aluminium — C
iii) Sodium chloride — A iv) Iodine — B [1 mark for each]

Answers

2) **Magnesium** has a metallic crystal lattice (it has metallic bonding) [1 mark]. It has positive ions [1 mark] and a sea of electrons/delocalised electrons/freely moving electrons [1 mark], which allow it to conduct electricity in the solid or liquid state [1 mark].
Sodium chloride has a (giant) ionic lattice [1 mark]. It doesn't conduct electricity when it's solid [1 mark] because its ions don't move freely, but vibrate about a fixed point [1 mark]. Sodium chloride conducts electricity when liquid/molten [1 mark] or in aqueous solution [1 mark] because it has freely moving ions (not electrons) [1 mark].
Graphite is giant covalent/macromolecular [1 mark]. It has delocalised/freely moving electrons [1 mark] between the layers [1 mark]. It conducts electricity along the layers in the solid state [1 mark].

Section 4 — Elements of the Periodic Table

Page 35 — The Periodic Table

1) a) Sodium $1s^2\ 2s^2\ 2p^6\ 3s^1$
b) s block
c) Bromine $1s^2\ 2s^2\ 2p^6\ 3s^2\ 3p^6\ 3d^{10}\ 4s^2\ 4p^5$
d) p block

Page 37 — Periodic Trends

1) Regular repeating patterns of variations of properties of elements with atomic number [1 mark] and position in the periodic table [1 mark].
2) Mg has more delocalised electrons [1 mark] and the ion has a greater charge density due to its smaller ionic radius [1 mark] (because of the greater nuclear charge). This gives Mg a stronger metal-metal bond, resulting in a higher boiling point [1 mark].
3) a) Si has a macromolecular (or giant molecular) structure [1 mark] consisting of very strong covalent bonds [1 mark].
b) Sulphur (S_8) has a larger molecule than phosphorus (P_4) [1 mark]. which results in larger van der Waals forces of attraction between molecules [1 mark].
4) a) Electronegativity is a measure of the attraction an atom has for bonding electrons [1 mark].
b) Electronegativity increases from element to element across the period [1 mark]. Elements on the left side lose electrons to achieve a stable structure [1 mark]. Elements on the right side gain electrons to achieve a stable structure [1 mark].
5) The atomic radius decreases across the period from left to right [1 mark]. The number of protons increases, so nuclear charge increases [1 mark]. Electrons are pulled closer to the nucleus [1 mark]. (The electrons are all added to the same outer shell, so there's little effect on shielding) [1 mark].

Page 39 — Ionisation Energy Trends

1) a) Increasing number of protons means a stronger pull from the positively charged nucleus [1 mark] making it harder to remove an electron from the outer shell [1 mark]. There are no extra inner electrons to add to the shielding effect [1 mark].
b) (i) Boron has the configuration $1s^2 2s^2 2p_x^{\ 1}$ compared to $1s^2 2s^2$ for beryllium [1 mark]. The 2p shell is at a slightly higher energy level than the 2s shell. As a result, the extra distance and partial shielding of the 2s orbital make it easier to remove the outer electron [1 mark].
(ii) Oxygen has the configuration $1s^2 2s^2 2p_x^{\ 2} 2p_y^{\ 1} 2p_z^{\ 1}$ compared to $1s^2 2s^2 2p_x^{\ 1} 2p_y^{\ 1} 2p_z^{\ 1}$ for nitrogen [1 mark]. Electron repulsion in the $2p_x$ sub-shell makes it easier to remove an electron in oxygen [1 mark].
2) Sulphur has a lower ionisation energy than phosphorus [1 mark]. It is easier to remove an electron from the $3p_x$ sub-shell [1 mark], due to repulsion between the two paired electrons in the $3p_x$ orbital [1 mark].
3) Neon has the configuration $1s^2 2s^2 2p^6$ and sodium $1s^2 2s^2 2p^6 3s^1$. [1 mark] The extra distance of sodium's outer electron from the nucleus and electron shielding make it easier to remove an electron from the 3s sub-shell [1 mark].

Page 41 — Oxidation and Reduction

1) a) $H_2SO_4\ (aq) + 8HI\ (aq) \rightarrow H_2S\ (g) + 4I_2\ (s) + 4H_2O\ (l)$ [1 mark]
b) Ox. No. of S in $H_2SO_4 = +6$ [1 mark]
Ox. No. of S in $H_2S = -2$ [1 mark]
c) $2I^- \rightarrow I_2 + 2e^-$ [1 mark]
d) $H_2SO_4 + 8H^+ + 8e^- \rightarrow H_2S + 4H_2O$
[all species correct — 1 mark, balancing — 1 mark]
e) Iodide [1 mark] — it donates electrons / its oxidation number increases [1 mark]
The ionic equations here are pretty tricky. Use the equation you're given as much as possible. For part d), sulphur is being reduced from +6 to −2, so it's gaining 8 electrons. You also need to add H^+s and H_20's to balance it. With ionic equations, always make sure the charges balance. E.g. in part d), charge on left = +8 − 8 = 0 = right-hand side.

Page 43 — S-Block Metals

1) Mg $1s^2\ 2s^2\ 2p^6\ 3s^2$ Ca $1s^2\ 2s^2 2p^6 3s^2 3p^6\ 4s^2$ [1 mark]
First ionisation energy of Ca is smaller [1 mark]
because Ca has (one) more electron shell(s) [1 mark]. This reduces the attraction between the nucleus and the outer electrons OR increases shielding effect [1 mark]. The outer shell of Ca is also further from the nucleus [1 mark].

2) Cs Rb Na Mg [1 mark]
Group I metals increase in reactivity down the group (so Cs is more reactive than Rb, which is more reactive than Na) [1 mark].
Group I metals are more reactive than Group II metals in the same period, so Na is more reactive than Mg [1 mark].
OR
an explanation based on the relative sizes of the atoms, Cs>Rb>Na>Mg [1 mark] The larger the atom, the easier it is to lose an electron (lower ionisation energy) and so the more reactive the metal is [1 mark].

3) a) Energy is absorbed and electrons move to higher energy levels. [1 mark] Energy is released in the form of coloured light when the electrons fall back to the lower levels [1 mark].
b) When viewed through a spectroscope, a line spectrum [1 mark] will be observed. Only certain wavelengths are present (if there were no energy levels you'd expect a continuous spectrum of all wavelengths) [1 mark].

Page 45 — Reactions of the S-Block Metals

1) a) Ra would react very rapidly [1 mark].
Bubbles of (H_2) gas [1 mark]
$Ra_{(s)} + 2H_2O_{(l)} \rightarrow Ra(OH)_{2(aq)} + H_{2(g)}$ [1 mark]
When you look it up, you'll find radium at the bottom of Group II. Since reactivity increases down the group, you know it's going to be a pretty vigorous reaction.
b) Universal indicator would turn purple or blue [1 mark]
... because it's a hydroxide, which means it's alkaline.
2) a) $Ca_{(s)} + Cl_{2(g)} \rightarrow CaCl_{2(s)}$ [1 mark]
b) From 0 to +2 [1 mark]
c) White [1 mark] solid [1 mark]
d) Ionic [1 mark]
...because as everybody who's anybody knows, Group II compounds (including oxides) are generally white ionic solids.
3) a) Y [1 mark]
b) Y has the largest radius [1 mark] so it will be furthest down the group / have the smallest ionisation energy [1 mark].

Page 47 — Compounds of S-Block metals

1) **A** = CO_2 [1 mark] (it turns limewater cloudy)
B = CaO [1 mark] (CO_2 is released when a carbonate is heated, leaving an oxide)
C = $CaCO_3$ [1 mark] (the precipitate formed in the reaction between CO_2 and limewater)
Original compound = $CaCO_3$ [1 mark] (CO_2 is released when a carbonate is heated, so the original compound must have been calcium carbonate)
...the easiest one to get is gas A because it's just describing the limewater test for CO_2. Getting the others isn't hard either, but you've got to really know all equations from page 47 — or you'll get muddled up.

Answers

2) a) $2NaNO_{3(s)} \rightarrow 2NaNO_{2(s)} + O_{2(g)}$ [1 mark]
b) O_2 gas relights a glowing splint. [1 mark]
c) magnesium nitrate   sodium nitrate   potassium nitrate [1 mark]
Group II nitrates decompose more easily than Group I (the greater the charge on cation, the less stable the nitrate anion) [1 mark].
The further down the group, the more stable the nitrate (the larger the cation, the less distortion to the nitrate anion) [1 mark].

3) Rain containing dissolved carbon dioxide falls onto limestone rocks [1 mark], dissolving some of the limestone [1 mark]
$CaCO_{3(s)} + CO_{2(g)} + H_2O_{(l)} \rightarrow Ca(HCO_3)_{2(aq)}$ [1 mark]

Page 49 — Solubilities and Uses of S-Block Compounds

1) a) $NaHCO_3 + HCl \rightarrow NaCl + H_2O + CO_2$ [1 mark]
b) Wind/burping etc. [1 mark]
c) Magnesium hydroxide [1 mark] – NB many other of the compounds would be either toxic or harmful.
$Mg(OH)_2 + 2HCl \rightarrow MgCl_2 + 2H_2O$ [1 mark]

2) Add barium chloride (or nitrate) solution to both [1 mark]
Zinc chloride would not change/no reaction [1 mark]
Zinc sulphate solution would give a white precipitate [1 mark]
$BaCl_{2(aq)} + ZnSO_{4(aq)} \rightarrow BaSO_{4(s)} + ZnCl_{2(aq)}$ [1 mark]
(or suitable equation using $Ba(NO_3)_{2(aq)}$)
OR $Ba^{2+}_{(aq)} + SO_4^{2-}{}_{(aq)} \rightarrow BaSO_{4(s)}$ [1 mark]
(or a test with silver nitrate for the chloride ions could be done.)

3) Test A $BaCl_2$ [1 mark]. Most soluble hydroxide. [1 mark]
Test B $MgSO_4$ [1 mark]. Addition of $BaCl_{2(aq)}$ to a sulphate gives a white precipitate [1 mark].
Test C $BeCl_{2(aq)}$ [1 mark]. $BeCl_{2(aq)}$ is acidic (because $BeCl_2$ is covalent and reacts with water) [1 mark]

It's getting really hard now. Question 3 is a real stinker, so don't cry if you got stuck. The trick for Tests A and B is to realise they're about solubilities — then, if you know the info on the page, you're most of the way there. Test C is easy if you've remembered that $BeCl_2$ is covalent, making it acidic. I recommend a good scream to release stress before moving on...

Page 51 — Group VII — The Halogens

1) a) $I_2 + 2At^- \rightarrow 2I^- + At_2$
b) The (sodium) astat<u>ide</u>

2) a) $2I^- + ClO^- + H_2O \rightarrow I_2 + Cl^- + 2OH^-$
[2 marks — 1 for correct formulas, 1 for balancing the equation.]
b) Iodine: -1 to 0 — oxidation [1 mark]
Chlorine: +1 to -1 — reduction [1 mark]
c) From colourless to brown [1 mark] solution.
The colour formed would be due to the iodine.
Most solutions of compounds of halogens are colourless.

3) a) MgF_2 [1 mark] (oxidation state of fluoride = -1)
b) KBrO [1 mark] (oxidation state of bromate(I) = +1, and the name brom**ate** indicates oxygen is present)
c) $NaClO_3$ [1 mark] (oxidation state of chlorate(V) = +5, and the name chlor**ate** indicates oxygen is present)

Page 53 — Sources of the Halogens

1) a) $2H^+ + 2e^- \rightarrow H_2$ [1 mark]
b) $2Cl^- \rightarrow Cl_2 + 2e^-$ [1 mark]
c) $2NaCl_{(aq)} + 2H_2O_{(l)} \rightarrow 2NaOH_{(aq)} + Cl_{2(g)} + H_{2(g)}$ [1 mark for correct balanced equation. 1 mark for state symbols].

Page 55 — Uses of the Halogens

1) a) $2OH^- + Cl_2 \rightarrow OCl^- + Cl^- + H_2O$ [1 mark]
Disproportionation is simultaneous oxidation and reduction of an element in a reaction [1 mark]. Cl_2 has been reduced to Cl^- [1 mark] and oxidised to OCl^- [1 mark].
b) In the presence of H^+ [1 mark], chlorate(I) oxidises chloride ions to chlorine gas [1 mark], which is toxic [1 mark].

2) Number of moles of sodium thiosulphate solution
$= \frac{21.6}{1000} \times 0.1 = 0.00216$ moles
One mole of iodine reacts with 2 moles of sodium thiosulphate, so the number of moles of iodine in 25 cm^3 of solution $= \frac{0.00216}{2}$
$= 0.00108$ moles.
So the concentration of iodine solution $= 0.00108 \times \frac{1000}{25}$
$= \mathbf{0.0432\ mol\ dm^{-3}}$

Page 57 — Halide Ions

1) **Aqueous** solutions of both halides are tested. [1 mark]
a) **Sodium chloride** — silver nitrate gives white precipitate which dissolves in dilute ammonia solution [1 mark].
$Ag^+ + Cl^- \rightarrow AgCl$ [1 mark]
Sodium bromide — silver nitrate gives cream precipitate which is only soluble in concentrated ammonia solution [1 mark].
$Ag^+ + Br^- \rightarrow AgBr$ [1 mark]
b) **Sodium chloride** — Misty fumes [1 mark]
$NaCl + H_2SO_4 \rightarrow NaHSO_4 + HCl$ [1 mark]
Sodium bromide — Misty fumes [1 mark]
$NaBr + H_2SO_4 \rightarrow NaHSO_4 + HBr$ [1 mark]
Choking / irritating odour [1 mark]
Orange / brown vapour [1 mark]
$2HBr + H_2SO_4 \rightarrow Br_2 + SO_2 + 2H_2O$ [1 mark]

2) a) NaI (via HI) reduces H_2SO_4 to H_2S [1 mark]. The reducing power of halide ions increases down the group [1 mark] and At is below I in the group [1 mark], so H_2S will be produced [1 mark].
b) AgI is insoluble in concentrated ammonia solution [1 mark], solubility of halides in ammonia solution decreases down the group [1 mark], so AgAt will **NOT** dissolve. [1 mark]

Question 2 is the kind of question that could completely throw you if you're not really clued up on the facts. If you really know p56, then in part b) you'll go "ah - ha!!! Reactions of Halides with H_2SO_4 — reducing power increases down the group..." If not, you basically won't have a clue. The moral is... it really is just about learning all the facts. Boring, but true.

Page 59 — Extracting Iron

1) a) reduction [1 mark]
b) oxygen [1 mark]
c) Pure oxygen is blown into molten iron [1 mark] to convert excess carbon and other impurities into their oxides, which are easily removed [1 mark].

Wahey — this stuff's dead easy...

Page 61 — Extracting Aluminium and Titanium

1 a) Aluminium oxide dissolved [1 mark] in molten cryolite [1 mark]
b) Cathode: $Al^{3+} + 3e^- \rightarrow Al$ [1 mark]
Anode: $2O^{2-} \rightarrow O_2 + 4e^-$ [1 mark]
c) High energy costs of extracting Al [1 mark].

2 a) Sodium or magnesium [1 mark],
$TiCl_{4\,(g)} + 4Na_{(l)} \rightarrow Ti_{(s)} + 4NaCl_{(s)}$ or
$TiCl_{4\,(g)} + 2Mg_{(l)} \rightarrow Ti_{(s)} + 2MgCl_{2\,(l)}$ [1 mark]
b) Some of the carbon reacts with the titanium to produce titanium carbide [1 mark], which makes the metal brittle and useless [1 mark].

Section 5 — Energetics

Page 63 — Enthalpy Changes

1) a)

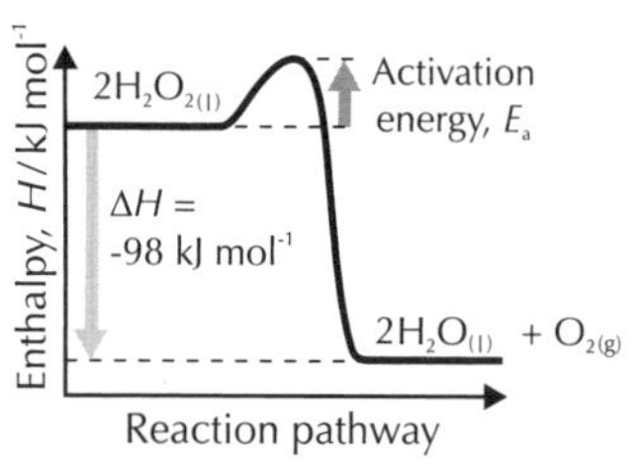

Enthalpy, H/kJ mol^{-1}
$2H_2O_{2(l)}$
Activation energy, E_a
ΔH = -98 kJ mol^{-1}
$2H_2O_{(l)} + O_{2(g)}$
Reaction pathway

Reactants lower in energy than products [1 mark]. Activation energy correctly labelled [1 mark]. ΔH correctly labelled with arrow pointing **downwards** [1 mark].

Answers

For an exothermic reaction, the ΔH arrow points downwards, but for an endothermic reaction it points upwards. The activation energy arrow always points upwards though.

b) i) *Hydrogen peroxide is thermodynamically unstable compared to the products (since products are more stable than reactants for an exothermic reaction) [1 mark]. It is kinetically stable since it doesn't readily decompose (due to a high E_a) [1 mark].*

ii) *It has a high activation energy [1 mark].*

2) a) $CH_3OH_{(l)} + 1\frac{1}{2}O_{2(g)} \rightarrow CO_{2(g)} + 2H_2O_{(l)}$

Correct balanced equation [1 mark]. Correct state symbols [1 mark].

It is perfectly OK to use halves to balance equations. Make sure that only

1 mole of CH_3OH is combusted, as it says in the definition for ΔH_c°.

b) $C_{(s)} + 2H_{2(g)} + \frac{1}{2}O_{2(g)} \rightarrow CH_3OH_{(l)}$

Correct balanced equation [1 mark]. Correct state symbols [1 mark].

c) *H_2O should be formed under standard conditions (i.e. liquid, not gas).*

[1 mark]. Only 1 mole of C_3H_8 should be shown according to the definition of ΔH_c° [1 mark].

You really need to know the definitions of the standard enthalpy changes off by heart. There's loads of nit-picky little details they could ask you questions about.

Page 65 — Calculating Enthalpy Changes

1) ΔH_r° = *sum of ΔH_f°(products) — sum of ΔH_f°(reactants) [1 mark]*

$= [0 + (3 \times -602)] - [-1676 + (3 \times 0)]$ *[1 mark]*

$=$ ***-130 kJ mol^{-1}*** *[1 mark]*

Don't forget the units. It's a daft way to lose marks.

2) *No. of moles of $CuSO_4$* $= \frac{0.200 \times 50}{1000}$ *[1 mark] = 0.01 moles [1 mark]*

From the equation, 1 mole of $CuSO_4$ reacts with 1 mole of Zn.

So, 0.01 moles of $CuSO_4$ reacts with 0.01 moles of Zn [1 mark].

Heat produced by reaction= $mc\Delta T$ [1 mark]

$= 50 \times 4.18 \times 2.6 = 543.4$ *J [1 mark]*

0.01 moles of zinc produces 543.4 J of heat, therefore 1 mole of zinc produces $\frac{543.4}{0.01}$ *[1 mark]* $= 54\ 340$ J ≈ 54.3 kJ

*So the enthalpy change is **-54.3 kJ mol^{-1}** (you need the minus sign because it's exothermic) [1 mark for correct number, 1 mark for minus sign].*

It'd be dead easy to work out the heat produced by the reactions, breathe a sigh of relief and sail on to the next question. But you need to find out the enthalpy change when 1 mole of zinc reacts. It's always a good idea to reread the question and check you've actually answered it.

Page 67 — Bond Enthalpy and Entropy Changes

1) *The negative charge density [1 mark] between carbon and oxygen in C=O is greater than in C–O [1 mark].*

Attraction between the positive nuclei [1 mark] of carbon and oxygen for this electron density is stronger for C=O. [1 mark].

So the bond enthalpy of C=O is higher [1 mark] and the atoms are closer together in C=O [1 mark], giving a shorter bond length.

2) a)

$2\Delta H_f^\circ NH_{3(g)}$ *[1 mark]*

$N_{2(g)} + 3H_{2(g)} \rightarrow 2NH_{3(g)}$

$2\Delta H_{at}^\circ N_2$ *[1 mark]* ; $6\Delta H_{at}^\circ H_2$ *[1 mark]* ; $6E$(N–H) *[1 mark]*

$2N_{(g)} + 6H_{(g)}$

b) $(2 \times +473) + (6 \times +218) = (-46.2 \times 2) + (6 \times E(N\text{–}H))$ *[1 mark]*

$6 \times E(N\text{–}H) = +946 + 1308 - (-92.4) = 2346.4$ *[1 mark]*

$E(N\text{–}H) = \frac{2346.4}{6}$ *[1 mark]* $\approx +391$ kJ mol^{-1} *[1 mark]*

Remember — there's 6 N–H bonds to be broken in $2NH_3$.

c) *391 kJ mol^{-1} is the average N–H bond energy in ammonia [1 mark]. The data book value of N–H is an average of N–H bond energies in many molecules [1 mark], like amines and acid amides.*

Section 6 — Kinetics

Page 69 — Reaction Rates

1) *The molecules don't always have enough energy [1 mark].*

Collisions don't always happen in the right orientation (the molecules mightn't be facing each other in the best way and will just bounce off each other) [1 mark].

2) *The particles in a liquid move freely and all of them are able to collide with the solid particles [1 mark]. Particles in solids just vibrate about fixed positions, so only those on the touching surfaces between the two solids will be able to react. [1 mark]*

Page 71 — Catalysts

1) a)

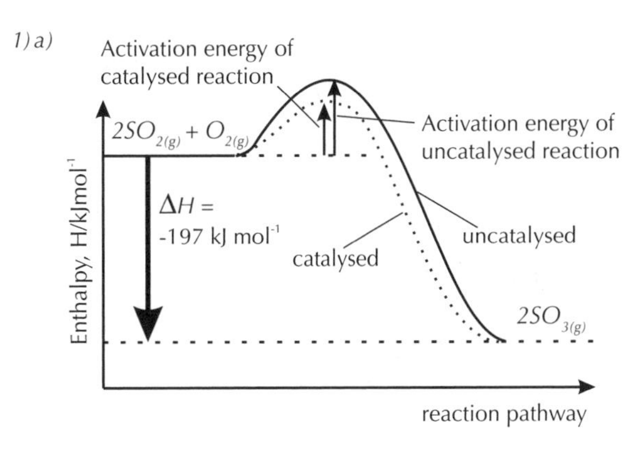

*Curve showing activation energy [1 mark]. This must link reactants and products. Showing exothermic change (products **lower** in energy than reactants), with ΔH correctly labelled and a **downward** arrow [1 mark]. Correctly labelling activation energy (from reactants to highest energy peak) [1 mark].*

Label your axes correctly. (No, not the sharp tools for chopping wood or heads off — you know what I mean.)

b) *See the diagram above. Reaction profile showing a **greater** activation energy than for the catalysed reaction [1 mark].*

Remember — catalysts lower the activation energy. So uncatalysed reactions have greater activation energies.

c) *Catalysts increase the **rate** of the reaction by providing an **alternative reaction pathway** [1 mark], with a **lower activation energy** [1 mark].*

d) *Catalysts are made ineffective by poisons [1 mark]. The arsenic probably clings to the surface of the platinum and stops it getting involved in the reaction [1 mark].*

Vanadium(V) oxide's solid, but the reactants are gases — so it's a heterogeneous catalyst. This is how they're normally poisoned.

2) a) $2H_2O_{2(l)} \rightarrow 2H_2O_{(l)} + O_{2(g)}$

Correct symbols [1 mark] and balancing equation [1 mark]. You get the marks even if you forgot the state symbols.

b)

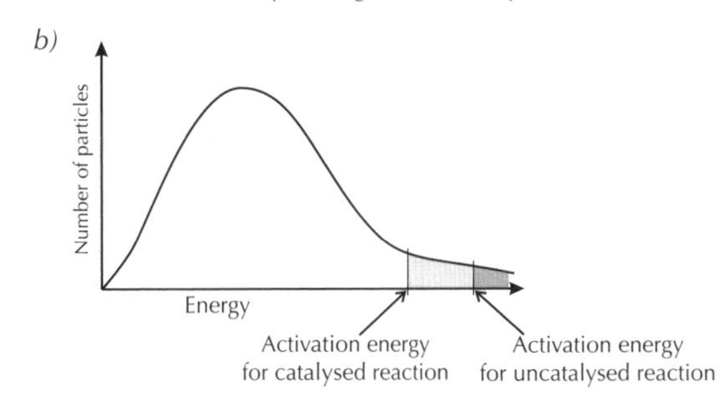

Correct general shape of the curve [1 mark]. Correctly labelling the axes [1 mark]. Activation energies marked on the horizontal axis — the catalysed activation energy must be lower than the uncatalysed activation energy [1 mark].

You don't have to draw another curve for the catalysed reaction. Just mark the lower activation evergy on the one you've already done.

Answers

c) Manganese(IV) oxide lowers the activation energy by providing an alternative reaction pathway [1 mark]. So, more reactant molecules have the activation energy [1 mark], meaning there are more successful collisions in a given period of time, and so the rate increases [1 mark].

Page 73 — Homogeneous and Heterogeneous Catalysts

1)

smaller activation energies
uncatalysed reaction
Enthalpy (or energy)
reactants
products
intermediates formed here
Progress of Reaction

Curve for uncatalysed reaction. [1 mark]
Curve for catalysed reaction with lower activation energy. [1 mark]
Two humps and label for intermediate. [1 mark]
Both axes correctly labelled. [1 mark]

2) In heterogeneous catalysis, the solid catalyst provides a surface where the reaction can take place and be speeded up [1 mark].
The iron needs to be finely divided so that it provides the largest possible surface area where the reaction can proceed [1 mark].

Section 7 — Equilibria

Page 75 — Reversible Reactions

1) a) If a reaction at equilibrium is subjected to a change in concentration, pressure or temperature, the equilibrium will shift to try to oppose (counteract) the change. [1 mark].
Examiners are always asking for definitions so learn them — they're easy marks.

b) (i) There's no change [1 mark]. There's the same number of molecules/moles on each side of the equation [1 mark].
(ii) Reducing temperature removes heat. So the equilibrium shifts in the exothermic direction to release heat [1 mark]. The reverse reaction is exothermic (since the forward reaction is endothermic). So, the position of equilibrium shifts left [1 mark].
(iii) Removing nitrogen monoxide reduces its concentration. The equilibrium position shifts right to try and increase the nitrogen monoxide concentration again [1 mark].

c) No effect [1 mark].
Catalysts don't affect the equilibrium position. They just help the reaction to get there sooner.

Page 77 — Equilibrium in Industrial Processes

1) a) At low temperatures the gas molecules will move more slowly [1 mark]. This reduces the chances of successful collisions [1 mark]. So, the rate of reaction decreases [1 mark].

b) High pressures are expensive to produce and maintain [1 mark]. These high costs may exceed the value of the extra product [1 mark].

c) i) The catalyst increases the rate of reaction [1 mark], by lowering the activation energy for the reaction (it provides an alternative reaction pathway) [1 mark].
ii) A catalyst has no effect on the position of the equilibrium [1 mark].

d) Refrigeration allows the ammonia to be liquefied and removed [1 mark]. Nitrogen and hydrogen are then recycled to produce more ammonia [1 mark].

Page 79 — Acids and Bases

1) a) A strong acid is one that almost completely dissociates into ions in aqueous solution [1 mark].

$HClO_{4(aq)} \rightarrow H^+_{(aq)} + ClO_4^-{}_{(aq)}$ [1 mark]

Don't forget — it's a one-way arrow for a strong acid.

b) $CaCO_{3(s)} + 2HClO_{4(aq)} \rightarrow Ca(ClO_4)_{2(aq)} + H_2O_{(l)} + CO_{2(g)}$

[1 mark for the state symbols, 1 mark for all the correct formulas and 1 mark for the correct balance.]

c) i) $2Li_{(s)} + 2H^+_{(aq)} \rightarrow 2Li^+_{(aq)} + H_{2(g)}$

[1 mark for the correct formulas and 1 mark for the correct balance.]
The SO_4^{2-} ions are left out of the ionic equation — they're spectator ions that don't get involved in the reaction.

ii) $2KOH_{(aq)} + H_2SO_{4(aq)} \rightarrow K_2SO_{4(aq)} + 2H_2O_{(l)}$

[1 mark for the correct formulas and 1 mark for the correct balance.]

Page 81 — The Atmosphere

1) Infra-red radiation makes the air warmer [1 mark]. This happens because infra-red radiation is of the right energy (or frequency) to give the molecules more vibrational or rotational energy [1 mark].

2) $E = h\nu$
$E = (6.63 \times 10^{-34}) \times (8.19 \times 10^{13})$ [1 Mark]
$E = \mathbf{5.43 \times 10^{-20}\ J}$ [1 Mark]

Section 8 — Organic Chemistry

Page 83 — Basic Stuff

1) a) butan-1-ol: H–C(H)(H)–C(H)(H)–C(H)(H)–C(H)(H)–OH   1-bromobutane: H–C(H)(H)–C(H)(H)–C(H)(H)–C(H)(H)–Br

[1 mark for each correct structure]

b) –OH (hydroxyl) [1 mark].
It could be attached to the first or second carbon OR butan-2-ol also exists [1 mark].

c) (i) M_r of $C_4H_9OH = (4 \times 12) + (9 \times 1) + 16 + 1 = 74$ g [1 mark]

Number of moles of $C_4H_9OH = \frac{8.0}{74} = \mathbf{0.108\ moles}$ [1 mark]

(ii) 1 mole of C_4H_9OH produces 1 mole of C_4H_9Br, so 0.108 moles of C_4H_9OH will produce **0.108** moles of C_4H_9Br [1 mark].
(iii) M_r of $C_4H_9Br = (4 \times 12) + (9 \times 1) + 80 = 137$ g [1 mark]
Theoretical yield (mass of C_4H_9Br) $= 0.108 \times 137 = \mathbf{14.8\ g}$ [1 mark]

d) (i) Percentage yield $= \frac{6.5}{14.8} \times 100$ [1 mark] $=$ **43.9%** [1 mark]

(ii) Reaction was incomplete OR product was lost in transfers/purification OR side reactions occurred [1 mark for any valid point].
See — you need to use the equation 'number of moles = mass/M_r' absolutely loads in Chemistry. It's dead handy.

Page 85 — Isomerism

1) a) (i)

hexane
2-methylpentane
2,3-dimethylbutane
3-methylpentane
2,2-dimethylbutane

[1 mark for each correctly drawn isomer, 1 mark for each correct name]

(ii) The same molecular formula [1 mark] but different arrangements of the carbon skeleton [1 mark].
Watch out — the atoms can rotate around the single C–C bonds, so these two aren't isomers — they're just the same molecule bent a bit.

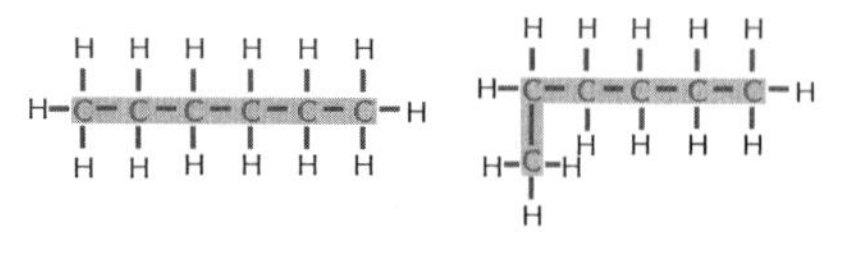

Answers

b) (i)

cis-1-chloropropene trans-1-chloropropene

[1 mark for each correctly drawn isomer, 1 mark for each correct name]

(ii)

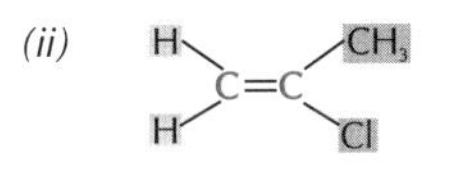

2-chloropropene

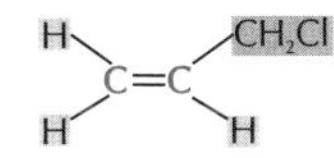

3-chloropropene

[1 mark for each correctly drawn isomer, 1 mark for each correct name]

c) A group of compounds represented by the same general formula OR having the same functional group OR with similar chemical properties [1 mark]. Each successive member differs by $-CH_2-$ [1 mark].

Page 87 — Alkanes

1) a) One with no double bond OR the maximum number of hydrogens OR single bonds only [1 mark]. It contains only hydrogen and carbon atoms [1 mark].

b) It has non-polar bonds/it's a non-polar molecule [1 mark], so it does not attract/react with polar reagents [1 mark].

c) $C_2H_{6(g)} + 3\frac{1}{2}O_{2(g)} \rightarrow 2CO_{2(g)} + 3H_2O_{(g)}$
[1 mark for correct symbols, 1 mark for balancing]

d) $CH_3CH_3 + Br_2 \xrightarrow{U.V.} CH_3CH_2Br + HBr$ [1 mark]

Initiation: $Br_2 \xrightarrow{U.V.} 2Br\cdot$ [1 mark]

Propagation: $CH_3CH_3 + Br\cdot \rightarrow CH_3CH_2\cdot + HBr$ [1 mark]

$CH_3CH_2\cdot + Br_2 \rightarrow CH_3CH_2Br + Br\cdot$ [1 mark]

Termination: $CH_3CH_2\cdot + Br\cdot \rightarrow CH_3CH_2Br$

Or: $CH_3CH_2\cdot + CH_3CH_2\cdot \rightarrow CH_3CH_2CH_2CH_3$ [1 mark]

[1 mark for mentioning U.V.]
It's a free-radical [1 mark] substitution [1 mark] reaction

Page 89 — Petroleum

1) a) (i) There's greater demand for smaller fractions [1 mark] for motor fuels [1 mark] OR for alkenes [1 mark] to make petrochemicals/polymers [1 mark].

(ii) Carbocation mechanism [1 mark].

(iii) E.g. $C_{12}C_{26} \rightarrow C_2H_4 + C_{10}H_{22}$ [1 mark]. There's loads of possible answers — just make sure the C's and H's balance and there's an alkane and an alkene.

b) (i) A measure [1 mark] of the tendency of the petrol to auto-ignite [1 mark] — the higher the number, the lower the tendency [1 mark].

(ii) Branched-chain alkanes, cycloalkanes and arenes [1 mark for each].
They promote efficient combustion/reduce knocking [1 mark].

(iii)

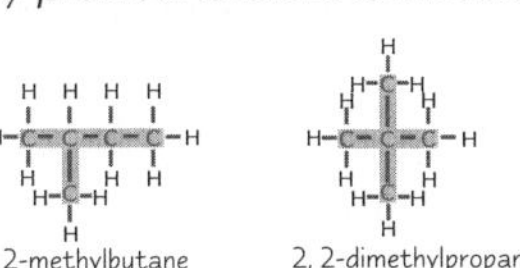

2-methylbutane 2, 2-dimethylpropane

[1 mark for each structure, 1 mark for each name]

2,2-dimethylpropane will increase the octane rating most [1 mark].

This is cos shorter, more branched alkanes increase the octane rating more. Don't worry about why — just remember that they do.

Page 91 — Fuels

1) a) M_r of hexane $(C_6H_{14}) = (12 \times 6) + (1 \times 14) = 86$ g [1 mark]

So 86 g gives out 4163 kJ of heat energy.

$1\ dm^3 = 1000\ cm^3$, $30\ dm^3 = 30\ 000\ cm^3$

Mass of $30\ dm^3$ of hexane = density × volume
= 0.7 × 30 000
= 21 000 g [1 mark]

So $1\ dm^3$ of hexane gives out $\frac{21\ 000}{86} \times 4163$ [1 mark]

= **1 016 547 kJ** (≈ **1 017 000 kJ**) of heat energy when it burns. [1 mark]

Cor blimey, that's a big number.

b) 1 mole of H_2 gas gives out -286 kJ heat energy when it burns.

Number of moles of $H_2 = \frac{1\ 016\ 547}{286} = 3554.4$ moles. [1 mark]

This has a volume of 3554.4 × 24 ≈ **85 300 dm³** [1 mark]

It's really vital that you show ALL your working. Cos, if you make a mistake early on which makes the rest of your calculations wrong, you should still get most of the marks for going through the right steps.

Page 93 — Alkenes

1) It's unsaturated because more atoms can be added [1 mark] across the double bond [1 mark]. (It doesn't have as many bonds as it can.)

2) a) C_nH_{2n} [1 mark]

b) (i) $C_{10}H_{16}$ [1 mark]

(ii) Three [1 mark]

The equivalent alkane would be $C_{10}H_{22}$, and each double bond removes 2 hydrogens.

(iii)

[2 marks]

c) You can extract the compound from the leaves without destroying it. [1 mark]

Page 95 — Reactions of Alkenes

1) a) Shake the alkene with bromine water [1 mark], and the solution goes colourless if a double bond is present [1 mark].

b) Electrophilic [1 mark] addition [1 mark].

c) (i)

2–bromobutane

[1 mark] [1 mark for correct intermediate] [1 mark]

Check that your curly arrows are exactly right, or you'll lose marks. They have to go from exactly where the electrons are from, to where they're going to.

(ii) The secondary carbocation OR the carbocation with the most attached alkyl groups [1 mark] is the most stable intermediate and so is the most likely to form [1 mark].

Page 97 — Polymers

1) a) (i)

(you can also put CH_2=CH_2) [1 mark] [1 mark]

(ii) The chains can't pack closely together OR it has an amorphous structure [1 mark]. So van der Waals forces OR instantaneous/temporary dipole-induced dipole OR dispersion forces are reduced [1 mark]. However, polar C–Cl bonds [1 mark] create permanent dipole-dipole interactions between polymer chains making the plastic hard and rigid [1 mark].

b) (i) Crystalline means packed in a regular arrangement [1 mark].

(ii) It makes polymers stronger [1 mark], less flexible/more rigid [1 mark], have higher melting points [1 mark]. [up to a maximum of 2 marks]

(iii) C–F bonds are strong/not easily broken/have high bond enthalpy OR fluorine atoms surround and protect the carbon chain [1 mark].

(iv) Any non-stick coating, e.g. on pans, stainproofing/waterproofing fabrics, protecting containers from corrosion.
[1 mark for any valid answer]

Answers

Page 99 — Polymers

1) a) *Low-density poly(ethene) is flexible, tough and is deformed by heat [1 mark]. This is because the polymer chains in LDPE have lots of branches, so they can't pack closely together [1 mark].*
High-density poly(ethene) is rigid, easy to mould and isn't deformed by heat. It has a higher density than LDPE [1 mark]. This is because the polymer chains in HDPE have very few branches so the polymer chains line up and pack very closely together [1 mark].

b) *Low-density poly(ethene) — bags, squeezy bottles, etc.*
[1 mark for each valid suggestion, up to a maximum of 2 marks]
High-density poly(ethene) — car petrol tanks, water pipes, etc.
[1 mark for each valid suggestion, up to a maximum of 2 marks]

c) *Low-density poly(ethene) — a temperature of 170 °C [1 mark], a pressure of 1400 atm [1 mark] and organic peroxide [1 mark].*
High-density poly(ethene) — a temperature of 70 °C [1 mark], a pressure of 2 atm [1 mark] and a Ziegler-Natta catalyst [1 mark].

Page 101 — Epoxyethane

1) a) (i) $2C_2H_4 + O_2 \longrightarrow 2$ (O bridging H_2C—CH_2)

[1 mark for correctly balanced equation, 1 mark for correctly drawn product.]

(ii) *Silver OR Ag [1 mark].*

(iii) *Epoxyethane is flammable OR explosive [1 mark].*
Epoxyethane is toxic OR irritant to lungs/causes respiratory failure OR harmful to nervous system/causes neurological effects [1 mark].

(iv) *The ring/molecule is strained OR bond angles are only 60° [1 mark]*

(b) (i) OH OH on H_2C—CH_2 *[1 mark]*

ethane-1,2-diol [1 mark]

(ii) *antifreeze OR production of/feedstock for polyesters [1 mark]*
Whatever you do, don't mix the reaction with water up with the reaction with alcohol, or you'll have to kick yourself really hard.

Page 103 — Haloalkanes

1) a) *Chlorofluorocarbon [1 mark]*

b) *Non-toxic / non-flammable / unreactive OR very stable / gases liquefy easily when compressed [any 2 for 1 mark each]*

c) *Refrigerants / (aerosol) propellants / blowing plastics OR polystyrene / degreasing solvent [any 1 for 1 mark]*

d) *CFC molecules reach the stratosphere [1 mark]. There they are broken down by UV radiation [1 mark] to give chlorine radicals [1 mark]. These decompose ozone molecules (to oxygen) [1 mark]. This thins / depletes / creates a hole in the ozone layer [1 mark]. This layer protects us from harmful (ultraviolet) radiation [1 mark] [1 mark for each point. Maximum of 4 marks]*

e) ***Hydrochlorofluorocarbons (HCFCs)***
Advantage — these are less stable, so they decomposes lower in the atmosphere.
Disadvantage — they still contain chlorine OR they contribute to the greenhouse effect.
OR
Hydrofluorocarbons (HFCs)
Advantage — these are broken down lower in the atmosphere.
Disadvantage — they contribute to the greenhouse effect.
Alkanes
Advantage — cheap.
Disadvantage — flammable OR contribute to greenhouse effect.
[1 mark for name, 1 mark for advantage, 1 mark for disadvantage]
If this question left you floundering, read the information again and check out page 72 as well.

Page 105 — Haloalkanes

1) a) ***Reaction 1***
Reagent — NaOH/KOH/OH⁻ [1 mark]
Conditions — Aqueous solution/water as solvent, reflux [1 mark]
Reaction 2
Reagent — Ammonia/NH_3 [1 mark]
Conditions — Ethanolic/alcoholic, reflux [1 mark]
Reaction 3
Reagent — NaOH/KOH [1 mark].
Conditions — Ethanolic/alcoholic, reflux [1 mark]

b) *There'd be a faster reaction [1 mark]. The C–I bond is weaker/longer than C–Br, or C–I bond enthalpy is lower [1 mark].*

Page 107 — Alcohols

1) a) *Butan-1-ol [1 mark], primary [1 mark]*

b) *2-methylpropan-2-ol [1 mark], tertiary [1 mark]*

c) *Butan-2-ol [1 mark], secondary [1 mark]*

2) a) *Primary [1 mark]. The -OH group is bonded to a carbon with one alkyl group/other carbon atom attached [1 mark].*

b) (i) $C_6H_{12}O_{6(aq)} \rightarrow 2C_2H_5OH_{(aq)} + 2CO_{2(g)}$ *[1 mark]*
(ii) *Yeast [1 mark], temperature between 30 and 40 °C [1 mark], Anaerobic conditions OR air/oxygen excluded [1 mark]*

c) *Ethene is cheap and abundantly available [1 mark]. It's a low-cost/high-yield process [1 mark]. This might change in the future as crude oil reserves are running out [1 mark].*

d) *The -OH group can hydrogen-bond [1 mark] so ethanol can dissolve polar compounds [1 mark]. Its non-polar hydrocarbon chain [1 mark] dissolves non-polar compounds too [1 mark].*

Page 109 — Reactions of Alcohols

1) a) (i) *NaBr AND conc. H_2SO_4 [1 mark]*
HBr won't do here — it's a gas.
Reagents are things you can pick up off the shelf in bottles.
(ii) *CH_2=CH_2 (accept C_2H_4) AND H_2O [1 mark]*

b) (i) *nucleophilic [1 mark] substitution [1 mark].*
(ii) *Steamy/misty fumes [1 mark] which turn blue litmus red [1 mark].*

Page 111 — Oxidation of Alcohols

1) a)

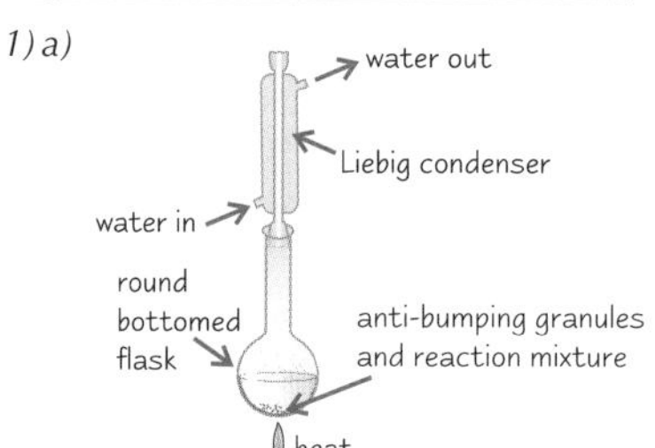

[1 mark for diagram]
You set up reflux apparatus in this way so that the reaction can be heated to boiling point [1 mark] without losing any materials/reactants/products OR so vapour will condense and drip back into the flask [1 mark]

b) (i) *Warm with Fehling's/Benedict's solution: turns from blue to brick-red OR warm with Tollen's reagent: a silver mirror is produced [1 mark for test, 1 mark for result]*
(ii) *Propanoic acid [1 mark]*
(iii) $CH_3CH_2CH_2OH + [O] \rightarrow CH_3CH_2CHO + H_2O$ *[1 mark]*
$CH_3CH_2CHO + [O] \rightarrow CH_3CH_2COOH$ *[1 mark]*
(iv) *Distillation [1 mark]. This is so aldehyde is removed immediately as it forms [1 mark].*
If you don't get the aldehyde out quick-smart, it'll be a carboxylic acid before you know it.

c) (i) (structure: H–C–H groups, H–C–C–OH, H–C–H) *[1 mark]*
(ii) *2-methylpropan-2-ol is a tertiary alcohol (which is more stable) [1 mark].*

Page 113 — Analytical Techniques

1) a) *Spectrum A: 1700 cm⁻¹ (accept 1700-1800) [1 mark], C=O [1 mark]*
Spectrum B: 1700 cm⁻¹ (accept 1700-1800) [1 mark], C=O [1 mark]
2900-3300 cm⁻¹ [1 mark], O–H [1 mark]

b) *A = ethanal, B = ethanoic acid [1 mark]*

c) *The absorption at 1700 cm⁻¹ would be missing [1 mark].*
Ethanol doesn't have a C=O bond. It's still got an O–H bond though.

Index

Index

Index

Some Random Bits and Bobs...

All the stuff on this page is worth learning. You'll be using the ion and gas tests a lot in your practicals. If I were you, I'd learn them now and save yourself faff when you need them...

Tests for the Common Ions...

Ion present	Test	Result
Carbonate, CO_3^{2-} or hydrogencarbonate, HCO_3^-	Add $HCl_{(aq)}$ to solid or solution	colourless gas (CO_2) given off, turns limewater cloudy.
Sulphate, SO_4^{2-} or sulphite, SO_3^{2-}	Add $BaCl_{2\,(aq)}$ to a solution, acidify with dilute $HCl_{(aq)}$	Both give a white precipitate; the sulphite redissolves in acid, the sulphate doesn't.
Chloride, Cl^- Bromide, Br^- Iodide, I^-	Acidify with dilute $HNO_{3\,(aq)}$, add $AgNO_{3\,(aq)}$	Cl^- gives white precipitate - dissolves in dilute $NH_{3(aq)}$ Br^- gives cream precipitate - dissolves in conc. $NH_{3(aq)}$ I^- gives yellow precipitate - insoluble in conc. $NH_{3(aq)}$
Nitrate, NO_3^-	Add $NaOH_{(aq)}$ to solution and powdered aluminium or Devarda's alloy and warm.	Gas given off (NH_3) that turns red litmus blue and has strong smell.
Ammonium, NH_4^+	Add $NaOH_{(aq)}$ to solution and warm.	Gas given off (NH_3) that turns red litmus blue and has strong smell.

Tests for the Common Gases...

Gas present	Test	Result
hydrogen, H_2	hold lighted splint in gas	get squeaky 'pop'
oxygen, O_2	hold glowing splint in gas	splint relights
carbon dioxide, CO_2	pass gas through limewater ($Ca(OH)_2$ solution)	cloudy white precipitate formed
ammonia, NH_3	hold moist red litmus paper in gas	litmus turns blue
chlorine, Cl_2	hold piece of moist indicator paper in gas	indicator paper is bleached
nitrogen dioxide, NO_2	note colour and hold piece of moist blue litmus paper in gas	brown gas, turns blue litmus paper red
sulphur dioxide, SO_2	hold a piece of filter paper dipped in potassium dichromate in gas	orange colour disappears - paper turns pale green

Reactivity Series for Metals...

Starting with the most reactive...

1) Potassium
2) Sodium
3) Calcium
4) Magnesium
5) Aluminium
(Carbon)
6) Zinc
7) Iron
8) Lead
(Hydrogen)
9) Copper
10) Silver
11) Gold
12) Platinum

Some Basic Solubility Rules...

Inorganic chemistry is so huge that all the facts can end up blurring into one. Here's some really handy rules for getting solubilities sorted...

All sodium, potassium and ammonium salts are soluble in water.

All nitrates are soluble in water.

Most chlorides are soluble in water. $PbCl_2$ and AgCl are common exceptions to this.

Most sulphates are soluble in water. $PbSO_4$ and $BaCl_2$ are common exceptions to this.

Most oxides, hydroxides and carbonates are insoluble in water
— those of sodium and potassium are exceptions to this.
— calcium hydroxide is slightly soluble in water.